LEVEL III PRACTICE EXAMS – VOLUME 2

D1449820

SCHWESER 2012 CFA LEVEL III PRACTICE EXAMS VOLUME 2

©2011 Kaplan, Inc. All rights reserved.

Published in 2011 by Kaplan Schweser.

Printed in the United States of America.

ISBN: 978-1-4277-3683-3 / 1-4277-3683-9

PPN: 3200-1746

HOW TO USE THE LEVEL III PRACTICE EXAMS

This volume contains three full-length Schweser practice exams. Answers to all item set questions contain full explanations, and since the goal for the morning session of the Level III exam is writing complete answers without consuming unnecessary time, essay questions have two answers—a **For the Exam** answer to help you practice writing short, correct answers for the exam, and a **Discussion** answer, which fully explains the concept behind the question and answer.

Important! Be sure to read the information under Figure 2 on how and where to answer essay questions.

I recommend that you save the Practice Exams for as late in the season as possible. A good strategy is to take one exam in each of the three weeks prior to the exam (two per week, if you have both practice exam volumes). Plan ahead; actually schedule the exam and take the entire exam in two, 3-hour sittings on the scheduled day. Do your best to mimic actual exam conditions. For example, time yourself, have someone work on a computer in the same room, and for distractions, have that person leave the room occasionally, turn the temperature in the room up and down, and talk to him- or herself. Remember, no matter how challenging we make our Practice Exams, the actual exam— and the exam experience, for that matter—will be different because you and everyone else in the room will be nervous and fidgety with the pressures of the day. Also, mainly due to nerves and the exam experience, your perception will be that the actual exam was much more difficult than our practice exams or even old CFA Exam questions you have studied.

The morning session of your exam (3 hours and 50% of the exam) will be entirely constructed response essay questions. The afternoon session (3 hours and 50%) will be 10 selected response item sets, each worth 18 points. You can expect any topic (e.g., portfolio management, derivatives, GIPS®) to be tested in either format. The Level III topic area weights, as presented on the CFA Institute® Web site, are shown in Figure 1.

Figure 1: Topic Area Weights for the Level III CFA Exam

Topic Area	Level III Weight
Ethical and Professional Standards	10%
Quantitative Methods	0%
Economics	0%
Financial Reporting and Analysis	0%
Corporate Finance	0%
Equity Investments	5–15%
Fixed Income	10–20%
Derivatives	5–15%
Alternative Investments	5–15%
Portfolio Management and Wealth Planning	45–55%

* *Note: These weights are intended to guide the curriculum and exam development processes. Actual exam weights may vary slightly from year to year. Please note that some topics are combined for testing purposes.*

Figure 2 shows the topic areas by study session. When you compare Figure 2 to Figure 1, the topic area weights in Figure 1 might appear a little confusing. You might have noticed that in Figure 2, Study Session 7 is titled Economic Concepts for Asset Valuation in Portfolio Management. Then, you see that the weight for Economics in Figure 1 is zero. As explained to me by a representative of CFA Institute, this is because Economics is tested as part of Portfolio Management. In fact, Study Sessions 3 through 18 all fall under the umbrella of Portfolio Management. Just how the individual topics will be combined and tested is somewhat of an unknown, so your focus is exactly the same as that for prior years' candidates—you must learn the entire Level III curriculum.

Figure 2: 2012 Level III Topic Areas by Study Session

Study Session	Topic Area	Title
1	Ethics and Standards	Code of Ethics and Professional Standards
2	Ethics and Standards	Ethical and Professional Standards in Practice
3	Portfolio Management	Behavioral Finance
4	Portfolio Management	Private Wealth Management
5	Portfolio Management	Portfolio Management for Institutional Investors
6	Portfolio Management	Capital Market Expectations in Portfolio Management
7	Portfolio Management	Economic Concepts for Asset Valuation in Portfolio Management
8	Portfolio Management	Asset Allocation
9	Portfolio Management	Management of Passive and Active Fixed Income Portfolios
10	Portfolio Management	Portfolio Management of Global Bonds and Fixed Income Derivatives
11	Portfolio Management	Equity Portfolio Management
12	Portfolio Management	Equity Portfolio Management
13	Portfolio Management	Alternative Investments for Portfolio Management
14	Portfolio Management	Risk Management
15	Portfolio Management	Risk Management Applications of Derivatives
16	Portfolio Management	Execution of Portfolio Decisions; Monitoring and Rebalancing
17	Portfolio Management	Performance Evaluation and Attribution
18	Portfolio Management	Global Investment Performance Standards

Do not underestimate Level III. A long-standing rumor is that Level II has the hardest curriculum and exam, and Level III has the most enjoyable curriculum—it's almost *easy reading*. However, this does not mean you should take the Level III exam lightly. At Levels I and II, all you had to do was search your mental data base for *the* answer. At Level III, you must know the entire curriculum well enough to integrate the topics and *construct* an answer. In other words, the vast proportion of your exam will require recalling and piecing together what you know.

Writing effective answers to essay questions. To be effective, the answer must be concise, yet fully address the question. CFA Institute's guideline answers for old exam questions are "perfect answers" (i.e., the one you would write if you had enough time). Also, CFA Institute typically gives you much more answer space on the exam than you need. You should not feel that you are expected to fill all the answer space provided. Your responses should be concise yet complete and most importantly, address the command words. This way, there can be no doubt that you are addressing the question.

Give the CFA answer. Graders use an answer key and don't give points for creative thought, either yours or theirs! That is, they are not allowed to read anything into your answer, so you must write exactly what you want to say. Also, organize your work and think before you write. If the graders can't find or decipher your work, you will receive no credit. By the way, be sure to answer every question, even if only a wild guess. Graders can only award points; they cannot deduct points for incorrect answers.

Where to write your answers. It is extremely important that you follow the exam proctors' directions, as well as directions written on the exam itself. For example, if a **template** is provided for a question, you will see, "Answer question X in the template provided," or similar language. When a template is provided, you must use the template to receive credit for your answers. Other essay questions will be followed by **lined pages** on which you are expected to write your answers. You must write your answers on the lined pages when these are provided. 2011 Level III candidates who wrote their answers directly on the question pages were told they would receive no credit for those answers!

For the Exam answers. To help make these exams a true learning experience, there are two answers for every constructed response essay question. The first answer is labeled **For the Exam**. These short, to-the-point answers would be awarded full credit on the exam. The second answer is labeled **Discussion**. This is more of an explanation of the concept, which should help you fully understand why you were correct or incorrect.

Be prepared. It should go without saying that you should get plenty of sleep the night before the exam. Bring all necessary items (including food) with you, and arrive early enough at the test site to get a decent parking space and a seat in the exam room that feels "right" to you. In fact, I recommend thoroughly checking out the site before exam day. **Important!** Be sure to read the CFA Institute guidelines for test day, which can be found on the CFA Institute Web site.

My thanks to the Schweser Level III team. I would like to thank all of my colleagues at Schweser, especially my friend and Level III partner Kurt Schuldes, CFA, CAIA; Kristen Rindfleisch, Lead Editor; and Jeff Faas, Lead Editor, for their incredible work ethic and commitment to quality. Schweser would not be the company it is, nor could we provide the quality products you see, without all the Schweser content and editing professionals.

Best regards,

Bruce Kuhlman

Dr. Bruce Kuhlman, Ph.D., CFA, CAIA
VP and Level III Manager
Kaplan Schweser

2012 PRACTICE EXAM ANSWERS AND EXPLANATIONS ARE ONLINE AT WWW.SCHWESER.COM

Answers and explanations for self-grading all practice exam essays and item sets are included at the end of this book. Explanations and calculations for the *item sets* are also available online at schweser.com. They also contain embedded links to supporting curriculum material for the relevant Learning Outcome Statements. In addition, you can access Performance Tracker, a tool that will provide you with exam diagnostics to target your review effort and allow you to compare your scores to those of other candidates.

USE YOUR SCHWESER *ONLINE ACCESS* ACCOUNT

You should have received an email with login information for Online Access. This is your login to view "What Every Level III Candidate Should Know" and volumes in the Schweser Library, to use the Schweser Study Planner and Performance Tracker, and (if you purchased any package) to get your questions answered during Instructor-Led Office Hours. Simply log in at www.schweser.com and select Online Access to use any of these features. You can access practice exam answers and explanations with the Practice Exams Vol. 2 left-hand menu item. If you need password help, go to www.schweser.com/password or use the Password Help link that appears if your login is unsuccessful.

PRACTICE EXAM ONLINE FEATURES AT A GLANCE

Answer Explanations
Our answer format contains explanations to help you understand why one answer is the best of all the choices. When using Performance Tracker, you can choose to get detailed explanations for only those item set questions you missed or for all item set questions.

Links to Curriculum
Within the answer explanations, we have embedded links to the relevant content for review. This can include multiple Learning Outcome Statements, concepts, definitions, or formulas.

Exam Diagnostics
When you access Performance Tracker, you can request a breakdown of your overall score on the afternoon session of any exam. You can even get the LOS references for questions you answered incorrectly to facilitate your review efforts.

Performance Comparison
Log in today and enjoy the benefits of the Schweser Library, Office Hours*, the Schweser Study Planner, expanded Practice Exam item set answers, and Performance Tracker.

* Included with the Essential, Premium, and Premium Plus study packages.

PRACTICE EXAM 1 MORNING SESSION QUESTION BREAKDOWN

MORNING SESSION		
Topic	Question	Points
Private Wealth Management	1A	12
Private Wealth Management	1B	10
Performance Evaluation and Attribution	1C	6
Asset Allocation	1D	4
Portfolio Management – Institutional	2A	12
Portfolio Management – Institutional	2B	18
Behavioral Finance	3	9
Global Investment Performance Standards	4	12
Equity Portfolio Management	5A	9
Equity Portfolio Management	5B	12
Equity Portfolio Management	5C	6
Performance Evaluation and Attribution	6A	6
Performance Evaluation and Attribution	6B	6
Performance Evaluation and Attribution	6C	6
Risk Management Applications of Derivatives	7A	6
Portfolio Management – Institutional	7B	6
Fixed Income Derivatives	7C	6
Private Wealth Management	8	12
Capital Market Expectations	9A	4
Capital Market Expectations	9B	8
Economic Concepts	9C	3
Economic Concepts	9D	3
Economic Concepts	9E	4
Total		180

PRACTICE EXAM 1 SCORE SHEET

MORNING SESSION		
Question	Max. Points	Your Approx. Score
1A	12	
1B	10	
1C	6	
1D	4	
2A	12	
2B	18	
3	9	
4	12	
5A	9	
5B	12	
5C	6	
6A	6	
6B	6	
6C	6	
7A	6	
7B	6	
7C	6	
8	12	
9A	4	
9B	8	
9C	3	
9D	3	
9E	4	
Total	180	

AFTERNOON SESSION		
Question	Max. Points	Your Approx. Score
1–6	18	
7–12	18	
13–18	18	
19–24	18	
25–30	18	
31–36	18	
37–42	18	
43–48	18	
49–54	18	
55–60	18	
Total	180	

Certain Passing Score: 252 of 360 (70%)
Probable Passing Score: 234 (65%)

Please note that we write these exams to be as challenging and representative as possible. However, due to the relaxed conditions that most candidates apply when they "take" these exams (e.g., "I need a break; I think I'll go to the refrigerator and get a snack"), you should adjust your score downward by 10–15 percentage points to get a more accurate measure of the score you would have actually received on exam day. Also, you must be honest with yourself for your score on this exam to have any meaning. Don't assume, for example, that if your essay answer is close, the graders will be generous with points.

Exam 1
Morning Session

QUESTION 1 HAS FOUR PARTS FOR A TOTAL OF 32 MINUTES

Ernie Marks, 62, is the owner of a regional construction company. Marks started the company when he was 20 years old, after receiving his grandfather's old pick-up truck as a birthday gift. Through conservative management and judicious use of bank debt, Marks was able to build the company to over 150 employees. The company is debt-free and generates all required operating funds from internal operations.

Marks' wife, Ellie, does not work and they have two children. Their daughter Allison, 28, suffers from a debilitating illness and requires constant attention. Their son Ernie Jr., 26, is in good health and graduated in the top 5% of his class at a prestigious New England liberal arts university. Marks wants to retire at 65 and wants Ernie Jr. to succeed him in running the company, but all efforts to train his son for succession have failed.

Marks has just sold the company to a national construction concern for cash. The after-tax proceeds from the sale plus the Marks' current investment portfolio total $5 million. The only requirement of the sale agreement is that Marks remain at the firm until he reaches 65, at which time he will retire and have no further obligations to the company.

Marks is seeking financial advice from Christopher Weber, CFA. In their first meeting, Marks makes the following statements:

- "Ellie and I owe nothing on the home in which we have lived for the past 30 years and we do not plan to move. The new owners of the company will pay me $150,000 next year, and that amount will grow at the general rate of inflation until I retire. They will provide medical benefits for Ellie and me for life, but I will not participate in their retirement plan."

- "I would prefer that the portfolio not lose more than 2% of its value in any one year. Since my bank account is earning only 1.5%, however, I realize that my portfolio may require some risk exposure."

- "Ellie and I estimate our personal living expenses will be $100,000 in the coming year, and I agree with you that they will probably grow at the general rate of inflation of 2% per year thereafter. My accountant indicates I will have a 33% average tax rate."

- "We have decided that Ellie can no longer care for Allison as in the past. Had Ellie not helped care for Allison over the past year, we estimate the total cost would have been $100,000, and there would have been no associated tax breaks. I would expect the cost of her care to increase at a rate of approximately 2% annually. It is our intention to provide for Allison's care as long as she lives."

- "Ernie Jr.'s 'free spirit' has essentially made him unemployable, so I want to provide him with a stipend of $50,000 per year with the first $50,000 paid in the coming year. I would also like the stipend to increase annually at the general rate of inflation. When Ellie and I have both passed away, the stipend will stop and Ernie Jr. is to receive a lump-sum payment equal to 50% of our estate. The remainder of the estate will go to charities that I will designate later."

A. **Formulate** the Marks' risk objective. **Calculate** the after-tax nominal rate of return that is required to meet all expenses for the coming year. **Show** your calculations.

Answer Question 1-A in the template provided.

(12 minutes)

Template for Question 1-A

Investment Policy Statement for the Marks	
Risk Objective	
Return Objective	

©2011 Kaplan, Inc.

B.   **Construct** the constraints portion of an investment policy statement for the Marks.

Answer Question 1-B in the template provided.

(10 minutes)

Template for Question 1-B

Time Horizon	
Liquidity	
Legal/ Regulatory	
Tax	
Unique Circumstances	

A recent analysis of market expectations has crossed Weber's desk, and he has formulated alternatives for allocating the assets from the sale proceeds. T-bill rates are 2%, and the characteristics of four alternative portfolio allocations are provided in the following table.

Asset Classes	Portfolios			
	A	B	C	D
U.S. stocks	50%	40%	20%	30%
Non-U.S. stocks	25%	20%	10%	0%
U.S. corporate bonds	10%	20%	30%	35%
Cash and equivalents	5%	10%	20%	10%
Real estate (REITs)	0%	5%	10%	10%
U.S. Treasury bills	10%	5%	10%	15%
Expected Sharpe ratio	0.66	0.70	0.77	1.17
After-tax expected return	8%	7.2%	6.3%	5.2%

C.   **Calculate** Roy's Safety First Ratio for the above portfolios and **explain** the information provided by the ratio.

(6 minutes)

D.   **Recommend** and **justify** one of the portfolios in the table.

(4 minutes)

QUESTION 2 HAS TWO PARTS FOR A TOTAL OF 30 MINUTES

Universal Insurance Company is an insurance mega-store selling life, property, and casualty insurance policies in all fifty states. The life insurance subsidiary sells products under the UniLife label, and the property and casualty subsidiary sells policies under the UniPC label.

UniLife's total assets are approximately $10 billion, which results in a surplus of $1 billion. As with most life insurance companies, UniLife's asset portfolio is segmented to cover the products sold and to achieve surplus growth to expand business. The segmentation of portfolio assets is a direct result of the increased competition in the life insurance industry and represents an attempt by UniLife to maintain an acceptable spread over their crediting rate of 5% and to more effectively price its products. Total expenses associated with business operations average 2% of assets. UniLife segments its asset base into three main asset classes: short-term/cash-like, long-term fixed-income, and equity instruments. The continued low interest rate environment, as well as improvement in equity markets, has strengthened the quality of UniLife's asset base. The following are statements made during a recent conversation by UniLife's management regarding the portfolio segments:

- "The main purpose of the short-term portfolio is to meet the liquidity requirements of our life insurance and annuity products. Hence, we expect this segment to be invested in assets exceeding or equivalent in safety to 90-day high-grade corporate commercial instruments. The improvement in overall quality of corporate paper has been encouraging."

- "The purpose of our long-term, fixed-income portfolio is to generate sufficient total returns that not only cover the crediting rate, but add to our net interest margin. Investment grade corporates (i.e., rated at least A1) with maturities ranging from 10–20 years are representative assets for this portfolio segment. Again, the improvement of corporate issues is encouraging."

- "The stock portfolio segment exists to provide longer-term growth in company surplus in the hopes of not only improving our financial condition, but also to better meet competitive pricing objectives. The majority of state regulations allow for ample investments in mid- to large-cap domestic equities, but only a small proportion (less than 5%) in international securities. Hence, the equity portfolio should generate returns exceeding the appropriate mid-to-large cap equity indexes such as the S&P MidCap or S&P 500 indexes. The equity market trend has also been positive."

A.   **Construct** the risk and return objectives portion of an investment policy statement for UniLife's portfolio segments.

Answer Question 2-A in the template provided.

(12 minutes)

Template for Question 2-A

Investment Policy Statement for UniLife Portfolio Segments	
Objectives	**Return Objectives** Short-term portfolio: Long-term bond portfolio: Stock portfolio:
	Risk Tolerance Short-term portfolio: Long-term bond portfolio: Stock portfolio:

B.   **Construct** the constraints portion of the investment policy statement for UniLife. Address the time horizon, liquidity, legal/regulatory, tax, and unique circumstances constraints. Address the time horizon and liquidity constraints for each of UniLife's portfolio segments.

Answer Question 2-B in the template provided.

(18 minutes)

Template for Question 2-B

Constraints	**Time Horizon** Short-term portfolio: Long-term portfolio: Stock portfolio:
	Liquidity Short-term portfolio: Long-term portfolio: Stock portfolio:
	Legal/regulatory:
	Taxes:
	Unique considerations:

QUESTION 3 HAS ONE PART FOR A TOTAL OF 9 MINUTES

Bernard Parker, CFA, is a portfolio manager at Wealth Enhancers, LLC. Recently, Parker attended a conference on the economic outlook for the next decade. During the conference, he spoke with Margaret Meriwether and Lloyd Allen of Foundation Specialists, Inc., a regional asset management firm specializing in portfolio management for non-profits.

Meriwether made the following statement:

- "One of our clients has experienced a change in management and is now willing to accept more risk in hopes of generating higher returns. They want to start thinking outside the box and are now open to strategies they haven't used before, such as short selling. Specifically, they want to short sell a large, popular foreign equity index. I suggested that they wait for a short period of time, because the index's weekly returns for the last four weeks have been below the long-run average weekly return, and I am expecting a correction before the index starts falling again."

Allen spoke of frustration with one of his clients:

- "One of my pension clients has well over 1,000 employees participating in their defined contribution plan. I have been trying over the last year to get them to educate their employees about the need to reallocate their portfolios as circumstances change. Some of the employees have had their plan portfolios for over two decades, and they have not made any significant changes to the portfolio allocation or even the way they want new contributions allocated."

In response, Parker says:

- "One of my clients is exactly the opposite. He is quite young and has inherited a large sum of money. Even though he has little investment experience and doesn't know much about portfolio theory, he is quite willing to make investments or even change his allocation based on small amounts of information. I can't tell you how many times he has said that he heard a Wall Street talk show person say this or that and it really resonated with him, so it made sense."

For each statement, **identify** the behavioral concept *most likely* exhibited by the individual making the statement or the behavior discussed. **Explain** each behavioral concept.

Answer Question 3 in the template provided.

(9 minutes)

Template for Question 3

Statement	Behavioral Concept	Explanation
"One of our clients has experienced a change in management and is now willing to accept more risk in hopes of generating higher returns. They want to start thinking outside the box and are now open to strategies they haven't used before, such as short selling. Specifically, they want to short sell a large, popular foreign equity index. I suggested that they wait for a short period of time, because the index's weekly returns for the last four weeks have been below the long-run average weekly return, and I am expecting a correction before the index starts falling again."		
"One of my pension clients has well over 1,000 employees participating in their defined contribution plan. I have been trying over the last year to get them to educate their employees about the need to reallocate their portfolios as circumstances change. Some of the employees have had their plan portfolios for over two decades, and they have not made any significant changes to the portfolio allocation or even the way they want new contributions allocated."		
"One of my clients is exactly the opposite. He is quite young and has inherited a large sum of money. Even though he has little investment experience and doesn't know much about portfolio theory, he is quite willing to make investments or even change his allocation based on small amounts of information. I can't tell you how many times he has said that he heard a Wall Street talk show person say this or that and it really resonated with him, so it made sense."		

QUESTION 4 HAS ONE PART FOR A TOTAL OF 12 MINUTES

Margaret Knight, CFA, is convinced that reporting portfolio performance according to the Global Investment Performance Standards (GIPS®) will provide her firm a competitive edge in the marketplace. After reading the latest information on the Standards, Knight formulates the following statements as a guide for how she will approach implementation of GIPS at her firm.

- "All composites will have the same beginning and ending annual dates. We will apply accrual accounting to all interest-accruing assets in our portfolios. Starting 2010 we will calculate time-weighted portfolio returns on the date of all large external cash flows. All discretionary, fee-paying portfolios will be included in at least one composite and composites will be defined according to investment strategy, mandate, and/or objectives."

- "My firm is approximately seven years old. Since GIPS only requires five years of annual investment performance, I can easily meet that requirement. Since my reporting systems are so effective, I also will have no problem maintaining the 5-year reporting requirement into the future."

- "My effective electronic systems will have no trouble capturing and maintaining cost and market values for portfolio valuations. My system automatically generates return information every quarter and, for my international composites, uses the same exchange rate sources for the portfolios and the benchmark."

- "All of my fee-paying portfolios will be included in at least one composite. When clients decide they no longer need my services, my system automatically recalculates previous portfolio performance to reflect the removal of the portfolios from relevant historical performance presentations."

Indicate whether each of Knight's statements is an accurate representation of GIPS. If you find these statements to be inaccurate, **explain** the reason(s) for the inaccuracies.

Answer Question 4 in the template provided.

(12 minutes)

Template for Question 4

Knight's statements	Accurate/inaccurate (circle one)	Reason(s) for inaccuracy
"All composites will have the same beginning and ending annual dates. We will apply accrual accounting to all interest-accruing assets in our portfolios. Starting 2010 we will calculate time-weighted portfolio returns on the date of all large external cash flows. All discretionary, fee-paying portfolios will be included in at least one composite and composites will be defined according to investment strategy and/or objectives."	Accurate Inaccurate	
"My firm is approximately seven years old. Since GIPS only requires five years of annual investment performance, I can easily meet that requirement. Since my reporting systems are so effective, I also will have no problem maintaining the 5-year reporting requirement into the future."	Accurate Inaccurate	

Knight's statements	Accurate/inaccurate (circle one)	Reason(s) for inaccuracy
"My effective electronic systems will have no trouble capturing and maintaining cost and market values for portfolio valuations. My system automatically generates return information every quarter and, for my international composites, uses the same exchange rate sources for the portfolios and the benchmark."	Accurate Inaccurate	
"All of my fee-paying portfolios will be included in at least one composite. When clients decide they no longer need my services, my system automatically recalculates previous portfolio performance to reflect the removal of the portfolios from relevant historical performance presentations."	Accurate Inaccurate	

QUESTION 5 HAS THREE PARTS FOR A TOTAL OF 27 MINUTES

Julie Carter and Jenny Dumas are senior analysts for Oleander Associates. Oleander provides portfolio management and investment planning for wealthy individuals. Although Oleander has a staff consisting of both analysts and economists, they periodically use outside portfolio managers when appropriate.

Carter and Dumas are currently evaluating the expected performance for a group of portfolio managers they have hired for a subset of their clients' portfolios. For this subset, Carter and Dumas have decided to pursue a core-satellite approach. The data below show the managers' active risk and active returns. Diamond Management uses a value-oriented approach, SRI Advisors uses a socially responsible investing approach, and Wrightsville Managers uses a passive enhanced indexing approach.

	Expected Alpha	Expected Tracking Risk	Allocations
Diamond Management	2.80%	5.20%	10%
Hoke Associates	0%	0%	20%
Mosby Investors	2.00%	3.10%	25%
SRI Advisors	3.50%	6.80%	5%
Wrightsville Managers	1.10%	1.62%	40%

A.   **Calculate** the expected active return, expected active risk, and expected information ratio of this subset of managers, given the above allocations.

(9 minutes)

Based on the previous data, Carter and others make the following comments:

- "From your data it appears that your core investment is Hoke associates. Hoke should mitigate the overall risk of your strategy, while the four satellites provide an active return component."
- "The portfolio of Diamond Management is likely weighted towards utility and financial stocks."
- "I expect that investors who pursue an investment approach similar to Hoke Associates will generally have higher information ratios than other investment approaches."
- "We should carefully monitor the style of SRI Advisors because they likely have a bias toward value stocks, given their investment emphasis."

B.   **State** whether or not *each* of these comments is correct or incorrect and **explain** your selection. Rearranging a statement does not constitute an explanation for either a correct or incorrect statement.

Answer Question 5-B in the template provided.

(12 minutes)

Template for Question 5-B

Comment	Correct or incorrect? (circle one)	Explanation
"From your data it appears that your core investment is Hoke associates. Hoke should mitigate the overall risk of your strategy, while the four satellites should provide an active return component."	Correct Incorrect	
"The portfolio of Diamond Management is likely weighted towards utility and financial stocks."	Correct Incorrect	

"I expect that investors who pursue an investment approach similar to Hoke Associates will generally have higher information ratios than other investment approaches."	Correct Incorrect	
"We should carefully monitor the style of SRI Advisors because they likely have a bias toward value stocks, given their investment emphasis."	Correct Incorrect	

Oleander Associates periodically reviews the performance of and fees paid to its outside portfolio managers. Carter and Dumas are in charge of revising the manager questionnaire, reviewing the fee schedules, and preparing a report on the impact of a manager's investment approach on the costs to Oleander.

Under Oleander's current plan, managers are paid 0.40% for the first $20 million under management and 0.35% for asset amounts over $20 million. The primary concern at Oleander is that managers are not provided proper incentive. Under a proposed fee schedule, managers would be paid 0.35% for the first $10 million under management and 0.30% for asset amounts over $10 million plus 10% of all excess returns relative to the manager's benchmark.

During their discussion on these items, Dumas makes the following comments:

- "Our proposed plan should contain high water mark provisions. These provisions state that managers will be paid no less than a certain amount during bear markets. This will prevent us from losing good managers during market downturns and, at the same time, help us avoid paying excess performance fees."
- "Your proposal to cap performance fees is illogical. The cap would discourage your managers from taking the risks necessary to obtain higher returns. Rather than aligning the managers' goals with your own, this could have a very negative effect."

C.   **State** whether *each* of these comments is correct or incorrect and **explain** your selection.

Answer Question 5-C in the template provided.

(6 minutes)

Template for Question 5-C

Comment	Correct or incorrect? (circle one)	Explanation
"Our proposed plan should contain high water mark provisions. These provisions state that managers will be paid no less than a certain amount during bear markets. This will prevent us from losing good managers during market downturns and, at the same time, help us avoid paying excess performance fees."	Correct Incorrect	
"Your proposal to cap performance fees is illogical. The cap would discourage your managers from taking the risks necessary to obtain higher returns. Rather than aligning the managers' goals with your own, this could have a very negative effect."	Correct Incorrect	

QUESTION 6 HAS THREE PARTS FOR A TOTAL OF 18 MINUTES

As part of an attribution analysis, Greg Roberts, CFA, has accumulated the following partial data for his portfolio:

Sectors	Portfolio Sector Weight (%)	Benchmark Sector Weight (%)	Portfolio Sector Return (%)	Benchmark Sector Return (%)
Agricultural	10.55	6.45	−0.82	+1.35
Capital Goods	8.52	8.99	−3.28	−4.34
Consumer Durables	36.22	37.36	1.96	1.98
Energy	5.24	4.65	0.44	0.24
Total Portfolio			1.34	0.56

A. Using the available data, **calculate** and **explain** the pure sector allocation contribution attributable to the agricultural sector allocation.

(6 minutes)

B.   Using the available data, **calculate** and **explain** the within-sector contribution attributable to the agricultural sector allocation.

(6 minutes)

C.   Using the available data, **calculate** and **explain** the allocation/selection interaction contribution attributable to the agricultural sector allocation.

(6 minutes)

QUESTION 7 HAS THREE PARTS FOR A TOTAL OF 18 MINUTES

Matrix Corporation has decided that since the company has sufficient liquid resources to make any required plan contributions in the future, it will maintain its current asset mix in the defined benefit plan, which is approximately 60% equities and 40% bonds over a wide range of maturities. Matrix officers believe that interest rates are temporarily low, and they do not want to increase the bond allocation for this reason.

Concern remains, however, that if they are wrong, further decreases in interest rates will worsen the underfunded status of the plan and require even greater funding by Matrix over the next several years. Matrix has decided to hedge this risk by taking a position in derivative securities.

Matrix is considering three derivative strategies to provide the hedge described above: exchange-traded interest rate put options, options on Treasury bonds, and futures on Treasury bonds. For each of the alternatives, **describe** the most appropriate strategy, given the goals stated above. For each alternative, **determine** whether the strategy will achieve the stated goal, **support** your conclusion, and **indicate** any potential problems with the strategy.

A.   Exchange-traded interest rate put options.

(6 minutes)

B.   Treasury bond options.

(6 minutes)

C.   Treasury bond futures.

(6 minutes)

QUESTION 8 HAS ONE PART FOR A TOTAL OF 12 MINUTES

Derek May, CFA, recently attended a retirement planning conference on using Monte Carlo techniques in the retirement planning decision. Since it has been a year since May formulated some of his clients' Investment Policy Statements, he decided it might be a good idea to apply some of the concepts discussed at the meeting. May scheduled a meeting with Lacy Dayne, who just returned from her travel abroad and has recently been named executive vice president of marketing for a global provider of wireless portal equipment. In the meeting, May makes the following statements:

- "Since all has gone according to plan since our first meeting a year ago, I think it is time we focus efforts on your retirement. The most important objective is to determine an exact future value goal for your portfolio, integrating an expected rate of return, inflation, and your tax position to produce your retirement profile."

- "Once we have generated the single point estimate for the value of your retirement portfolio, we can apply some Monte Carlo techniques to see various other outcomes. Monte Carlo techniques will generate various portfolio values at retirement but, unfortunately, will not account for the risks inherent in our investment decisions. So, we will just have to pay a little more attention to the various portfolio levels."

- "Think of the various portfolio levels as a range of potential outcomes your portfolio can achieve in ten years. The primary focus when evaluating those outcomes, however, will still be on the risks you wish to avoid in the present, and not necessarily any risks that may occur along the way."

- "Although we can incorporate taxes in our Monte Carlo techniques, the compounding assumptions we made in the single point estimate of portfolio value is just fine. Compounding does not play that much of a role with Monte Carlo, which simplifies the application of the procedure."

State whether you agree or disagree with each of May's statements. **Justify** your answer with a discussion of either a virtue or shortcoming associated with *each* statement.

Answer Question 8 in the template provided.

(12 minutes)

Template for Question 8

Statement	Agree or Disagree (circle one)	Explanation, if incorrect
"Since all has gone according to plan since our first meeting a year ago, I think it is time we focus efforts on your retirement. The most important objective is to determine an exact future value goal for your portfolio, integrating an expected rate of return, inflation, and your tax position to produce your retirement profile."	Agree Disagree	
"Once we have generated the single point estimate for the value of your retirement portfolio, we can apply some Monte Carlo techniques to see various other outcomes. Monte Carlo techniques will generate various portfolio values at retirement but, unfortunately, will not account for the risks inherent in our investment decisions. So, we will just have to pay a little more attention to the various portfolio levels."	Agree Disagree	

"Think of the various portfolio levels as a range of potential outcomes your portfolio can achieve in ten years. The primary focus when evaluating those outcomes, however, will still be on the risks you wish to avoid in the present, and not necessarily any risks that may occur along the way."	Agree Disagree	
"Although we can incorporate taxes in our Monte Carlo techniques, the compounding assumptions we made in the single point estimate of portfolio value is just fine. Compounding does not play that much of a role with Monte Carlo, which simplifies the application of the procedure."	Agree Disagree	

QUESTION 9 HAS FIVE PARTS FOR A TOTAL OF 22 MINUTES

Polly Nurnberg and Lilly Hoey are analysts for Greenville Management. Greenville manages the money for individuals and small institutions. Nurnberg and Hoey have been assigned the responsibility of identifying attractive national stock markets. They do so by evaluating the macroeconomic conditions in a country, the strength of its currency, and its future outlook.

Nurnberg and Hoey are currently evaluating the economic data for the European Union, North America, and South America. During a discussion amongst themselves and junior analysts, Nurnberg and Hoey discuss the economic data and prospects of these economies. Hoey has gathered the following data for the Canadian economy:

Neutral rate for Canada	4.0%
Inflation target for Canada	3.5%
GDP long-term trend for Canada	4.5%
Expected Canadian inflation	7.5%
Expected Canadian GDP	6.5%

Based on these figures, Hoey makes the following comments:

- "Using the Taylor rule, I expect the Canadian central bank to target an interest rate of about 6.0%."

- "Based on the information I have gathered, we should be advising clients interested in the Canadian economy to invest in Canadian cash instruments, rather than stocks or bonds."

A.   **State** whether *each* of these comments is correct or incorrect. If incorrect, **explain** or **demonstrate** why.

Answer Question 9-A in the template provided.

(4 minutes)

Template for Question 9-A

Comment	Correct or incorrect? (circle one)	Explanation, if incorrect
"Using the Taylor rule, I expect the Canadian central bank to target an interest rate of about 6.0%."	Correct Incorrect	
"Based on the information I have gathered, we should be advising clients interested in the Canadian economy to invest in Canadian cash instruments, rather than stocks or bonds."	Correct Incorrect	

Later in the discussion, Nurnberg makes the following comments regarding the prospects of other economies and currencies:

- "The European Central Bank has been cutting interest rates. One potential impact on the euro is to decrease its value because investors will seek higher returns elsewhere. Unlike most analysts, however, I use a capital flows approach which projects that the euro will actually increase in value."

- "Short-term interest rates on government bonds in Great Britain are 3.2% and 10-year rates are 5.9%. This indicates that, for an investor considering investing in Britain, British corporate bonds would be a better investment than British stocks."

- "Mexico's largest trading partner is the United States. Given that the United States is in the early stages of an economic expansion, Mexican stocks would be attractive investments."

- "Economists project that in the coming months, business confidence in Japan will increase. The Bank of Japan will continue to accommodate growth by keeping interest rates low. Japanese government spending will increase as Japan puts a renewed emphasis on defense spending. Inflation in Japan will fall or remain stable. Given this outlook, I suggest that for an investor with a time horizon of a few years, an allocation to Japanese bonds is warranted."

B.   **State** whether *each* of these comments is correct or incorrect. If incorrect, **explain** why.

Answer Question 9-B in the template provided.

(8 minutes)

Template for Question 9-B

Comment	Correct or incorrect? (circle one)	Explanation, if incorrect
"The European Central Bank has been cutting interest rates. One potential impact on the euro is to decrease its value because investors will seek higher returns elsewhere. Unlike most analysts, however, I use a capital flows approach which projects that the euro will actually increase in value."	Correct Incorrect	
"Short-term interest rates on government bonds in Great Britain are 3.2% and 10-year rates are 5.9%. This indicates that, for an investor considering investing in Britain, British corporate bonds would be a better investment than British stocks."	Correct Incorrect	

"Mexico's largest trading partner is the United States. Given that the United States is in the early stages of an economic expansion, Mexican stocks would be attractive investments."	Correct Incorrect	
"Economists project that in the coming months, business confidence in Japan will increase. The Bank of Japan will continue to accommodate growth by keeping interest rates low. Japanese government spending will increase as Japan puts a renewed emphasis on defense spending. Inflation in Japan will fall or remain stable. Given this outlook, I suggest that for an investor with a time horizon of a few years, an allocation to Japanese bonds is warranted."	Correct Incorrect	

As part of their analysis of developing economies, Nurnberg and Hoey estimate the rate of growth in economic output. The following table contains economic data for one of the markets in their analysis:

Expected growth in total factor productivity	2.0%
Expected growth in the labor	3.5%
Expected growth in capital stock, $\alpha = 0.35$	1.0%

C. Using the data from the table, **estimate** the growth (i.e., percentage change) in real economic output for this market over the coming year.

(3 minutes)

D. Nurnberg and Hoey are arguing over the value and interpretation of the Solow residual for another economy. In the space provided, using only the data provided in the table below, **estimate** and **interpret** the Solow residual for the economy:

Expected growth in real economic output	3.5%
Expected growth in the labor	2.5%
Expected growth in capital stock, $\alpha = 0.6$	1.5%
Expected rate of inflation	3.3%

(3 minutes)

E.   The following data pertain to the primary market index for one of the economies that Nurnberg and Hoey are evaluating. Nurnberg argues that the equity market is overvalued.*

Last dividend (D_0)	100
Forecast earnings per share	300
Current and sustainable long-term growth rate	2.1%
Required return	7.5%

*The index is currently at 2050.

Using only the data in the table, **determine** whether you would agree or disagree with Nurnberg's assertion. Show your calculations in the space below.

(4 minutes)

END OF MORNING SESSION

EXAM 1 AFTERNOON SESSION TOPIC BREAKDOWN

Question	Topic	Minutes
1–6	Ethical and Professional Standards	18
7–12	Ethical and Professional Standards	18
13–18	Portfolio Management – Institutional/GIPS	18
19–24	Global Bonds and Fixed Income Derivatives and Risk Management Applications of Derivatives	18
25–30	Management of Active and Passive Fixed Income Portfolios and Global Bonds and Fixed Income Derivatives	18
31–36	Global Bonds and Fixed Income Derivatives	18
37–42	Alternative Investments	18
43–48	Portfolio Management – Individual	18
49–54	Global Bonds and Fixed Income Derivatives, Risk Management, and Risk Management Applications of Derivatives	18
55–60	Execution of Portfolio Decisions: Monitoring and Rebalancing	18
Total		180

Exam 1 Selected Response Item Set Answer Sheet

The afternoon session of the Level III exam contains 10 Selected Response Item Sets, each with six questions, and you must answer them by filling in a bubble sheet with a number 2 or HB pencil. For realism, we suggest that you use this answer sheet and darken the bubbles corresponding to your answers. This sheet will also facilitate entering your answers into our online Performance Tracker. You have 180 minutes for this session of the exam. That equates to 3 minutes per item set question, so budget your time well.

#	A	B	C		#	A	B	C
1.	Ⓐ	Ⓑ	Ⓒ		31.	Ⓐ	Ⓑ	Ⓒ
2.	Ⓐ	Ⓑ	Ⓒ		32.	Ⓐ	Ⓑ	Ⓒ
3.	Ⓐ	Ⓑ	Ⓒ		33.	Ⓐ	Ⓑ	Ⓒ
4.	Ⓐ	Ⓑ	Ⓒ		34.	Ⓐ	Ⓑ	Ⓒ
5.	Ⓐ	Ⓑ	Ⓒ		35.	Ⓐ	Ⓑ	Ⓒ
6.	Ⓐ	Ⓑ	Ⓒ		36.	Ⓐ	Ⓑ	Ⓒ
7.	Ⓐ	Ⓑ	Ⓒ		37.	Ⓐ	Ⓑ	Ⓒ
8.	Ⓐ	Ⓑ	Ⓒ		38.	Ⓐ	Ⓑ	Ⓒ
9.	Ⓐ	Ⓑ	Ⓒ		39.	Ⓐ	Ⓑ	Ⓒ
10.	Ⓐ	Ⓑ	Ⓒ		40.	Ⓐ	Ⓑ	Ⓒ
11.	Ⓐ	Ⓑ	Ⓒ		41.	Ⓐ	Ⓑ	Ⓒ
12.	Ⓐ	Ⓑ	Ⓒ		42.	Ⓐ	Ⓑ	Ⓒ
13.	Ⓐ	Ⓑ	Ⓒ		43.	Ⓐ	Ⓑ	Ⓒ
14.	Ⓐ	Ⓑ	Ⓒ		44.	Ⓐ	Ⓑ	Ⓒ
15.	Ⓐ	Ⓑ	Ⓒ		45.	Ⓐ	Ⓑ	Ⓒ
16.	Ⓐ	Ⓑ	Ⓒ		46.	Ⓐ	Ⓑ	Ⓒ
17.	Ⓐ	Ⓑ	Ⓒ		47.	Ⓐ	Ⓑ	Ⓒ
18.	Ⓐ	Ⓑ	Ⓒ		48.	Ⓐ	Ⓑ	Ⓒ
19.	Ⓐ	Ⓑ	Ⓒ		49.	Ⓐ	Ⓑ	Ⓒ
20.	Ⓐ	Ⓑ	Ⓒ		50.	Ⓐ	Ⓑ	Ⓒ
21.	Ⓐ	Ⓑ	Ⓒ		51.	Ⓐ	Ⓑ	Ⓒ
22.	Ⓐ	Ⓑ	Ⓒ		52.	Ⓐ	Ⓑ	Ⓒ
23.	Ⓐ	Ⓑ	Ⓒ		53.	Ⓐ	Ⓑ	Ⓒ
24.	Ⓐ	Ⓑ	Ⓒ		54.	Ⓐ	Ⓑ	Ⓒ
25.	Ⓐ	Ⓑ	Ⓒ		55.	Ⓐ	Ⓑ	Ⓒ
26.	Ⓐ	Ⓑ	Ⓒ		56.	Ⓐ	Ⓑ	Ⓒ
27.	Ⓐ	Ⓑ	Ⓒ		57.	Ⓐ	Ⓑ	Ⓒ
28.	Ⓐ	Ⓑ	Ⓒ		58.	Ⓐ	Ⓑ	Ⓒ
29.	Ⓐ	Ⓑ	Ⓒ		59.	Ⓐ	Ⓑ	Ⓒ
30.	Ⓐ	Ⓑ	Ⓒ		60.	Ⓐ	Ⓑ	Ⓒ

Exam 1
Afternoon Session

Questions 1–6 relate to Ethical and Professional Standards.

Theresa Bair, CFA, a portfolio manager for Brinton Investment Company (BIC), has recently been promoted to lead portfolio manager for her firm's new small capitalization closed-end equity fund, the Horizon Fund. BIC is an asset management firm headquartered in Holland with regional offices in several other European countries.

After accepting the position, Bair received a letter from the three principals of BIC. The letter congratulated Bair on her accomplishment and new position with the firm and also provided some guidance as to her new role and the firm's expectations. Among other things, the letter stated the following:

> "Because our firm is based in Holland and you will have clients located in many European countries, it is essential that you determine what laws and regulations are applicable to the management of this new fund. It is your responsibility to obtain this knowledge and comply with appropriate regulations. This is the first time we have offered a fund devoted solely to small capitalization securities, so we will observe your progress carefully. You will likely need to arrange for our sister companies to buy and sell Horizon Fund shares over the first month of operations. This will provide sufficient price support to allow the fund to trade closer to its net asset value, giving the perception that our fund is more desirable than other small-cap closed-end funds."

Bair heeded the advice from her firm's principals and collected information on the laws and regulations of three countries: Norway, Sweden, and Denmark. So far, all of the investors expressing interest in the Horizon Fund are from these areas. Based on her research, Bair decides the following policies are appropriate for the fund:

Note: Laws mentioned in the following are assumed for illustrative purposes.

- For clients located in Norway the fund will institute transaction crossing, since, unlike in Holland, the practice is not prohibited by securities laws or regulations. The process will involve internally matching buy and sell orders from Norwegian clients whenever possible. This will reduce brokerage fees and improve the fund's overall performance.

- For clients located in Denmark, account statements that include the value of the clients' holdings, number of trades, and average daily trading volume will be generated on a monthly basis as required by Denmark's securities regulators, even though the laws in Holland only require such reports to be generated on a quarterly basis.
- For clients located in Sweden, the fund will not disclose differing levels of service that are available for investors based upon the size of their investment. This policy is consistent with the laws and regulations in Holland. Sweden's securities regulations do not cover this type of situation.

Three months after the inception of the fund, its market value has grown from $200 million to $300 million and Bair's performance has earned her a quarter-end bonus. Since it is now the end of the quarter, Bair is participating in conference calls with companies in her fund. Bair calls into the conference number for Sunrise Petroleum. The meeting doesn't start for another five minutes, however, and as Bair waits, she hears the CEO and CFO of Sunrise discussing the huge earnings restatement that will be necessary for the financial statement from the previous quarter. The restatement will not be announced until the year's end, six months from now. Bair does not remind the officers that she can hear their conversation. Once the call has ended, Bair rushes to BIC's compliance officer to inform him of what she has learned during the conference call. Bair ignores the fact that two members of the firm's investment banking division are in the office while she is telling the compliance officer what happened on the conference call. The investment bankers then proceed to sell their personal holdings of Sunrise Petroleum stock. After her meeting, Bair sells the Horizon Fund's holdings of Sunrise Petroleum stock.

1. Do the suggestions in the letter from the principals of BIC violate any CFA Institute Standards of Professional Conduct?
    A. Yes, buying and selling shares between divisions of a firm is an example of "priming the pump" and is not an acceptable practice.
    B. Yes, the suggested trades are intended to manipulate market data in order to attract investors for the fund.
    C. No, even though Blair is responsible for knowing the laws, the compliance officer is responsible for making sure the firm is in compliance.

2. With regard to the treatment of clients in Norway and Denmark, do the policies that Bair has selected for the Horizon Fund violate any CFA Institute Standards of Professional Conduct?

	Norway	Denmark
A.	No	Yes
B.	Yes	No
C.	No	No

3. With regard to the treatment of clients in Sweden, does the policy that Bair has selected for the Horizon Fund violate any CFA Institute Standards of Professional Conduct?
    A. Yes, Bair's policy will violate Standard III(B) Fair Dealing.
    B. No, because disclosure in Sweden would disadvantage clients residing in other countries.
    C. No, because disclosure in any country would break the confidentiality that Bair owes to her clients.

4. After her conference call with Sunrise Petroleum, Bair should have:
    A. included the information in a research report to make it public before selling the holdings from the Horizon Fund.
    B. attempted to have Sunrise publicly disclose the earnings restatement before informing the compliance officer of the information.
    C. informed the compliance officer and then publicly disclosed the information in a research report before selling the Sunrise stock.

5. By selling their personal holdings of Sunrise Petroleum, did the employees of BIC's investment banking division violate any CFA Institute Standards of Professional Conduct?
    A. Yes, because they breached their fiduciary duty and were disloyal to the clients of the Horizon Fund.
    B. Yes, because they did not maintain the confidentiality of the information they overheard in the compliance officer's office.
    C. Yes, because they knowingly traded on information that, if it had been publicly known, would have affected the price of Sunrise stock.

6. By selling the Horizon Fund's shares of Sunrise Petroleum, did Bair violate any CFA Institute Standards of Professional Conduct?
    A. Yes, Bair violated Standard II Integrity of Capital Markets.
    B. No, because she ensured public dissemination of the earnings restatement information before she traded the shares.
    C. Yes, because waiting to trade the stock would severely disadvantage investors in her fund and would have violated her duty of loyalty to her clients.

Questions 7–12 relate to Ethical and Professional Standards.

Stephanie Mackley is a portfolio manager for Durango Wealth Management (DWM), a regional money manager catering to wealthy investors in the southwestern portion of the United States. Mackley's clients vary widely in terms of their age, net worth, and investment objectives, but all must have at least $1 million in net assets before she will accept them as clients.

Many of Mackley's clients are referred to her by Kern & Associates, an accounting and consulting firm. DWM does not provide any direct compensation to Kern & Associates for the referrals, but Mackley, who is the president of her local CFA Society, invites Kern & Associates to give an annual presentation to the society on the subject of tax planning and minimization strategies that Kern & Associates provides for its clients. Kern & Associates' competitors have never received an invitation to present their services to the society. When Mackley receives a referral, she informs the prospect of the arrangement between DWM and Kern & Associates.

DWM maintains a full research staff that analyzes and recommends equity and debt investments. All of the in-house research is provided to the firm's portfolio managers and their clients. In addition, DWM provides a subscription service to outside investors and portfolio managers. Aaron Welch, CFA, a private contractor, researches and reports on high-tech firms in the United States and other developed countries for several portfolio management clients. One of his latest reports rated InnerTech, Inc., a small startup that develops microscopic surgical devices, as a strong buy. After reviewing the report carefully, Mackley decides to purchase shares of InnerTech for clients with account values over $6 million. She feels that accounts with less than this amount cannot accept the risk level associated with InnerTech stock.

Two days after purchasing InnerTech for her clients, the stock nearly doubles in value, and the clients are ecstatic about the returns on their portfolios. Several of them give her small bouquets of flowers and boxes of chocolates, which she discloses to her supervisor at DWM. One client even offers her the use of a condo in Vail, Colorado for two weeks during ski season, if she can reproduce the results next quarter. Mackley graciously thanks her clients and asks that they refer any of their friends and relatives who are in need of asset management services. She provides brochures to a few clients who mention that they have friends who would be interested. The brochure contains a description of Mackley's services and her qualifications. At the end of the brochure, Mackley includes her full name followed by "a Chartered Financial Analyst" in bold font of the same size as her name. Following is an excerpt from the brochure:

"DWM can provide many of the investment services you are likely to need. For those services that we do not provide directly, such as estate planning, we have standing relationships with companies that do provide such services. I have a long history with DWM, serving as an investment analyst for six years and then in my current capacity as a portfolio manager for twelve years. My clients have been very satisfied with my past performance and will likely be very satisfied with my future performance, which I attribute to my significant investment experience as well as my participation in the CFA Program. I earned the right to use the CFA designation thirteen years ago. All CFA charterholders must pass a series of three rigorous examinations that cover investment management and research analysis."

Two weeks later, some of Mackley's clients request that she provide supporting documentation for the research report on InnerTech, so they can familiarize themselves with how DWM analyzes investment opportunities. Mackley asks Welch for the documents, but Welch is unable to provide copies of his supporting research since he disposed of them, according to the company's policy, one week after issuing and distributing the report. Mackley informs Welch that obtaining the supporting documents is of the utmost importance, since one of the clients requesting the materials, Craig Adams, is about to inherit $20 million and as a result will be one of the firm's most important clients. Welch agrees to recreate the research documents in order to support the firm's relationship with Adams.

7. Does the arrangement between Mackley and Kern & Associates violate any CFA Institute Standards of Professional Conduct?
    A. Yes.
    B. No, because the referral agreement is fully disclosed to all clients and prospects before they employ Mackley's services.
    C. No, because Mackley only accepts clients with net assets above $1 million who are likely to know that the arrangement is common in the industry.

8. Were any CFA Institute Standards of Professional Conduct violated in conjunction with Welch's report on InnerTech and Mackley's purchase of InnerTech stock?

	Welch	Mackley
A.	No	Yes
B.	Yes	No
C.	Yes	Yes

9. According to the Standards of Professional Conduct, Mackley must do which of the following regarding the gifts offered to her by her clients? She may:

   A. not accept use of the condo without prior disclosure to her employer in writing.

   B. not accept the gifts or use of the condo without disclosing them to her employer in writing.

   C. accept the gifts and use of the condo as they represent little or no monetary value to her or cost to her clients.

10. Does Mackley's signature at the end of her brochure violate any CFA Institute Standards of Professional Conduct?

   A. Yes. Including "a Chartered Financial Analyst" after her name indicates that she is a Chartered Financial Analyst.

   B. No. Although writing out "a Chartered Financial Analyst" is discouraged, doing so does not represent a violation.

   C. Yes. Mackley may include "a Chartered Financial Analyst" in bold type only if the rest of her name is also in bold type.

11. In her marketing brochure, did Mackley violate any CFA Institute Standards of Professional Conduct in her reference to her investment performance or her reference to the CFA Program?

	Performance	CFA Program
A.	Yes	Yes
B.	No	Yes
C.	Yes	No

12. In her discussions with Welch, where she asks him to recreate the supporting research for the InnerTech report, has Mackley violated any CFA Institute Standards of Professional Conduct?

   A. No.

   B. Yes, because the request creates a conflict of interest between Mackley and Welch.

   C. Yes, because she failed to preserve the confidentiality of her client's information.

Questions 13–18 relate to Portfolio Management for Institutional Investors and GIPS.

Jack Rose and Ryan Boatman are analysts with Quincy Consultants. Quincy provides advice on risk management and performance presentation to pension plans, insurance firms, and other institutional portfolio managers throughout the United States and Canada.

Rose and Boatman are preparing an analysis of the defined benefit pension plans for four mature corporations in the United States. In an effort to ascertain the risk to the firms' shareholders, Rose and Boatman gather the information in Figure 1.

Figure 1: Pension Plan Data

	Firm A	Firm B	Firm C	Firm D
Market value of plan assets ($ million)	$1,300	$980	$1,400	$710
Market value of plan liabilities ($ million)	$1,460	$900	$1,330	$870
Percentage of plan assets in bonds	35%	57%	65%	25%

While discussing how the weighted average cost of capital (WACC) for a corporation can be adjusted to incorporate pension asset risk, Rose and Boatman make the following comments:

- Rose: "From what I understand, in order to calculate a true weighted average cost of capital, management should consider the assets held in their pension plan. Because pension plans hold equity securities as assets, the plan assets usually have a higher weighted average beta than the sponsoring firm's operating assets. This means the typical firm's weighted average asset beta and cost of capital are higher than when calculated using only the operating assets. If management bases their accept/reject decisions on a weighted average cost of capital that considers only operating assets, they might accept projects that really should have been rejected."
- Boatman: "I'm not sure I agree with you. To match the maturity of their liabilities, pension plans like to hold at least half their assets in long maturity bonds. Then, since the bonds have a long weighted average duration, they have considerable interest rate sensitivity. This is really what makes the pension assets riskier than the firm's operating assets. However, since debt securities have zero betas, they have a low weighted average asset beta and the firm has a lower weighted average cost of capital when pension assets are considered than when they are not considered. The result of considering only the operating assets is that the weighted average cost of capital is inflated and management tends to incorrectly reject projects that could have been accepted."

In a visit to the headquarters of Beeman Enterprises, Rose and Boatman explain how in an expanded balance sheet format, a change in a pension plan's asset allocation can result in a change in the firm's financial ratios. To illustrate the concept to the firm's chief financial officer, they provide three different scenarios (shown in Figure 2) indicating necessary changes in the firm's capital structure under the assumption that the firm's pension plan increases its allocation to equity and management wants to keep the sponsoring firm's cost of equity capital constant (i.e., constant equity beta).

Figure 2: Cost of Capital Scenarios

	Debt to Equity Ratio	Total Assets Beta	Equity Beta	Amount of Equity Capital
Scenario A	Increase	Constant	Constant	Increase
Scenario B	Decrease	Increase	Constant	Increase
Scenario C	Decrease	Decrease	Constant	Constant

Quincy Consultants has also provided advice to Monroe Portfolio Managers. Among its investments, Monroe has a real estate portfolio that invests in shopping centers and office buildings throughout the southern United States. The firm has provided the following data to calculate and report quarterly returns to current and prospective investors. Additionally, the capital contribution came on day 47 (0.52 into the quarter) and the capital disbursement came on day 67 (0.74 into the quarter).

Total capital as of	1/1/2010	$18,000,000
Capital contribution on	2/16/2010	2,300,000
Capital disbursement on	3/8/2010	850,000
Capital expenditure		1,000,000
Property taxes paid		219,000
Property sales		1,820,000
Total non-recoverable expenses		178,000
Interest paid on borrowed funds		152,000
Accrued investment income		58,000
Market value — beg. of quarter	1/1/2010	19,100,000
Market value — end of quarter	3/31/2010	20,200,000

After calculating the capital return and income return for the portfolio, Rose and Boatman discuss the performance presentation standards for real estate and private equity portfolios. Discussing the differences between the general provisions of the GIPS standards and those for real estate and private equity portfolios, Rose states the following:

1. For periods beginning on or after January 1, 2011, the GIPS general provisions require valuation in accordance with the definition of fair value and the GIPS valuation principles. Real estate portfolios can be valued quarterly, but real estate investments must be valued at least annually by an independent third party qualified to perform such valuations.

2. For periods beginning on or after January 1, 2011, in addition to a minimum of annual valuations, private equity provisions require the annualized since-inception internal rate of return (SI-IRR) using daily cash flows. Stock distributions must be considered cash flows.

3. In presentations for real estate composites, firms are required to disclose their definition of discretion as well as their internal valuation methodologies for the most recent period presented. In addition, for real estate closed-end composites, firms must present the since-inception paid-in capital and since-inception distributions for each year.

4. For periods beginning on or after January 1, 2011, the GIPS real estate requirements state that the income return and capital return must be calculated separately. Prior to that, the standards permitted simply stating that the capital return and income return were adjusted so that they summed to the total return.

13.   From the data provided in Figure 1, determine the firm or firms that *probably* have the greatest risk arising from pension plan assets.
A. Firm A.
B. Firms B and C.
C. Firm D.

14.   Regarding the comments by Rose and Boatman on the incorporation of pension plan risk into the weighted average cost of capital, determine whether they are correct or incorrect.
A. Only Rose is correct.
B. Only Boatman is correct.
C. Neither is correct.

15.   Of the three scenarios (see Figure 2) presented to the Beeman Enterprises executives, which would represent the appropriate reaction to increasing the pension plan allocation to equity, if management wishes to maintain its current equity beta?
A. Scenario A.
B. Scenario B.
C. Scenario C.

16.   The capital return and income return for Monroe are *closest* to:

Capital return	Income return
A. 5.8%	–2.6%
B. 7.6%	0.3%
C. 10.2%	–2.6%

17.   Determine whether Rose's statements 1 and 2 on the GIPS standards are correct or incorrect.
A. Only statement 1 is correct.
B. Only statement 2 is correct.
C. Both statements are correct.

18.   Determine whether Rose's statements 3 and 4 on the GIPS standards are correct or incorrect.
A. Only statement 3 is correct.
B. Only statement 4 is correct.
C. Both statements are correct.

Questions 19–24 relate to Management of Active and Passive Fixed Income Portfolios, Portfolio Management of Global Bonds and Fixed Income Derivatives, and Risk Management Applications of Derivatives.

Daniel Castillo and Ramon Diaz are chief investment officers at Advanced Advisors (AA), a boutique fixed-income firm based in the United States. AA employs numerous quantitative models to invest in both domestic and international securities.

During the week, Castillo and Diaz consult with one of their investors, Sally Michaels. Michaels currently holds a $10,000,000 fixed-income position that is selling at par. The maturity is 20 years, and the coupon rate of 7% is paid semiannually. Her coupons can be reinvested at 8%. Castillo is looking at various interest rate change scenarios, and one such scenario is where the interest rate on the bonds immediately changes to 8%.

Diaz is considering using a repurchase agreement to leverage Michaels's portfolio. Michaels is concerned, however, with not understanding the factors that impact the interest rate, or repo rate, used in her strategy. In response, Castillo explains the factors that affect the repo rate and makes the following statements:

1. "The repo rate is directly related to the maturity of the repo, inversely related to the quality of the collateral, and directly related to the maturity of the collateral. U.S. Treasury bills are often purchased by Treasury dealers using repo transactions, and since they have high liquidity, short maturities, and no default risk, the repo rate is usually quite low."

2. "The greater control the lender has over the collateral, the lower the repo rate. If the availability of the collateral is limited, the repo rate will be higher."

Castillo consults with an institutional investor, the Washington Investment Fund, on the effect of leverage on bond portfolio returns as well as their bond portfolio's sensitivity to changes in interest rates. The portfolio under discussion is well-diversified, with small positions in a large number of bonds with an average duration of 7.2. Of the $200 million value of the portfolio, $60 million was borrowed. The duration of borrowed funds is 0.8. The expected return on the portfolio is 8% and the cost of borrowed funds is 3%.

The next day, the chief investment officer for the Washington Investment Fund expresses her concern about the risk of their portfolio, given its leverage. She inquires about the various risk measures for bond portfolios. In response, Diaz distinguishes between the standard deviation and downside risk measures, making the following statements:

1. "Portfolio managers complain that using variance to calculate Sharpe ratios is inappropriate. Since it considers all returns over the entire distribution, variance and the resulting standard deviation are artificially inflated, so the resulting Sharpe ratio is artificially deflated. Since it is easily calculated for bond portfolios, managers feel a more realistic measure of risk is the semi-variance, which measures the distribution of returns below a given return, such as the mean or a hurdle rate."

2. "A shortcoming of VAR is its inability to predict the size of potential losses in the lower tail of the expected return distribution. Although it can assign a probability to some maximum loss, it does not predict the actual loss if the maximum loss is exceeded. If Washington Investment Fund is worried about catastrophic loss, shortfall risk is a more appropriate measure, because it provides the probability of not meeting a target return."

AA has a corporate client, Shaifer Materials with a €20,000,000 bond outstanding that pays an annual fixed coupon rate of 9.5% with a 5-year maturity. Castillo believes that euro interest rates may decrease further within the next year below the coupon rate on the fixed rate bond. Castillo would like Shaifer to issue new debt at a lower euro interest rate in the future. Castillo has, however, looked into the costs of calling the bonds and has found that the call premium is quite high and that the investment banking costs of issuing new floating rate debt would be quite steep. As such, he is considering using a swaption to create a synthetic refinancing of the bond at a lower cost than an actual refinancing of the bond. He states that in order to do so, Shaifer should buy a payer swaption, which would give Shaifer the option to pay a lower floating interest rate if rates drop.

Diaz retrieves current market data for payer and receiver swaptions with a maturity of one year. The terms of each instrument are provided below:

Payer swaption fixed rate	7.90%
Receiver swaption fixed rate	7.60%
Current Euribor	7.20%
Projected Euribor in one year	5.90%

Diaz states that, assuming Castillo is correct about falling interest rates, Shaifer can exercise a swaption in one year to effectively call in their old fixed rate euro debt paying 9.5% and refinance at a floating rate, which would be 7.5% in one year.

©2011 Kaplan, Inc.

19. Calculated in bond equivalent yield terms, Michaels's return over the next year, if interest rates change as expected, is *closest* to:
    A. 2.56%.
    B. −2.56%.
    C. 3.50%.

20. Determine whether each of Castillo's statements about repos is correct or incorrect.
    A. Statement 1 is correct.
    B. Statement 2 is correct.
    C. Neither statement is correct.

21. If the Washington Investment Fund portfolio earns the expected 8% over the next year, its net return will be *closest* to:
    A. 7.14%.
    B. 10.14%.
    C. 11.00%.

22. The leveraged duration on the Washington Investment Fund portfolio is *closest* to:
    A. 6.4.
    B. 8.0.
    C. 9.9.

23. Regarding the statements made by Diaz about downside risk measures, are the statements correct?
    A. Only statement 1 is correct.
    B. Only statement 2 is correct.
    C. Neither statement is correct.

24. Regarding their statements concerning the synthetic refinancing of the Shaifer Materials fixed rate euro debt, are the statements correct?
    A. Only Castillo is correct.
    B. Only Diaz is correct.
    C. Both Castillo and Diaz are incorrect.

Questions 25–30 relate to Management of Active and Passive Fixed Income Portfolios and Portfolio Management of Global Bonds and Fixed Income Derivatives.

Ellen Truxel is a principal at Truxel Investment Management. Her firm uses bonds for income enhancement as well as capital gains. She occasionally uses sector-quality bets and yield curve positioning to exploit her beliefs on the relative changes in sector credit quality and the direction of interest rates. She has recently hired John Timberlake to assist her in preparing data for the analysis of bond portfolios. Timberlake is a recent graduate of an outstanding undergraduate program in finance.

Truxel is considering investing in international bonds, as this is an arena she has previously ignored. During conversations, Truxel says it is her understanding that changes in international bond markets have made it easier to manage the duration of an international bond portfolio. Timberlake notes that the European Monetary Union has increased the availability of corporate bonds, making it easier to rotate across sectors.

In the domestic arena, Truxel is considering constructing a portfolio that matches the index on quality, call, sector, and cash flow dimensions and tilts the portfolio duration small amounts to take advantage of predictions of yield curve shifts. She states that this would be referred to as enhanced indexing with minor mismatches. Timberlake tells her that the most important determinant of her performance relative to other bond managers will be her ability to perform credit analysis.

Truxel then tells Timberlake that before they venture into new areas, she wants him to prepare an analysis of their current positions. Timberlake obliges and presents the following data on Truxel's current portfolio.

Bond Rating	Percent Weight in Truxel Portfolio	Sector Effective Duration	Percent Weight in Index Portfolio
AAA	12%	5.3	35%
AA	30%	5.4	30%
A	30%	5.5	25%
BBB	28%	5.0	10%

25. Regarding the conversation on the attributes of international bond investing, are Truxel and Timberlake correct or incorrect?
    A. Both are correct.
    B. Neither is correct.
    C. One is correct.

26. Regarding the conversation on domestic bond portfolio management, are Truxel and Timberlake correct or incorrect?
    A. Both are correct.
    B. Neither is correct.
    C. One is correct.

27. Given a parallel shift in the yield curve of 60 basis points for Treasury yields, the percentage change in the value of the Truxel portfolio is *closest* to:
    A. 3.2.
    B. 3.4.
    C. 5.3.

28. If the OAS for all bond sectors changes by 60 basis points while Treasury yields remain unchanged, the approximate percent change in the Truxel portfolio is *closest* to:
    A. 3.2.
    B. 3.4.
    C. 5.3.

29. If the OAS for all bond sectors changes by 100 basis points while Treasury yields remain unchanged, which sector or sectors would contribute the most to tracking error for Truxel's portfolio?
    A. BBB.
    B. AAA.
    C. AA and A, which contribute about the same.

30. In evaluating relative valuation methodologies, which of the following rationales for trading in the secondary bond market is *least* appropriate?
    A. Cash flow reinvestment.
    B. New issue swaps.
    C. Seasonality.

Questions 31–36 relate to Portfolio Management of Global Bonds and Fixed Income Derivatives.

Mark Rolle, CFA, is the manager of the international bond fund for the Ryder Investment Advisory. He is responsible for bond selection as well as currency hedging decisions. His assistant is Joanne Chen, a candidate for the Level I CFA Exam.

Rolle is interested in the relationship between interest rates and exchange rates for Canada and Great Britain. He observes that the spot exchange rate between the Canadian dollar (C$) and the British pound is C$1.75/£. Also, the 1-year interest rate in Canada is 4.0% and the 1-year interest rate in Great Britain is 11.0%. The current 1-year forward rate is C$1.60/£.

Rolle is evaluating the bonds from the Knauff company and the Tatehiki company, for which information is provided in the table below. The Knauff company bond is denominated in euros and the Tatehiki company bond is denominated in yen. The bonds have similar risk and maturities, and Ryder's investors reside in the United States.

Return on Knauff bond in euros	8.00%
Risk-free rate in the European Union	5.00%
Expected change in the euro relative to the U.S. dollar	−1.20%
Return on Tatehiki bond in yen	6.00%
Risk-free rate in Japan	2.00%
Expected change in the yen relative to the U.S. dollar	2.00%
Risk-free rate in United States	4.80%

Provided this information, Rolle must decide which country's bonds are most attractive if a forward hedge of currency exposure is used. Furthermore, assuming that both countries' bonds are bought, Rolle must also decide whether or not to hedge the currency exposure.

Rolle also has a position in a bond issued in Korea and denominated in Korean won. Unfortunately, he is having difficulty obtaining a forward contract for the won on favorable terms. As an alternative hedge, he has entered a forward contract that allows him to sell yen in one year, when he anticipates liquidating his Korean bond. His reason for choosing the yen is that it is positively correlated with the won.

One of Ryder's services is to provide consulting advice to firms that are interested in interest rate hedging strategies. One such firm is Crawfordville Bank. One of the certificates of deposit (CDs) Crawfordville has outstanding is a jumbo CD requiring the payment of LIBOR plus 150 basis points. The chief financial officer at Crawfordville is worried that interest rates may increase and would like to hedge this exposure. Rolle is contemplating either an interest rate cap or an interest rate floor as a hedge.

Additionally, Rolle is analyzing the best hedge for Ryder's portfolio of fixed-rate coupon bonds. Rolle is contemplating using either a call or a put on T-bond futures.

31. Given the current forward rate of C$1.60/£, the exact forward premium or discount for the £ against the C$ is *closest* to:
   A. –9.37%.
   B. –8.57%.
   C. 8.57%.

32 Based solely on the current interest rates and spot and 1-year forward exchange rates, describe the possible arbitrage transaction between the Canadian dollar (C$) and the pound (£).
   A. There is no arbitrage opportunity.
   B. An arbitrageur could buy Canadian dollars today and simultaneously sell Canadian dollars forward.
   C. An arbitrageur could sell Canadian dollars today and simultaneously buy Canadian dollars forward.

33. Assuming Rolle uses forward contracts to effectively hedge the currency risk of either bond investment, determine which bond is the better investment.
   A. The Knauff bond because its return is 8.0%.
   B. The Tatehiki bond because its excess return is 4.0%.
   C. The Knauff bond because its excess currency return is 3.2%.

34. Calculate the expected return for both bonds if Rolle uses forward contracts to hedge the currency risk of the Knauff company bond and leaves the Tatehiki company bond unhedged.

Knauff bond	Tatehiki bond
A. 6.8%	8.1%
B. 6.8%	8.8%
C. 7.8%	8.1%

35. The hedge that Rolle uses to hedge the currency exposure of the Korean bond is *best* referred to as a:
   A. proxy hedge.
   B. cross hedge.
   C. forward hedge.

36. The *best* hedges of the Crawfordville position and the Ryder portfolio are:

Crawfordville	Ryder
A. Cap	Call
B. Cap	Put
C. Floor	Call

Questions 37–42 relate to Alternative Investments for Portfolio Management.

Cynthia Farmington, CFA, manages the Lewis family's $600 million securities portfolio. Farmington and the Lewis family have agreed that they should hire a manager of alternative investments to manage a portion of the portfolio containing those assets. As part of the hiring process, they attempted to perform the necessary due diligence. They assessed each manager's organization, the relative efficiency of the markets each manager has invested in, the character of each manager, and the service providers, such as lawyers, that each manager has used. In particular, they hoped to find a manager who has run an operation with low employee turnover, has invested in efficient and transparent markets, has sound character, and has utilized reputable providers of external services.

Eventually, Farmington hires the firm owned and managed by Bruce Carnegie, CFA, to diversify the Lewis portfolio into alternative investments. Carnegie will manage the portion of the portfolio containing these assets, and Farmington will continue to manage the remainder of the portfolio in a mix of approximately 50/50 high-grade stocks and bonds. Over the past ten years, the stock portion of the portfolio has closely tracked the S&P 500 and the bond portfolio has closely tracked a broad bond index.

Carnegie and Farmington meet to discuss how Carnegie should proceed. Farmington mentions that she and the Lewis family have agreed that the main goal of the alternative investments that Carnegie will manage should be to enhance the return of the overall portfolio. Diversification is only a secondary goal. In particular, Farmington says the Lewis family has expressed an interest in having the portfolio take positions in private equity. Farmington says that she envisions that Carnegie should take five positions of about $5 million each in distinct private equity investments, and each position should have about a 5-year horizon.

Farmington states that she has grown very dependent on benchmarks for her investing activities, and she has concerns with respect to how she and Carnegie will monitor the success of the portfolio allocation in private equity. She has read that there can be a problem with the valuation of private equity indices in that they depend on price-revealing events like IPOs, mergers, and new financing. Thus, the repricing of the index occurs infrequently. Carnegie concludes that the solution is to follow the commonly accepted practice of creating their own private equity benchmark.

Farmington asks Carnegie to explain the choices that exist in the private equity market. Carnegie explains that there are two basic categories: venture capital funds and buyout funds. Farmington asks that Carnegie explain the pros and cons of one over the other. Carnegie states that although buyout funds would probably have lower return potential, they tend to have fewer losses, earlier cash flows, and less error in the measurement of the returns.

Carnegie comments that before he proceeds he will need to communicate with the clients. Farmington says this communication is not necessary because the Lewis family has largely followed her advice with very few questions. Even when the market has fallen and the portfolio has not done well, the Lewis family has not asked for any changes.

37. With respect to the criteria that Farmington used to choose a manager of alternative assets, which of the following is not a due diligence checkpoint? Finding a manager who:
    A. has low staff turnover.
    B. invests only in efficient and transparent markets.
    C. has stable providers of external services.

38. Given that Farmington states that increased return is more important than diversification, the choice to focus on private equity is:
    A. not appropriate because private equity offers good diversification, but the returns are comparatively low.
    B. appropriate because private equity offers a high return but relatively low diversification.
    C. appropriate because private equity offers both a high return and good diversification.

39. Regarding Farmington's recommended private equity allocations and time horizon, which of her guidelines is *least* appropriate?
    A. The horizon is too short.
    B. Too few positions for proper diversification.
    C. Too much invested given the size of the overall portfolio.

40. With respect to the issue of benchmarks, Farmington made an observation concerning the potential problem with benchmarks, and Carnegie offered a solution. With respect to their discussion, are Farmington and Carnegie correct or incorrect?
    A. Only Farmington is correct.
    B. Only Carnegie is correct.
    C. Both are correct.

41. Regarding Carnegie's statement comparing buyout funds to venture capital funds, the statement is true:
    A. even though venture capital funds tend to have lower average returns than buyout funds.
    B. with regard to mega-cap buyout funds only, because middle-market buyout funds' returns tend to be delayed.
    C. with regard to middle-market buyout funds only, because mega-cap buyout funds' returns tend to be more uncertain.

42.	With respect to the special issues that an alternative investment manager should address with a private wealth client, from the conversation between Farmington and Carnegie, Carnegie will need to discuss all of the following with the possible exception of:

A.	tax issues.

B.	other closely held investments.

C.	decision risk.

Questions 43–48 relate to Private Wealth Management.

Bill Ogilvey, CFA, manages money for clients residing in various countries. Some of them reside in countries that do not currently have tax-advantaged accounts. Ogilvey keeps current on the tax laws to be able to quickly advise his clients if and when new tax-advantaged accounts become available.

Ogilvey often counsels his clients with regard to how they should manage their investment accounts for tax purposes. One of his newest clients, Tilly Beamer, lives in a country with a tax regime that has a flat rate for ordinary income, dividends, and capital gains, but provides favorable treatment for interest income. Her portfolio is in a taxable account and is equally allocated among interest-paying assets, dividend-paying assets, and non-dividend-paying growth stocks.

Beamer is interested in Ogilvey's advice about her retirement planning and which tax-advantaged account(s) would be most beneficial to her. Beamer is young and her income is modest, but she has a high degree of job security and expects her income to increase dramatically over the upcoming ten years. Her objective is to fund a retirement income approximately equal to her wage income at retirement. She is specifically concerned with managing her risk exposure and wonders how a planned reduction in her portfolio risk will affect her expected returns, investment time horizon, and tax drag.

Ogilvey has another client, Steven Vance, who lives in a country with a heavy capital gains tax regime. The current tax law in Vance's country does not provide for tax-advantaged accounts, but that is expected to change, as tax-exempt accounts may soon become available.

To fund a new tax-exempt account, Vance will need to sell some appreciated stock, and he is concerned with the ramifications of reorganizing gains. In specific, Vance has a position in TTT stock, which he accumulated over several years at successively higher prices. If this position is liquidated, taxes will be payable on his investment gains. He asks Ogilvey his advice concerning the best way to handle the sale of the shares and how to measure the tax consequences of realizing the gains.

43.   The tax regime in Beamer's country can be *best* classified as:
        A. Flat and Heavy.
        B. Flat and Light.
        C. Heavy Capital Gain Tax.

44.   Assume that Beamer's interest paying assets are held in a taxable
        account. The account is currently worth €1,000,000, the pretax interest
        income is 7%, and the tax rate, assessed annually, is 25%. If there are
        no deposits or withdrawals from this account and compounding is
        annual, in 15 years the value of the account will be approximately:
        A. €2,069,274.
        B. €2,154,426.
        C. €2,759,032.

45.   Beamer's plan to reduce her investment risk will *most likely*:
        A. decrease her investment horizon because the resulting tax drag will
           be less than the applicable tax rate.
        B. increase her investment horizon but result in tax drag that is less
           than the applicable tax rate.
        C. increase both her investment horizon and result in tax drag that
           exceeds the applicable tax rate.

46.   Assume that Vance sells some of his TTT stock. The pretax return on the
        TTT stock averaged 12% per year over 10 years, the capital gains tax rate
        is 35%, and the cost basis is $250,000. What is the after-tax gain on the
        investment?
        A. $254,700.
        B. $342,200.
        C. $592,200.

47.   Which of the following is *closest* to the percentage tax drag Vance will
        experience with sale of the TTT stock?
        A. 25%.
        B. 35%.
        C. 40%.

48.   Suppose that Vance's after-tax proceeds on his TTT stock sale were
        $150,000, his cost basis was $60,000, the pre-tax return was 13%, and
        the holding period was 9 years. The accrual equivalent after-tax return is
        closest to:
        A. 10.7%.
        B. 17.7%.
        C. 27.8%.

Questions 49–54 relate to Portfolio Management of Global Bonds and Fixed Income Derivatives, Risk Management, and Risk Management Applications of Derivatives.

Gabrielle Reneau, CFA, and Jack Belanger specialize in options strategies at the brokerage firm of York and York. They employ fairly sophisticated strategies to construct positions with limited risk, to profit from future volatility estimates, and to exploit arbitrage opportunities. York and York also provide advice to outside portfolio managers on the appropriate use of options strategies. York and York prefer to use, and recommend, options written on widely traded indices such as the S&P 500 due to their higher liquidity. However, they also use options written on individual stocks when the investor has a position in the underlying stock or when mispricing and/or trading depth exists.

In order to trade in the one-year maturity puts and calls for the S&P 500 stock index, Reneau and Belanger contact the chief economists at York and York, Mark Blair and Fran Robinson. Blair recently joined York and York after a successful stint at a London investment bank. Robinson has been with York and York for the past ten years and has a considerable record of success in forecasting macroeconomic activity. In his forecasts for the U.S. economy over the next year, Blair is quite bullish, for both the U.S. economy and the S&P 500 stock index. Blair believes that the U.S. economy will grow at 2% more than expected over the next year. He also states that labor productivity will be higher than expected, given increased productivity through the use of technological advances. He expects that these technological advances will result in higher earnings for U.S. firms over the next year and over the long run.

Reneau believes that the best S&P 500 option strategy to exploit Blair's forecast involves two options of the same maturity, one with a low exercise price, and the other with a high exercise price. The beginning stock price is usually below the two option strike prices. She states that the benefit of this strategy is that the maximum loss is limited to the difference between the two option prices.

Belanger is unsure that Blair's forecast is correct. He states that his own reading of the economy is for a continued holding pattern of low growth, with a similar projection for the stock market as a whole. He states that York and York may want to pursue an options strategy where a put and call of the same maturity and same exercise price are purchased. He asserts that such a strategy would have losses limited to the total cost of the two options.

Reneau and Belanger are also currently examining various positions in the options of Brendan Industries. Brendan Industries is a large-cap manufacturing firm with headquarters in the midwestern United States. The firm has both puts and calls sold on the Chicago Board Options Exchange. Their options have good liquidity for the near money puts and calls and for those puts and calls with maturities less than four months. Reneau believes that Brendan Industries will benefit from the economic expansion forecasted by Mark Blair, the York and York economist. She decides that the best option strategy to exploit these expectations is for her to pursue the same strategy she has delineated for the market as a whole.

Shares of Brendan Industries are currently trading at $38. The following are the prices for their exchange-traded options.

Option Type	Strike Price	Maturity	Price
Call	$35	30 days	$4.50
Call	$40	30 days	$1.50
Put	$35	30 days	$1.80
Put	$40	30 days	$3.50

As a mature firm in a mature industry, Brendan Industries stock has historically had low volatility. However, Belanger's analysis indicates that with a lawsuit pending against Brendan Industries, the volatility of the stock price over the next 60 days is greater by several orders of magnitude than the volatility implied by the options. He believes that York and York should attempt to exploit this projected increase in Brendan Industries' volatility by using an options strategy where a put and call of the same maturity and same exercise price are utilized. He advocates using the least expensive strategy possible.

During their discussions, Reneau cites a counter example to Brendan Industries from last year. She recalls that Nano Networks, a technology firm, had a stock price that stayed fairly stable despite expectations to the contrary. Expecting the price to remain fairly stable yet protecting against the downside, she utilized an options strategy incorporating three different call prices on Nano stock.

Later that week, Reneau and Belanger discussed various credit option strategies during a lunch time presentation to York and York client portfolio managers. During their discussion, Reneau describes a credit option strategy that pays the holder a fixed sum, which is agreed upon when the option is written, and occurs in the event that an issue or issuer goes into default. Reneau declares that this strategy can take the form of either puts or calls. Belanger states that this strategy is known as either a credit spread call option strategy or a credit spread put option strategy.

Reneau and Belanger continue by discussing the benefits of using credit options. Reneau mentions that credit options written on an underlying asset help protect against declines in the asset's value. Belanger says that credit spread options protect against adverse movements of the credit spread over a referenced benchmark. Calls help protect against narrowing spreads, and puts help protect against widening spreads.

49.   Regarding their statements concerning the use of options strategies to exploit changes in the broad stock market, are Reneau and Belanger correct or incorrect?
A. Only Belanger is correct.
B. Only Reneau is correct.
C. Both are correct -OR- both are incorrect.

50.   If Brendan Industries will experience the same growth as the overall economy (as projected by Blair), the breakeven stock price and maximum loss on Reneau's intended option strategy are *closest* to:

	Breakeven	Maximum loss
A.	$38	Unlimited
B.	$43	$6
C.	$38	$3

51.   If Belanger is correct regarding Brendan Industries' volatility, and if the stock price at expiration is $45 and he pursues a lower cost strategy, his described strategy has a profit at expiration of:
A. $3.70.
B. $5.00.
C. $0.00.

52.   Assume Reneau applies the options strategy used earlier for Nano Networks. Assuming there is a 30-day 45 call on Brendan Industries trading at $1.00, calculate the maximum gain and maximum loss on this position.

	Max gain	Max loss
A.	$2.50	–$2.50
B.	$5.00	–$5.00
C.	$3.00	–$2.00

53.   Regarding their comments concerning the credit option strategy that pays the holder a fixed sum, are Reneau and Belanger correct or incorrect?
A. Only Belanger is correct.
B. Only Reneau is correct.
C. Both are correct.

54.   Regarding their comments concerning the benefits of using credit options, are Reneau and Belanger correct or incorrect?
A. Only Belanger is correct.
B. Only Reneau is correct.
C. Both are correct.

Questions 55–60 relate to Execution of Portfolio Decisions: Monitoring and Rebalancing.

Wealth Management's top economist, Frederick Milton, is an economic cycle forecaster. Milton's economic forecasts indicate an economic upswing that will impact all goods and services sectors. Milton presents his economic findings to the rest of Wealth Management's professionals at their monthly meeting. All are excited about Milton's forecast of an improving economic condition that should translate into a steadily rising stock market.

Nathaniel Norton and Timothy Tucker have confidence in Milton's capabilities and decide to meet with their clients. Their first meeting is with Elizabeth Mascarella to whom Norton recommends a dynamic asset allocation strategy to take advantage of Milton's forecast. However, Mascarella is concerned because the somewhat persistent back-and-forth of economic activity has translated into an oscillating stock market. Mascarella questions Norton's recommendation and asks Tucker which strategy should be followed if the market continues as it has, instead of making such "wonderful" strides.

It is one year later and Frederick Milton's economic forecast has been correct, and the market has trended upward as expected. Mascarella's strategic allocation to equity, which was $600,000 of a total portfolio of $1,000,000, has increased 20%. Her overall portfolio, which contains equity, debt, and some cash, is now valued at $1,150,000. Tucker meets with Mascarella and indicates it may be time to rebalance her portfolio.

55. Assuming a steadily rising market, the *best* strategy for Mascarella is:
   A. buy and hold.
   B. constant mix.
   C. constant proportion portfolio insurance.

56. Determine the preferred dynamic rebalancing strategy if the market is expected to be highly volatile, but more or less flat.
   A. Buy and hold.
   B. Constant mix.
   C. Constant proportion portfolio insurance.

57. Which of the following statements about CPPI strategies is probably *least* correct?
   A. CPPI strategies represent the purchase of portfolio insurance because they buy stocks as they rise and sell them as they fall.
   B. CPPI strategies offer good upside potential because they increase exposure to risky assets as the market rises.
   C. Due to the concave nature of CPPI strategies, they offer good downside protection.

58.   Mascarella has instructed Tucker to rebalance annually to maintain a corridor of ± 5% for equity. Given the constraint, Tucker should:
       A. reallocate approximately $70,000 of the increase in equity to debt and cash.
       B. reallocate the entire $120,000 increase in equity to debt and cash.
       C. make no adjustments.

59.   Tucker has tried to make Mascarella understand the benefits of percentage-of-portfolio rebalancing relative to calendar rebalancing. Which of the following statements made by Tucker is probably *least* correct?
       A. Calendar rebalancing provides discipline while requiring less monitoring.
       B. Percentage-of-portfolio rebalancing minimizes the amount by which the allocations stray from their strategic levels.
       C. Percentage of portfolio rebalancing is better than calendar rebalancing because it keeps allocations closer to their strategic levels.

60.   Which of the following would generally suggest a narrower tolerance band?
       A. Assets in the portfolio tend to be illiquid.
       B. Highly volatile assets.
       C. Correlated portfolio assets.

END OF AFTERNOON SESSION

PRACTICE EXAM 2 MORNING SESSION QUESTION BREAKDOWN

MORNING SESSION		
Topic	Question	Points
Private Wealth Management	1	20
Behavioral Finance	2A	6
Portfolio Management – Institutional	2B	12
Portfolio Management – Institutional	2C	10
Fixed Income and Equity Portfolio Management and Alternative Investments	3	10
Capital Market Expectations	4A	12
Capital Market Expectations	4B	16
Equity Portfolio Management	5A	4
Equity Portfolio Management	5B	10
Equity Portfolio Management	5C	9
Asset Allocation	6A	9
Asset Allocation	6B	7
Asset Allocation	6C	6
Portfolio Management – Institutional	7	14
Global Investment Performance Standards	8	12
Performance Evaluation and Attribution	9A	8
Performance Evaluation and Attribution	9B	3
Performance Evaluation and Attribution	9C	3
Portfolio Management – Institutional	10A	6
Equity Portfolio Management	10B	3
Total		180

PRACTICE EXAM 2 SCORE SHEET

MORNING SESSION		
Question	Max. Points	Your Approx. Score
1	20	
2A	6	
2B	12	
2C	10	
3	10	
4A	12	
4B	16	
5A	4	
5B	10	
5C	9	
6A	9	
6B	7	
6C	6	
7	14	
8	12	
9A	8	
9B	3	
9C	3	
10A	6	
10B	3	
Total	180	

AFTERNOON SESSION		
Question	Max. Points	Your Approx. Score
1–6	18	
7–12	18	
13–18	18	
19–24	18	
25–30	18	
31–36	18	
37–42	18	
43–48	18	
49–54	18	
55–60	18	
Total	180	

Certain Passing Score: 252 of 360 (70%)
Probable Passing Score: 234 (65%)

Please note that we write these exams to be as challenging and representative as possible. However, due to the relaxed conditions that most candidates apply when they "take" these tests (e.g., "I need a break. I think I'll go to the refrigerator and get a snack"), you should adjust your score downward by 10–15 percentage points to get a more accurate measure of the score you would have actually received on exam day. Also, you must be honest with yourself for your score on this exam to have any meaning. Don't assume, for example, that if your essay answer is close, the graders will be generous with points.

Exam 2
Morning Session

QUESTION 1 HAS ONE PART FOR A TOTAL OF 20 MINUTES

Barney Smythe, 40, and his wife Heather, 39, are considering what to do with a recent windfall they received after the untimely death of Heather's mother. The windfall is estimated to be $2,500,000 (after taxes). Barney is currently a supervising mechanic at a local luxury car dealership and has a salary of $48,750 annually. Heather is, and always has been, a stay-at-home mom. The Smythes have two children, Lenny, 12, and Buford, 10. By design, the Smythes owe no debt and pay their expenses on a monthly basis. Family expenses last year amounted to approximately $150,000.

In addition to the inheritance they will receive, the Smthyes have an additional $1,250,000 in savings. Barney and Heather have approached Net Worth Enhancers, PC, for assistance in managing their portfolio. The Smythes made the following statements at a recent client discovery meeting:

- "One of our goals at this stage in our lives is to pay for the college education of our children. We would like both of them to go to Heather's alma mater, which is a prestigious liberal arts institution."
- "We expect our annual expenses to increase at the general rate of inflation of 2%."
- "We want to retire at 65 and be able to live comfortably, but not extravagantly."
- "We are taxed at 25% on both income and capital gains."
- "We believe our portfolio should never suffer an annual loss of more than 5%. In addition, we do not want to invest in any individual investment or security that is too risky."
- "We do not foresee any unusual expenses over the short term. As always, we would like to have enough cash on hand for emergencies."

Determine the Smythes' willingness and ability to take risk, their overall risk tolerance, and their required after-tax nominal return and liquidity constraint for the coming year. **Determine** the rest of the Smythes' investment constraints.

Answer Question 1 in the template provided.

(20 minutes)

Template for Question 1

Investment Policy Statement for the Smythes		
Objectives	Risk Tolerance	
	Return	
Constraints	Time Horizon	
	Liquidity	
	Legal/Regulatory	
	Taxes	
	Unique Circumstances	

QUESTION 2 HAS THREE PARTS FOR A TOTAL OF 28 MINUTES

Matrix Corporation is a multidivisional company with operations in energy, telecommunications, and shipping. Matrix sponsors a traditional defined benefit pension plan. Plan assets are valued at $5.5 billion, while recent declines in interest rates have caused plan liabilities to balloon to $8.3 billion. Average employee age at Matrix is 57.5, which is considerably higher than the industry average, and the ratio of active to retired lives is 1:1. Joe Elliot, Matrix's CFO, has made the following statement about the current state of the pension plan.

> "Recent declines in interest rates have caused our pension liabilities to grow faster than ever experienced in our long history, but I am sure these low rates are temporary. I have looked at the charts and estimated the probability of higher interest rates at more than 90%. Given the expected improvement in interest rate levels, plan liabilities will again come back into line with our historical position. Our investment policy will therefore be to invest plan assets in aggressive equity securities. This investment exposure will bring our plan to an over-funded status, which will allow us to use pension income to bolster our profitability."

A.   **Critique** Elliot's statement with respect to investing Matrix's plan assets by addressing the following three points:

   i. Behavioral characteristic exhibited.
   ii. Plan risk and return objectives.
   iii. Using pension plan income to bolster firm profitability.

(6 minutes)

B.   Based on the information provided, **formulate** a return objective and a risk objective for the Matrix Corporation pension plan. (No calculations required.)

Answer Question 2-B in the template provided.

(12 minutes)

Template for Question 2-B

Investment Policy Statement for Matrix Corporation	
Risk	
Return	

C.   Based on the information provided, **formulate** an appropriate constraints section for the investment policy statement for the pension fund.

Answer Question 2-C in the template provided.

(10 minutes)

Template for Question 2-C

Constraints	Time Horizon	
	Liquidity	
	Legal/ Regulatory	
	Taxes	
	Unique	

QUESTION 3 HAS ONE PART FOR A TOTAL OF 10 MINUTES

John Carpenter is considering using fixed income securities, hedge funds, and international stocks as vehicles for his more wealthy clients. Before doing so, he consults with Tom McKnealey, who is president of Benchmark Associates, a firm that specializes in the construction of benchmarks for portfolio managers. During a meeting with Carpenter, McKnealey makes the following statements about the proper construction of benchmarks for fixed income, hedge fund, and international stock portfolio managers:

- "The popularity bias can cause problems for measuring value-weighted hedge fund benchmark performance. The popularity bias argues that out-performing hedge funds as well as hedge fund styles tend to attract additional funding, so as they grow in popularity their performance tends to have a greater and greater impact on the value-weighted index's measured performance. This creates a double impact on the value-weighted hedge fund index return; the individual funds have good returns, and their increasing size means they have a greater weight in the index. The result is that the index's return has an upward bias. This bias, however, can be counteracted by utilizing two indices, one long and one short. Since most hedge fund managers attempt to generate alpha through both long and short positions, they can have a net zero weight or even a net negative weight. A single, long-only benchmark will not capture the performance of both strategies."

- "If an investor is averse to market value risk, the bond benchmark used should have a long maturity so they can lock in a yield to maturity."

- "The recommended solution to the 'free float' problem in international markets is to determine the amount of shares to be floated by an issuer in the upcoming year and use that to recalculate the issuer's weight in market capitalization weighted indices."

- "For bond investors such as foundations who desire a stable stream of income, long-term bond benchmarks should be used."

Determine which of McKnealey's statements are correct or incorrect, and if incorrect, **justify** your response.

Answer Question 3 in the template provided.

(10 minutes)

Template for Question 3

Comment	Is this statement correct or incorrect? (circle one)	Explanation, if incorrect
"The popularity bias can cause problems for measuring value-weighted hedge fund benchmark performance. The popularity bias argues that out-performing hedge funds as well as hedge fund styles tend to attract additional funding, so as they grow in popularity their performance tends to have a greater and greater impact on the value-weighted index's measured performance. This creates a double impact on the value-weighted hedge fund index return; the individual funds have good returns, and their increasing size means they have a greater weight in the index. The result is that the index's return has an upward bias. This bias, however, can be counteracted by utilizing two indices, one long and one short. Since most hedge fund managers attempt to generate alpha through both long and short positions, they can have a net zero weight or even a net negative weight. A single, long-only benchmark will not capture the performance of both strategies."	Correct Incorrect	

Comment	Is this statement correct or incorrect? (circle one)	Explanation, if incorrect
"If an investor is averse to market value risk, the bond benchmark used should have a long maturity so they can lock in a yield to maturity."	Correct Incorrect	
"The recommended solution to the 'free float' problem in international markets is to determine the amount of shares to be floated by an issuer in the upcoming year and use that to recalculate the issuer's weight in market capitalization weighted indices."	Correct Incorrect	
"For bond investors such as foundations who desire a stable stream of income, long-term bond benchmarks should be used."	Correct Incorrect	

QUESTION 4 HAS TWO PARTS FOR A TOTAL OF 28 MINUTES

William Barkley and David McFalls are economists for Irvington Advisors, a U.S.-based firm. Irvington provides independent economic and investment advice to portfolio managers, research analysts, and others. Barkley and McFalls are discussing the state of developed and emerging market economies and stock markets.

Barkley and McFalls use economic data from a variety of sources to form their forecasts of international economies. At their regular Monday morning staff meeting, the two economists discuss the usefulness of economic data with their junior economists and research analysts. During the meeting, Barkley makes the following comments:

- "The stock returns in emerging markets are quite impressive. The mean returns are quite high and the risk is lower than many investors expect. Consider the example of the country of Yalewian. An index of Yalewian stocks had high returns for the period January 1, 1995 to December 31, 2006. This includes the period of crisis for emerging market stocks in 1997 and 1998. Yalewian stocks escaped from this crisis unscathed as their returns were positive during these years."

- "After extensive research on stock price patterns in 30 developed and emerging markets, I have uncovered a turn of the month effect in the United States. Specifically, the returns for U.S. stocks are higher in the first half of every month compared to the returns during the latter part of the month. The reason why this pattern is found in the United States and not in the other countries is because U.S. investors tend to invest after they have been paid their wages at the end of the month."

- "U.S. inflation from 1960 to 2006 averaged 3.4%. Because it was measured over such a long period, it would be hard to argue that the rate of U.S. inflation for the next year would be different from this historical average."

- "After evaluating the historical data for the U.S. and European stock markets, I have found that when the central bank is increasing the growth of the money supply, stock returns are higher. When they are restricting the growth, stock returns are lower. In fact, the correlation between the central bank discount rate and stock returns is 0.74 on average, indicating that central bank monetary policy is very influential for stock returns."

A.   **State** whether or not *each* of these comments is susceptible to problems associated with using economic data to forecast. If susceptible, **identify** and **describe** the problem.

Answer Question 4-A in the template provided.

(12 minutes)

Template for Question 4-A

Comment	Is the statement susceptible to problems in using economic data to forecast? (circle one)	If yes, identify and describe the problem
"The stock returns in emerging markets are quite impressive. The mean returns are quite high and the risk is lower than many investors expect. Consider the example of the country of Yalewian. An index of Yalewian stocks had high returns for the period January 1, 1995 to December 31, 2006. This includes the period of crisis for emerging market stocks in 1997 and 1998. Yalewian stocks escaped from this crisis unscathed as their returns were positive during these years."	Yes No	
"After extensive research on stock price patterns in 30 developed and emerging markets, I have uncovered a turn of the month effect in the United States. Specifically, the returns for U.S. stocks are higher in the first half of every month compared to the returns during the latter part of the month. The reason why this pattern is found in the United States and not in the other countries is because U.S. investors tend to invest after they have been paid their wages at the end of the month."	Yes No	

"U.S. inflation from 1960 to 2006 averaged 3.4%. Because it was measured over such a long period, it would be hard to argue that the rate of U.S. inflation for the next year would be different from this historical average."	Yes No	
"After evaluating the historical data for the U.S. and European stock markets, I have found that when the central bank is increasing the growth of the money supply, stock returns are higher. When they are restricting the growth, stock returns are lower. In fact, the correlation between the central bank discount rate and stock returns is 0.74 on average, indicating that central bank monetary policy is very influential for stock returns."	Yes No	

Barkley and McFalls are evaluating the stock returns for two economies, the country of Airedale and the country of Bermiese. Airedale is a developed country with mature capital markets and few restrictions on cross border capital flows. Bermiese is an emerging country that puts restrictions on investment in its stock market by foreign investors. Specifically, foreign investors in total may hold no more than 5% of the outstanding shares of a single stock. McFalls has gathered the following data for the two countries and is deciding whether they would be an attractive addition to a portfolio. He uses the MSCI World Index as the global portfolio and uses a financial equilibrium model approach to evaluate the markets.

Sharpe ratio of the MSCI World Index	0.26
Standard deviation of the MSCI World Index	10.00%
Risk-free rate of return	3.50%
Degree of market integration for Airedale	85.00%
Degree of market integration for Bermiese	65.00%
Standard deviation of Airedale stock returns	11.00%
Standard deviation of Bermiese stock returns	21.00%
Correlation of Airedale with MSCI World Index	0.79
Correlation of Bermiese with MSCI World Index	0.58
Estimated illiquidity premium for Airedale	0.00%
Estimated illiquidity premium for Bermiese	2.60%

B.   **Calculate** the expected returns and betas for the two countries' stock markets. **Calculate** the covariance between the two countries' stock markets.

(16 minutes)

©2011 Kaplan, Inc.

QUESTION 5 HAS THREE PARTS FOR A TOTAL OF 23 MINUTES

Aaron Bell, a portfolio manager, is focusing his attention on investment style, and whether style should be a factor in investment decision making. Bell decides to play it safe and investigate how he can use different instruments related to style indices or indexing strategies to see if he can add value to his customers' portfolios.

A.   **Explain** holdings-based style analysis. **Discuss** *one* disadvantage and *one* advantage of holdings-based style analysis over returns-based style analysis.

(4 minutes)

B.   **Explain** returns-based style analysis. **Reproduce** the general form of the regression equation used for returns-based style analysis, including any constraints, and label *each* component of the equation. **Discuss** *one* disadvantage and *one* advantage of returns-based style analysis over holdings-based style analysis.

(10 minutes)

C.   Bell is considering indexing strategies and a colleague has suggested three alternatives: full replication; stratified sampling; and optimization. **Explain** *each* along with the conditions under which each would be appropriate to use and provide *one* disadvantage for *each*.

(9 minutes)

QUESTION 6 HAS THREE PARTS FOR A TOTAL OF 22 MINUTES

Wyatt Washington is the portfolio manager for Mark Beitia, a recent retiree. He is currently exploring a change in Beitia's strategic asset allocation. He gathers data on the expected returns, standard deviations, and correlations for five assets. Using these market expectations, he derives an efficient frontier. Washington uses the following information in his construction of the asset allocation:

- Beitia's asset base = $5,000,000.
- Expected annual after-tax spending amount = $150,000.
- Estimate of future inflation = 3.5%.
- Beitia will donate $750,000 to his alma mater over the coming year in one lump sum.
- Risk-free rate = 4.0%.
- Beitia's tax rate = 25%.
- Beitia's risk aversion value = 5.0.

Washington forms four corner portfolios from his efficient frontier and calculates the following expected returns and standard deviations:

Corner Portfolio	Expected Before Tax Return	Expected Std. Dev.	Sharpe Ratio	Weights in assets 1 to 5				
				1	2	3	4	5
1	6.50%	4.10%	0.610	0%	20%	80%	0%	0%
2	7.75%	5.80%	0.647	0%	15%	85%	0%	0%
3	9.70%	7.80%	0.731	60%	10%	30%	0%	0%
4	13.50%	10.60%	0.896	100%	0%	0%	0%	0%

A.   **Calculate** the required before-tax return for Beitia's portfolio and Beitia's expected utility from holding each of the corner portfolios.

(9 minutes)

B.   Assuming that Washington combines two corner portfolios to meet Beitia's desired return (calculated in Part A), **calculate** the weights of the appropriate corner portfolios that will be used (assume no borrowing or short-selling) and the resulting portfolio standard deviation.

(7 minutes)

C.   Assuming that Washington combines a corner portfolio with the risk-free asset to meet Beitia's desired return (calculated in Part A), **calculate** the weights of the appropriate corner portfolio and the risk-free asset that will be used (assume no borrowing) and the resulting portfolio standard deviation.

(6 minutes)

QUESTION 7 HAS ONE PART FOR A TOTAL OF 14 MINUTES

A1 Casualty, Inc. writes property and casualty insurance policies for individuals, homeowners, and small businesses located in the Southeastern portion of the United States. For the last three years, market forces have caused A1 to more competitively price their policies to increase underwriting volume. This competitive pricing environment coincides with a somewhat slowing general business cycle. Two months ago, a massive hurricane hit the panhandle of Florida and southeast Alabama, causing unprecedented damages to property. Approximately 50% of A1's homeowners' policies are written in that geographic region, but as of yet, claims processing has been much less than expected from the area. Stan Carnay, A1's CEO, has been busy preparing the latest investment portfolio report for the Board of Directors' meeting in two weeks and has asked Eileen Carlyle, CFA, A1's most recent addition to the investment group, for assistance in updating a decades-old investment policy statement. In preliminary discussions, Carlyle indicated the following:

- "Underwriting activity, although somewhat improved over the past decade, has not been as profitable as expected during the last three years. The competitive marketplace in which we operate has directly impacted our ability to profitably price our insurance products."

- "We should count our blessings that so few claims from the recent hurricane have been submitted. Actuarial estimates indicate our potential exposure from this weather event is approximately $75 million, which represents 75% of our surplus portfolio. Since claim submission has been almost non-existent, we can transition our investment portfolio into a greater proportion of common stock, taking our stock to surplus ratio from 90% to close to 100%. That action should help strengthen our long-term competitive position."

- "Recent economic conditions have slowed, but numerous other comparable casualty companies are optimistic that economic conditions will improve over the next 9 to 12 months. Although market economists continue forecasting a slightly longer downturn in the national economy, we consider those forecasts overly pessimistic."

Without using calculations, **formulate** an investment policy statement appropriate for A1.

Answer Question 7 in the template provided.

(14 minutes)

Template for Question 7

Investment Policy Statement for A1 Casualty	
Objectives	Return Objectives
	Risk Tolerance
Constraints	Time Horizon
	Liquidity
	Legal/Regulatory
	Taxes
	Unique Circumstances

©2011 Kaplan, Inc.

QUESTION 8 HAS ONE PART FOR A TOTAL OF 12 MINUTES

Bailey Investments is a U.S.-based investment management firm. They began operations on January 1, 2006. Their client base has grown considerably over the last few years and in order to ensure accurate and consistent performance data they have decided to pursue GIPS® compliance. The following includes composite data and notes relating to the first presentation for one of their composites in which they claim GIPS compliance.

Year	Total Return (%)	Benchmark Return (%)	Number of Portfolios	Composite Dispersion (%)	Total Firm Asset ($ millions)
2007	6.54	7.25	15	2.5	86
2008	8.74	9.25	19	3.2	135
2009	9.45	8.67	28	4.1	276
2010	7.53	7.45	35	4.5	332

Bailey Investments has prepared and presented this report in compliance with the Global Investment Performance Standards (GIPS®).

Notes:

1. Valuations are obtained by Reuters and computed using the U.S. dollar.

2. Bailey Investments is a dedicated equity portfolio manager that invests entirely in U.S. securities and has no affiliates.

3. The benchmark composition is 100% S&P 500. The annualized compound benchmark return is 8.15%. The annualized compound composite return is 8.06%.

4. Composite dispersion is the annualized monthly standard deviation of composite returns.

5. No modifications to the composites as presented here have occurred as a result of changes in personnel or for any other reason at any time.

6. Performance results are presented before management and custodial fees but after all trading commissions.

7. The composite includes discretionary and non-discretionary fee-paying portfolios.

List *four* non-compliant items in the presentation. For *each*, **state** the necessary corrective action.

Answer Question 8 in the template provided.

(12 minutes)

Template for Question 8

Errors in presentation and corrective action.
1.
2.
3.
4.

QUESTION 9 HAS THREE PARTS FOR A TOTAL OF 14 MINUTES

One year has passed since HNW Advisors first started operations. Their overall equity portfolio has returned 28.2% versus a return of 22.4% for the S&P 500. The standard deviation of the S&P 500 is 20%, and Maggie Day, CFA, has estimated the standard deviation of HNW Advisor's equity portfolio at 45%. HNW Advisor's equity portfolio has a beta of 1.35, and the risk-free rate is 4.4%.

A major HNW client is attempting to evaluate the relative performance of HNW's equity fund. The client is unsure whether the Sharpe measure or the Treynor measure is appropriate for the HNW portfolio.

A.   Using the Sharpe and Treynor measures for the HNW portfolio and the S&P 500, **determine** how HNW has performed relative to the S&P 500.

(8 minutes)

B.   Assume that, using the Sharpe ratio to measure performance, the S&P 500 outperformed the HNW portfolio, but using the Treynor measure, the HNW portfolio outperformed the S&P 500. **Explain**, in terms of systematic and unsystematic risk, how this change in ranking could have occurred.

(3 minutes)

C.   **Compute** M^2 for the HNW portfolio, assuming management uses the market as a benchmark. **Explain**, in terms of relative returns and volatility, the circumstances under which M^2 for HNW would equal M^2 for the market.

(3 minutes)

QUESTION 10 HAS TWO PARTS FOR A TOTAL OF 9 MINUTES

Tom Groh is the President of Opportunity Banks. Opportunity has historically operated in the northeastern United States, with most of its business in Maryland, Delaware, and New Jersey. Opportunity has been in business since 1987 and has built its business on making mortgages and construction loans to residential developers. Opportunity has been very profitable, because developers value the services the bank provides. This allows Opportunity to price their construction loans with higher interest rates. Opportunity services and retains ownership of the its loans. It historically has had a near-zero leverage-adjusted duration gap.

In the most recent fiscal year, Opportunity has experienced important changes in their business as follows:

1. Due to pressure from local activists, Opportunity has stepped up lending in low-income areas. Groh expects the default rate on these loans to be higher than the loans currently in their portfolio.

2. Opportunity has bought a regional bank with operations in North Carolina, South Carolina, and Georgia. The acquired bank's loan portfolio consists mostly of commercial loans to small, local businesses.

3. A recent downturn in interest rates has caused many of Opportunity's variable rate mortgages to be refinanced to 15- and 30-year fixed-rate mortgages. Opportunity has retained the business of most of its customers who have refinanced.

A.   In each of the scenarios provided, **determine** *one* effect on the investment objectives, constraints, or investment policies of the bank's security portfolio. **Evaluate** *each* scenario in isolation from the others.

    Answer Question 10-A in the template provided.

                    (6 minutes)

Template for Question 10-A

Scenario	Effect on Securities Portfolio Policies
1. Due to pressure from local activists, Opportunity has stepped up lending to low-income areas. Groh expects the default rate on these loans to be higher than the loans currently in their portfolio.	
2. Opportunity has bought a regional bank with operations in North Carolina, South Carolina, and Georgia. The acquired bank's loan portfolio consists mostly of commercial loans to small, local businesses.	
3. A recent downturn in interest rates has caused many of Opportunity's variable rate mortgages to be refinanced to 15- and 30-year fixed rate mortgages. Opportunity has retained the business of most of its customers who have refinanced.	

B.   Groh is advising one of the bank's clients on the management of the client's family trust. Previously the family trust hired a portfolio manager whose fee was a fixed 1% of assets. The family is now considering another portfolio manager who is paid a lower fixed 0.30% of assets but also charges 20% of any excess return above their benchmark. **Discuss** *one* advantage and *two* disadvantages of the new manager's fee structure.

(3 minutes)

END OF MORNING SESSION

EXAM 2 AFTERNOON SESSION
TOPIC BREAKDOWN

Question	Topic	Minutes
1–6	Ethics and Professional Standards	18
7–12	Ethics and Professional Standards	18
13–18	Management of Active and Passive Fixed Income Portfolios, Portfolio Management of Global Bonds and Fixed Income Portfolios, and Risk Management Applications of Derivatives	18
19–24	Portfolio Management of Global Bonds and Fixed Income Derivatives and Risk Management	18
25–30	Management of Active and Passive Fixed Income Portfolios and Portfolio Management of Global Bonds and Fixed Income Derivatives	18
31–36	Alternative Investments for Portfolio Management	18
37–42	Portfolio Management of Global Bonds and Fixed Income Derivatives, Equity Portfolio Management, and Risk Management Applications of Derivatives	18
43–48	Management of Active and Passive Fixed Income Portfolios, Risk Management, and Risk Management Applications of Derivatives	18
49–54	Execution of Portfolio Decisions: Monitoring and Rebalancing	18
55–60	Risk Management and Performance Evaluation and Attribution	18
	Total	180

EXAM 2 SELECTED RESPONSE ITEM SET ANSWER SHEET

The afternoon session of the Level III exam contains 10 Selected Response Item Sets, each with six questions, and you must answer them by filling in a bubble sheet with a number 2 or HB pencil. For realism, we suggest that you use this answer sheet and darken the bubbles corresponding to your answers. This sheet will also facilitate entering your answers into our online Performance Tracker. You have 180 minutes for this session of the exam. That equates to 3 minutes per item set question, so budget your time well.

1. Ⓐ Ⓑ Ⓒ		31. Ⓐ Ⓑ Ⓒ
2. Ⓐ Ⓑ Ⓒ		32. Ⓐ Ⓑ Ⓒ
3. Ⓐ Ⓑ Ⓒ		33. Ⓐ Ⓑ Ⓒ
4. Ⓐ Ⓑ Ⓒ		34. Ⓐ Ⓑ Ⓒ
5. Ⓐ Ⓑ Ⓒ		35. Ⓐ Ⓑ Ⓒ
6. Ⓐ Ⓑ Ⓒ		36. Ⓐ Ⓑ Ⓒ
7. Ⓐ Ⓑ Ⓒ		37. Ⓐ Ⓑ Ⓒ
8. Ⓐ Ⓑ Ⓒ		38. Ⓐ Ⓑ Ⓒ
9. Ⓐ Ⓑ Ⓒ		39. Ⓐ Ⓑ Ⓒ
10. Ⓐ Ⓑ Ⓒ		40. Ⓐ Ⓑ Ⓒ
11. Ⓐ Ⓑ Ⓒ		41. Ⓐ Ⓑ Ⓒ
12. Ⓐ Ⓑ Ⓒ		42. Ⓐ Ⓑ Ⓒ
13. Ⓐ Ⓑ Ⓒ		43. Ⓐ Ⓑ Ⓒ
14. Ⓐ Ⓑ Ⓒ		44. Ⓐ Ⓑ Ⓒ
15. Ⓐ Ⓑ Ⓒ		45. Ⓐ Ⓑ Ⓒ
16. Ⓐ Ⓑ Ⓒ		46. Ⓐ Ⓑ Ⓒ
17. Ⓐ Ⓑ Ⓒ		47. Ⓐ Ⓑ Ⓒ
18. Ⓐ Ⓑ Ⓒ		48. Ⓐ Ⓑ Ⓒ
19. Ⓐ Ⓑ Ⓒ		49. Ⓐ Ⓑ Ⓒ
20. Ⓐ Ⓑ Ⓒ		50. Ⓐ Ⓑ Ⓒ
21. Ⓐ Ⓑ Ⓒ		51. Ⓐ Ⓑ Ⓒ
22. Ⓐ Ⓑ Ⓒ		52. Ⓐ Ⓑ Ⓒ
23. Ⓐ Ⓑ Ⓒ		53. Ⓐ Ⓑ Ⓒ
24. Ⓐ Ⓑ Ⓒ		54. Ⓐ Ⓑ Ⓒ
25. Ⓐ Ⓑ Ⓒ		55. Ⓐ Ⓑ Ⓒ
26. Ⓐ Ⓑ Ⓒ		56. Ⓐ Ⓑ Ⓒ
27. Ⓐ Ⓑ Ⓒ		57. Ⓐ Ⓑ Ⓒ
28. Ⓐ Ⓑ Ⓒ		58. Ⓐ Ⓑ Ⓒ
29. Ⓐ Ⓑ Ⓒ		59. Ⓐ Ⓑ Ⓒ
30. Ⓐ Ⓑ Ⓒ		60. Ⓐ Ⓑ Ⓒ

Exam 2
Afternoon Session

Questions 1–6 relate to Ethical and Professional Standards.

Rowan Brothers is a full service investment firm offering portfolio management and investment banking services. For the last ten years, Aaron King, CFA, has managed individual client portfolios for Rowan Brothers, most of which are trust accounts over which King has full discretion. One of King's clients, Shelby Pavlica, is a widow in her late 60s whose husband died and left assets of over $7 million in a trust, of which she is the only beneficiary.

Pavlica's three children are appalled at their mother's spending habits and have called a meeting with King to discuss their concerns. They inform King that their mother is living too lavishly to leave much for them or Pavlica's grandchildren upon her death. King acknowledges their concerns and informs them that, on top of her ever-increasing spending, Pavlica has recently been diagnosed with a chronic illness, a fact previously not known by her children.

Since the diagnosis could indicate a considerable increase in medical spending, he will need to increase the risk of the portfolio to generate sufficient return to cover the medical bills and spending and still maintain the principal. King restructures the portfolio accordingly and then meets with Pavlica a week later to discuss how he has altered the investment strategy, which was previously revised only three months earlier in their annual meeting.

During the meeting with Pavlica, King explains his reasoning for altering the portfolio allocation but does not mention the meeting with Pavlica's children. Pavlica agrees that it is probably the wisest decision and accepts the new portfolio allocation adding that she will need to tell her children about her illness, so they will understand why her medical spending requirements will increase in the near future. She admits to King that her children have been concerned about her spending. King assures her that the new investments will definitely allow her to maintain her lifestyle and meet her higher medical spending needs.

One of the investments selected by King for Pavlica's portfolio is a private placement offered to him by a brokerage firm that often makes trades for King's portfolios. The private placement is an equity investment in ShaleCo, a small oil exploration company. In order to make the investment, King sold shares of a publicly traded biotech firm, VNC Technologies. King also held shares of VNC, a fact that he has always disclosed to clients before purchasing VNC for their accounts. An hour before submitting the sell order for the VNC shares in Pavlica's trust account, King placed an order to sell a portion of his position in VNC stock.

By the time Pavlica's order was sent to the trading floor, the price of VNC had risen, allowing Pavlica to sell her shares at a better price than received by King.

Although King elected not to take any shares in the private placement, he purchased positions for several of his clients, for whom the investment was deemed appropriate in terms of the clients' objectives and constraints as well as the existing composition of the portfolios. In response to the investment support, ShaleCo appointed King to their board of directors. Seeing an opportunity to advance his career while also protecting the value of his clients' investments in the company, King gladly accepted the offer. King decided that since serving on the board of ShaleCo is in his clients' best interest, it is not necessary to disclose the directorship to his clients or his employer.

For his portfolio management services, King charges a fixed percentage fee based on the value of assets under management. All fees charged and other terms of service are disclosed to clients as well as prospects. In the past month, however, Rowan Brothers has instituted an incentive program for its portfolio managers. Under the program, the firm will award an all-expense-paid vacation to the Cayman islands for any portfolio manager who generates two consecutive quarterly returns for his clients in excess of 10%. King updates his marketing literature to ensure that his prospective clients are fully aware of his compensation arrangements.

1.   In discussing Pavlica's spending and medical condition with Pavlica's children, did King violate any CFA Institute Standards of Professional Conduct?
     A. No. Because the children are the remaindermen, King is obligated to manage the trust in the best interest of both Pavlica and the children.
     B. Yes, because he violated his client's confidentiality.
     C. Yes, because he created a conflict of interest between himself and his employer.

2.   In reallocating the portfolio after the meeting with Pavlica's children, did King violate any CFA Institute Standards of Professional Conduct?
     A. No, because King has discretion over the portfolio.
     B. Yes, he violated Standard III(A) Loyalty, Prudence, and Care.
     C. No, because he had a reasonable basis for making adjustments to the portfolio.

3.   In his statements to Pavlica after the reallocation, did King violate any CFA Institute Standards of Professional Conduct?
     A. No.
     B. Yes, because he misrepresented the expected performance of the strategy.
     C. Yes, because he met with her before their annual meeting which is unfair to clients who only meet with King annually.

4. Did King's actions with regard to allocating the private placement and the sale of VNC stock violate any CFA Institute Standards of Professional Conduct?

	Private placement	VNC sale
A.	Yes	Yes
B.	No	No
C.	No	Yes

5. According to the CFA Institute Standards of Professional Conduct, which of the following statements is correct concerning King's directorship with ShaleCo?
    A. King may not accept the directorship since it creates a conflict of interest.
    B. King may accept the directorship as long as it is disclosed to clients and prospects.
    C. King may accept the directorship as long as it is disclosed to his employer, clients, and prospects.

6. Does the fee structure at Rowan Brothers and King's disclosure of the compensation structure violate any CFA Institute Standards of Professional Conduct?

	Fee structure	Disclosure
A.	No	Yes
B.	Yes	No
C.	No	No

Questions 7–12 relate to Ethical and Professional Standards.

Johnny Bracco, CFA, is a portfolio manager in the trust department of Canada National (CNL) in Toronto. CNL is a financial conglomerate with many divisions. In addition to the trust department, the firm sells financial products and has a research department, a trading desk, and an investment banking division.

Part of the company's operating procedures manual contains detailed information on how the firm allocates shares in oversubscribed stock offerings. Allocation is effected on a pro rata basis based upon factors such as the size of a client's portfolio, suitability, and previous notification to participate in IPOs. Additionally, company policy discloses to clients that any trade needs to meet a minimum transaction size in an effort to control trading costs and to comply with best execution procedures.

One of Bracco's trust accounts is the Carobilo family trust, which contains a portion of nondiscretionary funds managed by Stephen Carobilo. Carobilo has a friend who runs a brokerage firm called First Trades, to which Carobilo tells Bracco to direct trades from the nondiscretionary accounts. Bracco has learned that First Trades charges a slightly higher trading fee than other brokers providing comparable services, and he discloses this to Carobilo.

Due to high prices and limited supplies of oil, Bracco has been following companies in the energy sector. He believes this area of the economy is in turmoil and should present some mispricing opportunities. One company he has been researching is Stiles Corporation, which is working on a new type of hydrogen fuel cell that uses fusion technology to create energy. To date, no one has been able to successfully sustain a fusion reaction for an extended period of time. Bracco has been in close contact with Stiles' pubic relations department, has toured their laboratories, and has thoroughly researched fusion technology and Stiles' competitors. Bracco is convinced from his research, based upon various public sources, that Stiles is on the verge of perfecting this technology and will be the first firm to bring it to the marketplace. Jerry McNulty, CFA and vice president of the investment banking division of CNL, has been working with Stiles to raise new capital via a secondary offering of Stiles common shares. One day Bracco happened to be in a stall in the bathroom when McNulty and a colleague came in and discussed the fact that Stiles had perfected the fuel-cell technology, which will greatly increase the price of Stiles' stock.

Stiles Corporation's board of directors includes Dr. Elaine James, who is a physics professor at the University of Toronto. She also works part-time for Stiles Corporation as a consultant in their fusion technology laboratory. Her husband is a materials engineer who recently started performing consulting work for Stiles.

A routine audit by the quality control department at CNL discovered trading errors in several of Bracco's accounts involving an oversubscribed IPO. Some accounts received shares they should not have and others did not receive shares they should have. Bracco and his supervisor Jaime Gun, CFA, are taking responsibility to reverse the incorrect trades. Bracco told Gun, "I'll correct the trades based on our clients' investment policy statements, previous notification of intent, and according to the company's formula for allocating shares on a pro rata basis. In so doing, we will fairly allocate shares so even small accounts that did not meet minimum size requirements will receive some shares of the IPO." Gun replied to Bracco by saying, "I'll credit short-term interest back to the accounts that should not have received the shares and subtract back interest from the accounts that should have received the shares."

That evening, Bracco and his wife attended the company holiday party for CNL employees and their spouses. Jerry McNulty, whose wife was ill and could not come to the party, arrived drunk from a meeting with Stiles' upper management. During the party McNulty made inappropriate advances toward many of the female employees and joked about the inadequacies of Stiles' managers.

While cleaning up after the party, a janitor found McNulty's pocket notebook that he apparently dropped accidentally during the party. In the notebook, McNulty wrote the recommended amount and date of the secondary offering as well as several details on the nature of the new product. Not knowing exactly what to do with the notebook, the janitor gave it to Burt Sampson, CFA, a trader at CNL. Later that night, Sampson called many of his relatives and friends and told them about the upcoming offering. First thing the following Monday morning, McNulty submitted an order to buy the stock for his personal portfolio.

7. Has Bracco violated any soft dollar standards regarding the Carobilo family trust? Bracco has:
   A. violated soft dollar standards because he did not satisfy the requirement of best execution.
   B. violated the soft dollar standards because client brokerage is to be used only for research purposes to benefit the client.
   C. not violated any soft dollar standards since Carobilo requested that the trades be sent to a specific broker.

8. If after overhearing McNulty's conversation in the bathroom Bracco placed trades to purchase shares of the Stiles Corporation for some of his clients, would Bracco have violated any of the Standards of Professional conduct?
   A. No, because the information regarding the Stiles Corporation was not acquired in a breach of confidence.
   B. No, because he did not base the trade solely on the information he overheard.
   C. Yes, because he is not allowed to trade on material, nonpublic information.

9.   Which of the following statements regarding Elaine James's participation on the board of directors of Stiles Corporation is *most* accurate? James's participation:
     A. does not violate effective corporate governance policies because she provides relevant expertise to the board.
     B. does not violate effective corporate governance policies since boards are allowed to hire outside consultants when making decisions.
     C. violates effective corporate governance policies because she is paid by the company as a consultant and is therefore not independent.

10. Regarding the statements made by Bracco and Gun on how to correct the trading errors:
     A. only Gun's statement is correct.
     B. only Bracco's statement is correct.
     C. both are correct or both are incorrect.

11. Did McNulty's behavior at the holiday party violate the:

Code of Ethics?	Standards of Professional Conduct?
A. Yes	Yes
B. No	Yes
C. Yes	No

12. Based solely on the information provided in the last paragraph, determine whether McNulty and/or Sampson violated the Code and Standards.

McNulty	Sampson
A. No	No
B. Yes	Yes
C. No	Yes

Questions 13–18 relate to Fixed Income Portfolio Management and Risk Management Applications of Derivatives.

Tiffany Morrison, CFA, a manager for Sierra Fund, is investigating the use of relative value methodologies for global corporate bond portfolio management. As a recent college graduate, Bernard Tabler has been assisting Morrison in data gathering and analysis.

Morrison is a firm believer that corporate yield spreads have a tendency to revert to their historical mean values. Accordingly, Tabler has compiled relevant information for three corporate issues. Morrison and Tabler use the information below to conduct mean reversion analysis.

Bond Issue	Current Spread	Mean Spread for Past 12 Months	Standard Deviation of Spread
VV	125	98	28
XX	100	75	15
YY	85	100	10

Note: All spreads are expressed in basis points.

Morrison's research has also included a study of the implications of secular and cyclical changes in the primary corporate bond market. As a result of her research, she states that the implication of both cyclical and secular changes in the primary corporate bond market for fixed-income portfolio management is that effective duration and aggregate interest rate risk will increase. Tabler adds that it also appears that credit-based derivatives will increasingly be used to achieve desired exposure to credit sectors, issuers, and structures.

During the presentation to a client, Morrison discusses corporate curve analysis. She states that corporate spread curves tend to change with the economic cycle, so in order to properly conduct this analysis the analyst must examine credit and yield curves carefully. Tabler adds that corporate spreads usually narrow during upturns and widen during downturns.

Morrison is also considering using repurchase agreements to fund some overnight investment activities. Watching the financial news, she observes that the Federal Reserve has increased the federal funds rate to combat potential inflation. She notes that this will increase the borrowing costs of investment strategies using repurchase agreements. Tabler chimes in that the strategy's interest cost could be reduced by using hot collateral such as on-the-run U.S. Treasuries.

Morrison is providing advice to a client on the best way to hedge a floating rate loan using a swap. The client is paying 120 basis points over LIBOR. Morrison suggests that the client enter a 5-year LIBOR-based swap. The swap fixed rate is 100 basis points over the U.S. Treasury rate. The floating rate is LIBOR flat. LIBOR is 5.60% and the Treasury rate is 5.20% when this swap is being considered.

13. Based on the mean-reversion analysis only, which of the three bonds is the most attractive candidate for Morrison to purchase for the Sierra Fund?
    A. VV.
    B. XX.
    C. YY.

14. Regarding their statements on the implications of secular and cyclical changes in the primary corporate bond market, **determine** if Morrison and Tabler are correct or incorrect.
    A. Only Morrison is correct.
    B. Only Tabler is correct.
    C. Both are incorrect.

15. Over lunch, Morrison and Tabler get into a heated debate over the relative performance of callable and non-callable bonds in a dynamic interest rate environment. In terms of relative performance, determine which of the following relationships is *least* accurate.
    A. If rates are significantly greater than coupon rates, embedded call options are practically worthless, so callable bonds perform as if they are non-callable.
    B. As interest rates increase, the option to call a callable bond decreases. If required returns are below coupon rates and expected to increase, non-callable bonds are probably better investments than callable bonds.
    C. The value of a callable bond is significantly affected by the value of the embedded call option. For example, as its required return falls below (increases above) its coupon rate, the value of the embedded option consumes an increasing (a decreasing) proportion of the total value of the bond.

16. Regarding their statements on corporate curve analysis, are Morrison and Tabler correct or incorrect?
    A. Both are correct.
    B. Neither is correct.
    C. One is correct.

17. Regarding their statements on investment strategies using repurchase agreements, are Morrison and Tabler correct or incorrect?
    A. Only Morrison is correct.
    B. Only Tabler is correct.
    C. Both are correct.

18. In the swap hedge of the floating rate loan, the net fixed rate that the client will pay is *closest* to:
    A. 5.8%.
    B. 7.4%.
    C. 7.8%.

Questions 19–24 relate to Portfolio Management of Global Bonds and Fixed-Income Derivatives and Risk Management.

Carl Cramer is a recent hire at Derivatives Specialists Inc. (DSI), a small consulting firm that advises a variety of institutions on the management of credit risk. Some of DSI's clients are very familiar with risk management techniques whereas others are not. Cramer has been assigned the task of creating a handbook on credit risk, its possible impact, and its management. His immediate supervisor, Christine McNally, will assist Cramer in the creation of the handbook and will review it. Before she took a position at DSI, McNally advised banks and other institutions on the use of value-at-risk (VAR) as well as credit-at-risk (CAR).

Cramer's first task is to address the basic dimensions of credit risk. He states that the first dimension of credit risk is the probability of an event that will cause a loss. The second dimension of credit risk is the amount lost, which is a function of the dollar amount recovered when a loss event occurs. Cramer recalls the considerable difficulty he faced when transacting with Johnson Associates, a firm which defaulted on a contract with the Grich Company. Grich forced Johnson Associates into bankruptcy, and Johnson Associates was declared in default of all its agreements. Unfortunately, DSI then had to wait until the bankruptcy court decided on all claims before it could settle the agreement with Johnson Associates.

McNally mentions that Cramer should include a statement about the time dimension of credit risk. She states that the two primary time dimensions of credit risk are current and future. Current credit risk relates to the possibility of default on current obligations, while future credit risk relates to potential default on future obligations. If a borrower defaults and claims bankruptcy, a creditor can file claims representing the face value of current obligations and the present value of future obligations. Cramer adds that combining current and potential credit risk analysis provides the firm's total credit risk exposure and that current credit risk is usually a reliable predictor of a borrower's potential credit risk.

As DSI has clients with a variety of forward contracts, Cramer then addresses the credit risks associated with forward agreements. Cramer states that long forward contracts gain in value when the market price of the underlying increases above the contract price. McNally encourages Cramer to include an example of credit risk and forward contracts in the handbook. She offers the following:

> *A forward contract sold by Palmer Securities has six months until the delivery date and a contract price of 50. The underlying asset has no cash flows or storage costs and is currently priced at 50. In the contract, no funds were exchanged upfront.*

Cramer also describes how a client firm of DSI can control the credit risks in their derivatives transactions. He writes that firms can make use of netting arrangements, create a special purpose vehicle, require collateral from counterparties, and require a mark-to-market provision. McNally adds that Cramer should include a discussion of some newer forms of credit protection in his handbook. McNally thinks credit derivatives represent an opportunity for DSI. She believes that one type of credit derivative that should figure prominently in their handbook is total return swaps. She asserts that to purchase protection through a total return swap, the holder of a credit asset will agree to pass the total return on the asset to the protection seller (e.g., a swap dealer) in exchange for a single, fixed payment representing the discounted present value of expected cash flows from the asset.

A DSI client, Weaver Trading, has a bond that they are concerned will increase in credit risk. Weaver would like protection against this event in the form of a payment if the bond's yield spread increases beyond LIBOR plus 3%. Weaver Trading prefers a cash settlement.

Later that week, Cramer and McNally visit a client's headquarters and discuss the potential hedge of a bond issued by Cuellar Motors. Cuellar manufactures and markets specialty luxury motorcycles. The client is considering hedging the bond using a credit spread forward because he is concerned that a downturn in the economy could result in a default on the Cuellar bond. The client holds $2,000,000 in par of the Cuellar bond, and the bond's coupons are paid annually. The bond's current spread over the U.S. Treasury rate is 2.5%. The characteristics of the forward contract are shown below.

Information on the Credit Spread Forward

Contract spread	3%
Risk factor	10
Spread at maturity	4.5%
Notional principal of credit spread forward	$2 million

19. Determine which of the following is *most likely* responsible for the difficulty Cramer faced when transacting with the firm Johnson Associates.
    A. A cross-default provision.
    B. A jump-to-default provision.
    C. A credit protection provision.

20. Regarding their statements concerning current and future credit risk, determine whether Cramer and McNally are correct or incorrect.
    A. Only Cramer is correct.
    B. Only McNally is correct.
    C. Both are correct.

21. Determine whether the forward contracts sold by Palmer Securities have current and/or potential credit risk.
    A. The contract has current credit risk only.
    B. The contract has potential credit risk only.
    C. The contract has neither potential credit risk nor current credit risk.

22. Regarding their statements concerning controlling credit risk, determine whether Cramer and McNally are correct or incorrect.
    A. Only Cramer is correct.
    B. Only McNally is correct.
    C. Both are incorrect.

23. Of the following, determine which would *most likely* provide the *best* hedge desired by Weaver Trading.
    A. Credit default swap.
    B. Credit spread call option.
    C. Credit spread put option.

24. Assuming the $2,000,000 in par of the Cuellar bond is hedged using the given credit spread forward, the payoff to the buyer or seller from the credit spread forward contract is *closest* to:
    A. $300,000 to the seller.
    B. $300,000 to the buyer.
    C. $100,000 to the buyer.

Questions 25–30 relate to Fixed Income Portfolio Management.

Jack Thomas and Tim Bentley are analysts for Bond Analytics (BA). BA provides bond analysis for mutual fund managers, hedge fund managers, and institutional money managers in the United States. BA specializes in the valuation of international bonds and callable bonds, using intrasector analysis to find undervalued bonds. In addition to valuing the bonds, they also advise clients on whether to hedge currency risk for international bonds. Thomas has been a particularly strong advocate of hedging the currency risk of international bonds, especially in emerging markets, using forward contracts when they are available.

At a morning meeting, Thomas and Bentley are trying to decide whether to hedge the currency risk of a large issue of bonds from a Thai manufacturer of pressed steel, Nakhon Metals. The client considering purchasing the bonds is a large U.S. mutual fund, Epsilon Funds. Epsilon has started to explore the possibility of earning higher returns through currency management using forward contracts. Thomas and Bentley discuss the various hedges of currency risk for the Nakhon Metals bond. One possibility is using a forward hedge position on the Thai baht. A second possibility is using forward contracts where the baht is delivered for Korean won. Thomas states that the second hedge would be pursued if the won was expected to appreciate more against the U.S. dollar than the baht. In the second hedge, the manager would sell won for dollars at the future spot rate.

Thomas and Bentley gather the following information on the expected changes in the various currencies, the 1-year cash rates in the respective countries, and the expected return on the Nakhon bond.

Yield on Nakhon Metals bond in Thai baht terms	5.20%
Cash rate in Thailand	2.50%
Expected change in the baht relative to the U.S. dollar	2.80%
Cash rate in Korea	3.20%
Expected change in the won relative to the U.S. dollar	6.40%
Cash rate in Japan	4.20%
Expected change in the yen relative to the U.S. dollar	3.50%
Cash rate in United States	6.50%

Additionally, the Nakhon Metals bond has a duration of 7.30 and is being compared against a bond denominated in U.S. dollars, issued by Powhatan Industries. The Powhatan bond has a duration of 4.2 and a yield of 4.50%. Whichever bond is purchased will be held for the next year. Thomas projects that the yield for the Nakhon Metals bond is expected to increase by 15 basis points, while the yield on the Powhatan Industries bond is expected to stay constant.

©2011 Kaplan, Inc.

The following day, Thomas and Bentley discuss the market for and valuation of callable and long duration bonds. They believe that interest rates are temporarily low and for this reason want to be careful about their bond investments. Although they could hedge interest rate risk, they prefer not to because they believe it reduces the ultimate long-term return.

Thomas says that due to secular changes in the bond market, bonds with structures are expected to become more scarce. He says that the problem with callable bonds has been that they typically trade at a premium due to their scarcity. Bentley states that bonds with very long durations also trade at a premium because they are scarce as well.

Thomas states that the performance of callables and non-callables may differ when interest rates change due to the inherent call risk. He discusses the relative performance under two scenarios:

- Scenario A: Interest rates are near coupon rates and fall for both callables and non-callables by the same amount.
- Scenario B: Interest rates are historically very low and rise for both callables and non-callables by the same amount.

25. The second hedge that Thomas recommends for the Nakhon Metals bond is *most likely* an example of which of the following currency hedging strategies?
    A. Cross hedge.
    B. Proxy hedge.
    C. Forward hedge.

26. Based on their cash rates determine which of the currencies (Thai baht, Korean won, and Japanese yen) should trade at forward discount to the dollar.
    A. Only the yen should trade at a forward discount.
    B. The baht and the won should trade at a forward discount.
    C. None of the currencies should trade at a forward discount.

27. Based on interest rate expectations and ignoring currency effects, determine whether the Nakhon Metals bond or Powhatan Industries bond should be more attractive over the one-year time horizon.
    A. The Nakhon Metals bond should be more attractive.
    B. The Powhatan Industries bond should be more attractive.
    C. Neither bond should be more attractive.

28.   After Thomas and Bentley review the cash rates and expectations data they have gathered on the won, baht, yen, and dollar, Thomas says, "I'm going to recommend to my U.S. managers that they remain unhedged in Japanese bond investments because they'll pick up an additional currency return not predicted by the market when they translate back into dollars."

Overhearing Thomas, a friend of Bentley's replies, "You're off your bean, old boy. The difference in the cash rates in the dollar and the yen is already reflected in their spot and forward rates. Since you have to exchange dollars for yen now and yen for dollars later, you won't gain anything that isn't already incorporated into the currencies."

Based on cash rates and expectations data provided above, determine whether Thomas and Bentley's friend are correct or incorrect.
A. Only Bentley's friend is correct.
B. Only Thomas is correct.
C. Both are incorrect.

29.   Determine whether Thomas and Bentley are correct or incorrect regarding their statements about the scarcity and pricing of callable and long duration bonds.
A. Only Thomas is correct.
B. Only Bentley is correct.
C. Both are correct.

30.   Which of the following *best* describes the relative performance of callables and non-callables under the two scenarios?
A. Callables will outperform non-callables under both scenarios.
B. Callables will outperform non-callables under scenario A only.
C. Callables will outperform non-callables under scenario B only.

Questions 31–36 relate to Alternative Investments for Portfolio Management.

William Bliss, CFA, runs a hedge fund that uses both managed futures strategies and positions in physical commodities. He is reviewing his operations and strategies to increase the return of the fund. Bliss has just hired Joseph Cantori, CFA, to help him manage the fund because he realizes that he needs to increase his trading activity in futures and to engage in futures strategies other than passively managed positions. Cantori is a registered commodity trading advisor (CTA) who generally uses a contrarian strategy to manage futures. Bliss also hired Cantori because of Cantori's experience with swaps, which Bliss hopes to add to his choice of investment tools.

Bliss explains to Cantori that his clients pay 2% on assets under management and a 20% incentive fee. The incentive fee is based on profits after having subtracted the risk-free rate, which is the fund's basic hurdle rate, and there is a high water mark provision. Bliss is hoping that Cantori can help his business because his firm did not earn an incentive fee this past year. This was the case despite the fact that, after two years of losses, the value of the fund increased 14% during the previous year. That increase occurred without any new capital contributed from clients. Bliss is optimistic about the near future because the term structure of futures prices is particularly favorable for earning higher returns from long futures positions.

Cantori says he has seen research that indicates inflation may increase in the next few years. He states this should increase the opportunity to earn a higher return in commodities and suggests taking a large, margined position in a broad commodity index. This would offer an enhanced return that would attract investors holding only stocks and bonds. Bliss mentions that not all commodity prices are positively correlated with inflation, so it may be better to choose particular types of commodities in which to invest. Furthermore, Bliss adds that commodities traditionally have not outperformed stocks and bonds either on a risk-adjusted or absolute basis. Cantori says he will research companies who do business in commodities because buying the stock of those companies to gain commodity exposure is an efficient and effective method for gaining indirect exposure to commodities.

Bliss agrees that his fund should increase its exposure to commodities and wants Cantori's help in using swaps to gain such exposure. Bliss asks Cantori to enter into a swap with a relatively short horizon to demonstrate how a commodity swap works. Bliss notes that the futures prices of oil for six months, one year, eighteen months, and two years are $55, $54, $52, and $51 per barrel, respectively, and the risk-free rate is less than 2%.

Bliss asks how a seasonal component could be added to such a swap. Specifically, he asks if either the notional principal or the swap price can be higher during the reset closest to the winter season and lower for the reset period closest to the summer season. This would allow the swap to more effectively hedge a commodity like oil, which would have a higher demand in the winter than the summer. Cantori says that a swap can only have seasonal swap prices, and the notional principal must stay constant. Thus, the solution in such a case would be to enter into two swaps: one that has an annual reset in the winter and one that has an annual reset in the summer.

31.   Given the information, the *most likely* reason that Bliss's firm did not earn an incentive fee in the past year was because:
A. of a high water mark provision.
B. the return did not exceed the risk-free rate.
C. the 2% asset-under-management fee is greater than the risk-free rate.

32.   Cantori's futures trading strategy can *best* be described as a:
A. market trading strategy.
B. discretionary trading strategy.
C. systematic trading strategy.

33.   Bliss is optimistic about the near future because the term structure of futures prices is particularly favorable for earning higher returns from long positions. This would be the case if the term structure is:
A. in contango.
B. relatively flat.
C. in backwardation.

34.   The points made by Cantori and Bliss during their discussion of commodity returns given high inflation expectations were correct with the exception of:
A. Cantori's assertions concerning the indirect method of investing in stocks to gain commodity exposure.
B. Bliss's assertion that not all commodities are positively correlated with inflation.
C. Cantori's assertion that a broad index would benefit from inflation.

35.   Based on the given information, the fixed price for the 2-year swap with semi-annual reset is probably:
A. closest to $53.
B. closest to $55.
C. undefined since the futures price decreases with the time horizon.

36.   Cantori's comment concerning seasonal swaps is:
A. not correct because neither swap price nor notional principal can be seasonal.
B. not correct because both a seasonal notional principal and swap price are possible.
C. not correct because it is the notional principal that can be seasonal and not the swap price.

Questions 37–42 relate to Global Bonds and Fixed-Income Derivatives, Equity Portfolio Management, and Risk Management Applications of Derivatives.

Jerry Edwards is an analyst with DeLeon Analytics. He is currently advising the CFO of Anderson Corp., a multinational manufacturing corporation based in Newark, New Jersey, USA. Jackie Palmer is Edwards's assistant. Palmer is well versed in risk management, having worked at a large multinational bank for the last ten years prior to coming to Anderson.

Anderson has received a $2 million note with a duration of 4.0 from Weaver Tools for a shipment delivered last week. Weaver markets tools and machinery from manufacturers of Anderson's size. Edwards states that in order to effectively hedge the price risk of this instrument, Anderson should sell a series of interest rate calls. Palmer states that an alternative hedge for the note would be to enter an interest rate swap as the fixed-rate payer.

As well as selling products from a Swiss plant in Europe, Anderson sells products in Switzerland itself. As a result, Anderson has quarterly cash flows of 12,000,000 Swiss franc (CHF). In order to convert these cash flows into dollars, Edwards suggests that Anderson enter into a currency swap without an exchange of notional principal. Palmer contacts a currency swap dealer with whom they have dealt in the past and finds the following exchange rate and annual swap interest rates:

Exchange Rate (CHF per dollar)	1.24
Swap interest rate in U.S. dollars	2.80%
Swap interest rate in Swiss franc	6.60%

Discussing foreign exchange rate risk in general, Edwards states that it is transaction exposure that is most often hedged because the amount to be hedged is contractual and certain. Economic exposure, he states, is less certain and thus harder to hedge.

To finance their U.S. operations, Anderson issued a $10 million fixed-rate bond in the United States five years ago. The bond had an original maturity of ten years and now has a modified duration of 4.0. Edwards states that Anderson should enter a 5-year semiannual pay floating swap with a notional principal of about $11.4 million to take advantage of falling interest rates. The duration of the fixed-rate side of the swap is equal to 75% of its maturity or 3.75 (= 0.75 × 5). The duration of the floating side of the swap is 0.25. Palmer states that Anderson's position in the swap will have a negative duration.

For another client of DeLeon, Edwards has assigned Palmer the task of estimating the interest rate sensitivity of the client's portfolios. The client's portfolio consists of positions in both U.S. and British bonds. The relevant information for estimating the duration contributions of the bonds and the portfolio's total duration is provided below.

U.S. dollar bond	$275,000
British bond	$155,000
British yield beta	1.40
Duration of U.S. bond	4.0
Duration of British bond	8.5

When discussing portfolio management with clients, Edwards recommends the use of emerging market bonds to add value to a core-plus strategy. He explains the characteristics of emerging market debt to Palmer by stating:

1. "The performance of emerging market debt has been quite resilient over time. After crises in the debt markets, emerging market bonds quickly recover, so long-term returns can be good."

2. "Emerging market debt is quite volatile due in part to the nature of political risk in these markets. It is therefore important that the analyst monitor the risk of these markets. I prefer to measure the risk of emerging market bonds with the standard deviation because it provides the best representation of risk in these markets."

37.   Regarding their statements concerning the hedge of the Weaver Tools note, determine if Edwards and Palmer are correct or incorrect.
       A. Both are correct.
       B. Only Palmer is correct.
       C. Only Edwards is correct.

38.   If Anderson enters a properly structured currency swap to convert the CHF 12,000,000 to dollars, the amount they will receive is *closest* to:
       A. $4,105,572.
       B. $7,071,429.
       C. $9,677,419.

39.   Regarding Edward's statements concerning the transaction exposure of currency risk, which of the following *best* describes his statement?
       A. It is inaccurate because transaction exposure is very uncertain.
       B. It accurately describes firms' currency exposures and hedging practices.
       C. It is inaccurate because firms more frequently hedge translation exposure.

40.   Regarding their statements concerning the hedge of the U.S. dollar-denominated bond Anderson issued, determine whether Edwards and Palmer are correct or incorrect.
       A. Only Edwards is correct.
       B. Only Palmer is correct.
       C. Both are correct.

41.   Which of the following is *closest* to the duration contribution of the British bond and the portfolio's total duration from a U.S. perspective?

	British bond	Portfolio duration
A.	2.19	4.75
B.	3.06	5.62
C.	4.29	6.85

42.   Regarding his two statements about the characteristics of emerging market debt, is Edwards correct?
       A. Only statement 1 is correct.
       B. Only statement 2 is correct.
       C. Both statements are incorrect.

Questions 43–48 relate to Management of Active and Passive Fixed Income Portfolios, Risk Management, and Risk Management Applications of Derivatives.

Mary Thomas works for Kershaw-Ross, a large investment bank located in London. Kershaw-Ross provides advice to portfolio managers, securities dealers, and hedge funds. Jack Bentley is Thomas's assistant.

Washington Capital Management, one of Thomas's clients, has a $5 million position in fixed-rate U.S. Treasury bonds. The firm would like to hedge this position using calls on Treasury bonds. The calls each cover $100,000 par value of bonds, have a delta of 0.4, and are out-of-the-money. To hedge this position, Thomas recommends that Washington Capital Management consider the delta for the call options written on these Treasury bonds.

Later that week, Thomas discusses the particulars of option hedges with Francis Steele, Vice President at Washington Capital Management. Thomas describes how using gamma, the change in delta relative to the change in the underlying asset price, can increase the precision of the hedge. She states that this would be particularly true if the bond portfolio used calls that were at-the-money. Bentley adds that, given the uncertainty surrounding U.S. Federal Reserve monetary policy, Kershaw-Ross has been advising clients to carefully monitor their bond positions for price changes. Bentley states that, in Washington Capital Management's case, if the price of the underlying bond increases by 1% due to a yield curve shift, the call hedge should be decreased because delta would have increased.

Thomas is analyzing the portfolio for one of his investors, Canopy Managers. Last year the portfolio had a market value of $4,881,000 and a dollar duration of $157,200. The current figures for the portfolio are provided below:

	Market Value	Duration	Dollar Duration
Bond 1	$780,000	4.5	$35,100
Bond 2	$2,500,000	3.4	$85,000
Bond 3	$524,000	2.7	$14,148
Bond 4	$413,000	1.9	$7,847
Portfolio	$4,217,000		$142,095

Canopy would like to alter the current dollar duration of the portfolio to last year's duration, and they would like to do so with the least amount of cash possible and a controlling position in one of the bonds.

Canopy Managers has also contracted to take out a 9-month loan for $5 million in three months at LIBOR. Canopy's chief financial officer has become concerned that interest rates might increase and has asked Thomas to investigate the possibility of hedging the position with a forward rate agreement. Thomas finds a forward rate agreement is available with the same maturity as Canopy's loan and a forward rate of 4.40%. The risk free rate is 3.8%, and LIBOR has increased to 4.60%.

The next week, Thomas and Bentley visit the headquarters of Capital Pension Management, one of Kershaw-Ross's largest clients. Capital is using contingent immunization to immunize a liability, but management is concerned about a possible rise in interest rates. Thomas states that if she were to recommend the most effective strategy to Capital, she would recommend that they use bonds with high yields because immunization will be cheaper. Bentley interjects that the risk from nonparallel shifts in the yield curve can be minimized by concentrating the cash flows around the horizon date.

Due to their tremendous success, Kershaw-Ross has outgrown their current headquarters and is going to expand their current building. Thomas's team has been charged with securing financing for the renovations. They currently are considering a remodeling and addition that would cost approximately £5,000,000.

Thomas has secured the financing necessary for the renovations at a floating interest rate of LIBOR plus 150 basis points, with payments made quarterly over three years. Thomas believes that Kershaw-Ross should be able to complete the renovation of the building and close on the loan in one year. She is concerned, however, that interest rates will increase in the interim and has obtained a swaption to hedge the loan. She states that Kershaw-Ross should use a payer swaption to hedge the loan. Bentley evaluates the forecasts for future swap fixed rates as well as the current terms of various swaptions, which are provided below:

Fixed rate for a 1-year payer swaption	= 8.50%
Fixed rate for a 1-year receiver swaption	= 8.60%
Projected swap fixed rate in one year	= 9.30%
Fixed rate for a 4-year payer swaption	= 9.40%
Fixed rate for a 4-year receiver swaption	= 9.70%
Projected swap fixed rate in four years	= 9.80%

43.　Determine the most appropriate action to delta hedge the Washington Capital Management's Treasury bond position.
　A.　Sell 20 Treasury bond calls.
　B.　Buy 20 Treasury bond calls.
　C.　Sell 125 Treasury bond calls.

44.　Regarding their statements to Steele concerning the hedge of Washington Capital Management's Treasury bond position, determine whether Thomas and Bentley are correct or incorrect.
　A.　Only Thomas is correct.
　B.　Only Bentley is correct.
　C.　Both are correct.

45.　To adjust the dollar duration of the Canopy portfolio to last year's level, the amount Canopy will need to purchase of Bond 1, acting as a controlling position, is *closest* to:
　A.　$335,667.
　B.　$862,916.
　C.　$1,115,667.

46.　The current credit risk to Canopy from the FRA agreement is *closest* to:
　A.　$7,183.
　B.　$7,250.
　C.　$7,292.

47.　Regarding their statements concerning the strategy of Capital Pension Management, determine whether Thomas and Bentley are correct or incorrect.
　A.　Only Thomas is correct.
　B.　Only Bentley is correct.
　C.　Both are correct.

48.　Assuming that their interest rate forecast is correct and they use the appropriate hedge, calculate Kershaw-Ross's first quarterly payment on the building expansion loan.
　A.　£125,000.
　B.　£126,250.
　C.　£136,250.

Questions 49–54 relate to Execution of Portfolio Decisions: Monitoring and Rebalancing.

Somerset Investment Limited is a Singapore-based money management firm that is conducting an appraisal of its investment performance. Cameron Li, CFA, has been charged with conducting the appraisal and is to report back to upper management with his findings.

Li is convinced that trade executions play a substantial role in overall portfolio performance, particularly for funds that have a relatively high level of turnover during the year. As a result, he is seeking methods that will allow him to evaluate the quality of trade executions.

He knows that the firm's traders use both market and limit orders, and he is wondering if a framework can be developed to ensure that the best order type is used under the specific circumstances for each trade. When he consults with the firm's head trader, Rick Gleeson, Gleeson tells him that market orders have price uncertainty but no execution uncertainty, while limit orders eliminate price uncertainty but have execution uncertainty. According to Gleeson, rebalancing and liquidity-motivated trades should use limit orders while value-motivated and information-motivated trades should use market orders.

Li knows that bid-ask spreads are a major component of trading costs and asks Gleeson for some recent trade data that he can use for analysis and presentation to management. He receives the following data relating to a series of buy trades for Sumatra Natural Resources (SNR), with all currency values in Singapore dollars:

Trades of Sumatra Natural Resources

Time	Bid Price	Ask Price	Execution Price	Shares Bought
10:30	$22.18	$22.36	$22.33	900
11:15	$22.23	$22.43	$22.43	600
13:45	$22.29	$22.48	$22.47	700
15:00	$22.37	$22.63	$22.65	800

Gleeson also tells Li that the portfolio manager had originally made the decision to purchase 5,000 SNR at 10:00 a.m. when the price was $22.36. The closing price for the day was Leeson's last trade at $22.65, at which point the order for the remaining 2,000 shares was cancelled.

49. Which of the following *correctly* summarizes Gleeson's comments concerning the differences between market and limit orders?
   A. He is correct concerning the nature of uncertainty; he is correct concerning when the order types should be used.
   B. He is correct concerning the nature of uncertainty; he is incorrect concerning when the order types should be used.
   C. He is incorrect concerning the nature of uncertainty; he is correct concerning when the order types should be used.

50. Concerning the Sumatra Natural Resources price and execution data, the average effective spread and weighted average effective spread are *closest* to:

	Average effective spread	Weighted average effective spread
A.	0.1957	0.1975
B.	0.0971	0.0908
C.	0.1975	0.1957

51. Assume that the four trades in Sumatra Natural Resources are the only trades in the security for the day. Determine which of the following statements concerning the volume weighted average price (VWAP) is *most* correct.
   A. The VWAP for the day is 22.470, and the trader's goal would be to have an average cost that is less than the VWAP.
   B. The VWAP for the day is 22.468, and the trader's goal would be to have an average cost that is greater than the VWAP.
   C. The VWAP for the day is 22.468, and the trader's goal would be to have an average cost that is less than the VWAP.

52. Calculate the implementation shortfall assuming total commissions paid by Gleeson when he purchased the 3,000 SNR were $210.
   A. 0.303%.
   B. 0.996%.
   C. 2.027%.

53. Which of the following statements concerning implementation shortfall and VWAP is incorrect?
   A. Implementation shortfall is greater than zero if any portion of the original order goes unfilled and is cancelled.
   B. For small trades in non-trending markets, VWAP is more appropriate than implementation shortfall.
   C. Implementation shortfall must be adjusted to accurately account for movements in the general market.

54. Determine which of the following statements concerning an algorithmic trading strategy is *most* incorrect. An algorithmic trading strategy:

   A. ensures that the portfolio does not become over-concentrated (in specific assets or sectors) because it is based on quantitative rules.

   B. involves the use of automated processes based on quantitative measures, such as the ratio of the trade size to average daily volume, to guide trading decisions.

   C. known as simple logical participation, breaks trades into small pieces to avoid detection and to minimize market impact costs.

Questions 55–60 relate to Risk Management and Performance Evaluation and Attribution.

Jack Mercer and June Seagram are investment advisors for Northern Advisors. Northern provides investment advice for pension funds, foundations, endowments, and trusts. As part of their services, they evaluate the performance of outside portfolio managers. They are currently scrutinizing the performance of several portfolio managers who work for the Thompson University endowment.

Over the most recent month, the record of the largest manager, Bison Management, is as follows. On March 1, the endowment account with Bison stood at $11,200,000. On March 16, the university contributed $4,000,000 that they received from a wealthy alumnus. After receiving that contribution, the account was valued at $17,800,000. On March 31, the account was valued at $16,100,000. Using this information, Mercer and Seagram calculated the time-weighted and money-weighted returns for Bison during March. Mercer states that the advantage of the time-weighted return is that it is easy to calculate and administer. Seagram states that the money-weighted return is, however, a better measure of the manager's performance.

Mercer and Seagram are also evaluating the performance of Lunar Management. Risk and return data for the most recent fiscal year are shown below for both Bison and Lunar. The minimum acceptable return (MAR) for Thompson is the 4.5% spending rate on the endowment, which the endowment has determined using a geometric spending rule. The T-bill return over the same fiscal year was 3.5%. The return on the MSCI World Index is used as the market index. The World index had a return of 9% in dollar terms with a standard deviation of 23% and a beta of 1.0.

	Bison	Lunar
Return	14.1%	15.8%
Standard Deviation	31.5%	34.7%
Beta	0.9	1.3
Standard Deviation of returns below the MAR	15.1%	15.9%

The next day at lunch, Mercer and Seagram discuss alternatives for benchmarks in assessing the performance of managers. The alternatives discussed that day are manager universes, broad market indices, style indices, factor models, and custom benchmarks. Mercer states that manager universes have the advantage of being measurable, but they are subject to survivor bias. Seagram states that manager universes possess only one quality of a valid benchmark.

Mercer and Seagram also provide investment advice for a hedge fund, Jaguar Investors. Jaguar specializes in exploiting mispricing in equities and over-the-counter derivatives in emerging markets. They periodically engage in providing foreign currency hedges to small firms in emerging markets when deemed profitable. This most commonly occurs when no other provider of these contracts is available to these firms. Jaguar is selling a large position in Mexican pesos in the spot market. Furthermore, they have just provided a forward contract to a firm in Russia that allows that firm to sell Swiss francs for Russian rubles in 90 days. Jaguar has also entered into a currency swap that allows a firm to receive Japanese yen in exchange for paying the Russian ruble.

55. The time-weighted and money-weighted returns for Bison during March (assuming compounding every half-month) are *closest* to:

Time-weighted	Money-weighted
A. 5.9%	6.8%
B. 5.9%	3.4%
C. 11.4%	6.8%

56. Regarding their statements about time-weighted and money-weighted returns, determine whether Mercer and Seagram are correct or incorrect.
    A. Only Mercer is correct.
    B. Both are correct.
    C. Neither is correct.

57. The M-squared measure for the Bison fund is *closest* to:
    A. 2.2%.
    B. 6.4%.
    C. 11.2%.

58. Determine which of the following best describes the relative diversification and performance of the Bison portfolio and Lunar portfolio:
    A. The Lunar portfolio is better diversified and, from a downside risk perspective, has superior performance.
    B. The Bison portfolio is better diversified, but from a downside risk perspective, the Lunar portfolio has superior performance.
    C. The Lunar portfolio is better diversified, but from a downside risk perspective, the Bison portfolio has superior performance.

59. Regarding their statements about manager universes, determine whether Mercer and Seagram are correct or incorrect.
    A. Only Mercer is correct.
    B. Only Seagram is correct.
    C. Both are correct.

60. Of the following risks, determine which was *most likely not* explicitly considered by Jaguar before entering the series of foreign currency derivative transactions.
   A. Credit risk.
   B. Herstatt risk.
   C. Operations risk.

END OF AFTERNOON SESSION

PRACTICE EXAM 3 MORNING SESSION QUESTION BREAKDOWN

MORNING SESSION		
Topic	Question	Points
Private Wealth Management	1A	14
Private Wealth Management	1B	6
Private Wealth Management and Asset Allocation	2A	4
Asset Allocation	2B	4
Private Wealth Management	2C	2
Private Wealth Management	3	8
Alternative Investments	4A	6
Alternative Investments	4B	3
Alternative Investments	4C	2
Alternative Investments	4D	3
Alternative Investments	4E	4
Alternative Investments	5A	3
Alternative Investments	5B	4
Alternative Investments	5C	3
Economic Concepts	6A	3
Economic Concepts	6B	2
Economic Concepts	6C	4

MORNING SESSION (CONTINUED)		
Topic	Question	Points
Performance Evaluation and Attribution	7A	10
Performance Evaluation and Attribution	7B	8
Performance Evaluation and Attribution	7C	6
Portfolio Management – Institutional	8A	6
Portfolio Management – Institutional	8B	5
Portfolio Management – Institutional	8C	4
Portfolio Management – Institutional	9A	6
Portfolio Management – Institutional	9B	4
Equity Portfolio Management	10A	4
Equity Portfolio Management and Economic Concepts	10B	5
Portfolio Management – Institutional	11A	12
Asset Allocation	11B	8
Asset Allocation	11C	6
Execution of Portfolio Decisions	12A	4
Execution of Portfolio Decisions	12B	4
Execution of Portfolio Decisions	12C	4
Portfolio Management – Individual	13	9
Total		180

Practice Exam 3 Score Sheet

MORNING SESSION		
Question	Max. Points	Your Approx. Score
1A	14	
1B	6	
2A	4	
2B	4	
2C	2	
3	8	
4A	6	
4B	3	
4C	2	
4D	3	
4E	4	
5A	3	
5B	4	
5C	3	
6A	3	
6B	2	
6C	4	
7A	10	
7B	8	
7C	6	
8A	6	
8B	5	
8C	4	
9A	6	
9B	4	
10A	4	
10B	5	
11A	12	
11B	8	
11C	6	

MORNING SESSION (CONTINUED)		
Question	Max. Points	Your Approx. Score
12A	4	
12B	4	
12C	4	
13	9	
Total	180	

AFTERNOON SESSION		
Question	Max. Points	Your Approx. Score
1–6	18	
7–12	18	
13–18	18	
19–24	18	
25–30	18	
31–36	18	
37–42	18	
43–48	18	
49–54	18	
55–60	18	
Total	180	

Certain Passing Score: 252 of 360 (70%)
Probable Passing Score: 234

Please note that we write these exams to be as representative of Level III exam questions as possible. However, due to the relaxed conditions that most candidates apply when they "take" these exams (i.e., "I'm getting a little tired, I think I'll go to the refrigerator and get a snack"), you should adjust your score downward by 10–15% to get a more accurate measure of the score you would have received on exam day. Also, you must be honest with yourself for your score on this exam to have any meaning. Don't assume, for example, that if your answer is close, the graders will be generous with points.

Practice Exam 3
Morning Session

QUESTION 1 HAS TWO PARTS FOR A TOTAL OF 20 MINUTES

Glyn Williams is a successful entrepreneur from Wales, and he is thinking about retiring in one year. Over the past 15 years or so, he has started and sold many small businesses. At age 40, Williams is now thinking about ending his entrepreneurial career to pursue a more comfortable lifestyle. He expects to earn £2.4 million this year from profits and £600,000 from the sale of his last small business. He is in the 40% tax bracket.

Williams has always managed his own investments, and as a result his growth equity portfolio has not had as much success as his businesses. His worst performing security is D&D, an investment he first made about five years ago. Instead of liquidating his position in response to extended decreases in D&D's share price, however, Williams acquired additional shares in order to lower his average cost per share. He totally avoids energy securities due to several investment losses he incurred in that industry during the 1980s. The rest of his growth equity portfolio has performed adequately. He also has commercial real estate investments that are expected to be cash-flow neutral this year (cash inflows ≈ outflows). Williams's assets are shown in Exhibit 1.

Exhibit 1: Glyn Williams's Personal Assets

Cash savings	£2,400,000
Growth equity portfolio*	£24,000,000
Commercial real estate investments	£8,400,000

*All dividends are reinvested

Williams expects the annual after-tax interest income on his cash savings to be £60,000 at the end of the year. He plans to pay cash for a £2.7 million ocean-front home when he receives the cash from the sale of his last business. Because Williams hasn't forgotten the difficulties he experienced growing up in poverty, he has started the Glyn Williams Children's Foundation to help the troubled youth in the community where he was raised. He plans to gift all of his commercial real estate investments to the foundation upon his retirement. During retirement, Williams plans to volunteer the majority of his time to the foundation and does not expect to receive any compensation from other sources.

Williams recently divorced his wife of 20 years, and they have twin daughters, age 10, both of whom live with their mother in London. He makes monthly child support payments that total £480,000 per year. These annual payments will end when his daughters turn 18 years old. Williams's living expenses are expected to be £720,000 this year. Both living expenses and child support payments will increase at the expected 4% annual inflation rate. All dividends from the equity portfolio are reinvested in the portfolio at no cost to Williams. Williams has stated that he wants to maintain the real value of his portfolio during his retirement, and he expects the portfolio to meet his living expenses for his expected 40 years of retirement. Justin Rabey, CFA, who was recently hired by Williams, expects the after-tax nominal annual return for growth equity to be 8.5%.

A.   i.   **Formulate** the return objective in Williams's investment policy statement. (No calculations necessary)

(2 minutes)

     ii. **Calculate** the *after-tax* nominal rate of return that is required during Williams's first year of retirement assuming there are no tax benefits or liabilities related to paying child support, living expenses, or gifting commercial real estate to his foundation. **Show** your calculations.

(12 minutes)

B.   i. **Identify** *two* factors in Williams's personal situation that increase his ability to take risk.

ii. **Identify** *two* factors in Williams's personal situation that decrease his ability to take risk.

iii. **Determine** whether Williams most likely has below-average, average, or above-average ability to take risk.

(6 minutes)

Answer Question 1-B in the template provided.

Template for Question 1-B

Two factors that increase Williams's ability to take risk:

Two factors that decrease his ability to take risk:

Determine Williams's ability to take risk (circle one)
Below Average   Average   Above Average

QUESTION 2 HAS THREE PARTS FOR A TOTAL OF 10 MINUTES

Jerome Bush, a 63-year-old recently retired commercial pilot, has accumulated a $2 million investment portfolio. Bush is meeting with Richard Gleason, CFA, to discuss his financial situation and plan for his retirement. He tells Gleason that he needs an asset allocation that can meet his retirement spending needs, and those needs would be difficult to decrease at any time. As he will receive no pension income of any kind, one of Bush's biggest concerns is that his assets will not sustain his desired lifestyle throughout his expected 20 years of retirement.

In response, Gleason constructs three alternative portfolios from which Bush can select his preferred allocation. He explains to Bush that the allocations, starting with Allocation 1, should be considered conservative, moderate, and aggressive, respectively. The allocations are shown in Exhibit 1.

Exhibit 1: Alternative Portfolio Allocations

Asset Class	Allocation 1 (conservative)	Allocation 2 (moderate)	Allocation 3 (aggressive)
Non-U.S. equities	5%	15%	25%
U.S. equities	20%	35%	50%
Cash equivalents	15%	10%	5%
Global fixed income	60%	40%	20 %

Bush believes the conservative asset allocation would provide the safety he needs in his portfolio, but he thinks a more aggressive allocation could provide the opportunity to increase the value of his portfolio and thus may be a better option for the long term. In their discussions, Gleason states:

> "I feel that, given your situation, an asset-liability management approach to strategic asset allocation is more appropriate than an asset-only approach. Incorporated into a Monte Carlo simulation, it will provide the data we need to determine the most appropriate allocation for your situation."

Gleason prepares the Monte Carlo simulation, which shows expected values of Bush's portfolio after 20 years, after meeting all of Bush's expected retirement expenses. The results are shown in Exhibit 2. Gleason explains the Monte Carlo output to Bush:

> "The data in the table denote expected values of your portfolio after 20 years. Using Allocation 1 as an example, there is a 95% probability that the portfolio will be worth $1,001,000 or less and a 5% probability that it will be worth more. There is a 50% probability it will be worth $321,000 or less and 50% probability that it will be worth more."

Exhibit 2: Monte Carlo Simulation Results

Projected Portfolio Values after 20 Years ($1,000)			
Percentile	Allocation 1	Allocation 2	Allocation 3
95th	1,001	2,536	7,938
90th	813	1,972	5,243
75th	686	1,164	2,818
50th	321	832	1,271
25th	143	318	458
10th	10	101	2
5th	0	15	0

A.   **Explain** *two* ways the Monte Carlo simulation and mean-variance analysis differ in a multi-period setting.

(4 minutes)

B.   **Explain** *two* advantages of using an asset-liability management approach for Bush's portfolio.

(4 minutes)

C.   **Recommend** the *most* appropriate allocation for Bush's portfolio based on the Monte Carlo simulation results. **Justify** your response with *one* reason.

(2 minutes)

QUESTION 3 HAS ONE PART FOR A TOTAL OF 8 MINUTES

Diego Investment Counseling has previously used a traditional approach to determine investors' personality classifications. The portfolio manager has categorized the investor based on the initial and periodic personal interviews with the investor and a review of past investment activity. While Diego believes past client risk assessments to be accurate, McCurdy's supervisor now believes this traditional approach needs to be supplemented by a questionnaire approach to better determine investors' personality types. To facilitate the development of the new questionnaires, McCurdy has been reviewing notes from past client interviews. Excerpts from four different client interviews are listed below.

1. "In general, I don't like to see much turnover in my account since I don't believe in market timing strategies. Those strategies seem likely to have a low probability of actually making money. What I find more important is preserving the value of my portfolio against inflation."

2. "Most of the time I don't want to be bothered with stock tips from my broker. I read the same research they read, and I often think the analysts writing the reports don't have a clue what they are talking about. The majority of my investments have been selected using my own careful research, but there are a few stocks in my portfolio that I just had a feeling about so I bought them."

3. "I like to have broad access to quality reports from analysts and economic researchers so I can stay abreast of key market developments. I do not appreciate, however, receiving calls from my stockbroker regarding the latest investment strategy that is also being sold to everyone else in the market. Most of the time the recommended strategy is too risky and doesn't fit with my portfolio."

4. "I need to have access to market information quickly so I can keep up-to-date on where the hot money is. I read research occasionally but the analysts are usually talking over my head about some boring blue-chip company. Everyone in my investment club generally agrees that the analysts are overrated. I like my portfolio to be reasonably liquid so I can move funds quickly."

For each of the client excerpts, **identify** the primary personality type and **justify** your choice with one reason.

(8 minutes)

Answer Question 3 in the template provided.

Template for Question 3

Client Statement	Investor Type	Explanation
"In general, I don't like to see much turnover in my account since I don't believe in market timing strategies. Those strategies seem likely to have a low probability of actually making money. What I find more important is preserving the value of my portfolio against inflation."	Cautious Methodical Spontaneous Individualistic	
"Most of the time I don't want to be bothered with stock tips from my broker. I read the same research they read, and I often think the analysts writing the reports don't have a clue what they are talking about. The majority of my investments have been selected using my own careful research, but there are a few stocks in my portfolio that I just had a feeling about so I bought them."	Cautious Methodical Spontaneous Individualistic	
"I like to have broad access to quality reports from analysts and economic researchers so I can stay abreast of key market developments. I do not appreciate, however, receiving calls from my stockbroker regarding the latest investment strategy that is also being sold to everyone else in the market. Most of the time the recommended strategy is too risky and doesn't fit with my portfolio."	Cautious Methodical Spontaneous Individualistic	
"I need to have access to market information quickly so I can keep up-to-date on where the hot money is. I read research occasionally but the analysts are usually talking over my head about some boring blue-chip company. Everyone in my investment club generally agrees that the analysts are overrated. I like my portfolio to be reasonably liquid so I can move funds quickly."	Cautious Methodical Spontaneous Individualistic	

QUESTION 4 HAS FIVE PARTS FOR A TOTAL OF 18 MINUTES

Max Cady is the chairman of the investment committee of Mitchum University (MU). The MU endowment is currently invested primarily in stocks (65% of assets) and bonds (25% of assets) with the remainder in cash. Cady would like to further diversify the MU endowment by adding an asset class—commodities. In particular, Cady is interested in gaining exposure to the energy sector. Rising energy costs have been a budgetary problem for MU, and Cady would like to derive some benefit from higher energy prices. Cady is uncertain as to how MU could best add the desired exposure to energy, and he has contacted Greg Peck, CFA, who serves as a consultant to the MU endowment.

Peck has suggested three alternatives:

1. Trading futures contracts on oil or some other energy-related commodity.

2. Overweighting energy stocks in the existing MU portfolio.

3. Buying exchange traded funds (ETFs) related to the energy sector.

Peck suggested an ETF based on the Goldman Sachs Commodity Index (GSCI). Cady is familiar with ETFs but is less knowledgeable about commodity futures contracts. Peck has provided Cady with a breakdown of commodity futures returns over the past 30 days for three upcoming oil futures contracts, shown in Exhibit 1.

Exhibit 1

Contract Maturity	Futures Price June 15	Futures Price May 15	Change in Spot Price
July	$83.25	$82.55	+$0.50
October	$82.35	$81.70	+$0.50
January	$81.75	$81.20	+$0.50

Cady is evaluating his alternatives.

A. For each of the three alternatives suggested by Peck, **select** whether the approach is a direct or an indirect commodity investment, and **comment** on how well each alternative could achieve Cady's objective of higher exposure to energy-related commodities.

(6 minutes)

Answer Question 4-A in the template provided.

Template for Question 4-A

Alternative	Type (circle one)	Comment
Trading futures contracts on oil or some other energy-related commodity.	Direct Indirect	
Overweighting energy stocks in the existing MU portfolio.	Direct Indirect	
Buying exchange traded funds (ETFs) related to the energy sector.	Direct Indirect	

B. **Calculate** the roll return, for the period May 15 to June 15, for the oil futures contracts maturing in July, October, and January, based on the data in Exhibit 1.

(3 minutes)

Template for Question 4-B

Contract	Roll yield calculation
July	
October	
January	

C. **Identify** the current oil futures pricing situation as backwardation or contango, and **justify** your response with *one* reason.

(2 minutes)

Template for Question 4-C

Futures pricing	Justification
Backwardation	
Contango	

©2011 Kaplan, Inc.

D.   Cady has been reviewing the recent performance of the GSCI, and has found that for the last 12 months, the GSCI has had a roll return of 6.4% and a spot return of 10.2%. If the collateral return on the GSCI over the past 12 months was 7.1%, **calculate** the total return on the GSCI.

(3 minutes)

E.   **Discuss** the potential benefits to the MU endowment of adding energy-related commodities as an asset class, in terms of:
   i. Inflation hedging.
   ii. Diversification.

(4 minutes)

QUESTION 5 HAS THREE PARTS FOR A TOTAL OF 10 MINUTES

Juan Ketter, CFA, conducts reviews of real estate fund and commingled real estate fund (CREF) managers for Fund Evaluators, Inc. (FEI). Ketter just completed his evaluation of the Von Wilstrom Real Estate Mutual Fund, which has a mandate to hold only apartment REITs. In an internal memorandum, a new FEI portfolio manager states the following:

> "Based solely on real estate benchmarks, it would appear that direct investment in real estate tends to be more volatile than indirect investment."

A summary of the performance of the fund and various benchmarks is provided below:

Exhibit 1: Performance Statistics

	Average Return	Standard Deviation
Von Wilstrom Fund	12%	28%
NAREIT index	20%	20%
NCREIF index	13%	10%
Apartment REITs	10%	30%
Office REITs	14%	26%

Ketter's supervisor, Eileen Davies, concludes that the Von Wilstrom Fund performed poorly during the evaluation period.

A.   **State** whether you agree or disagree with the new FEI portfolio manager's assessment of real estate benchmarks. **Justify** your decision with *two* reasons.

Answer Question 5-A in the template provided.

(3 minutes)

B.   **Explain** *one* strength and *one* weakness of using the NCREIF index as a benchmark for the performance of closed-end CREFs.

Answer Question 5-B in the template provided.

(4 minutes)

C.   **Indicate** whether Ketter should agree or disagree with Davies's conclusion about the performance of the Von Wilstrom Fund, and **justify** your response with *one* supporting reason.

Answer Question 5-C in the template provided.

(3 minutes)

Template for Question 5-A

FEI Memo	Justifications
Agree Disagree	1. 2.

Template for Question 5-B

Strength/ Weakness	Explanation
Strength	
Weakness	

Template for Question 5-C

Decision	Justification
Agree Disagree	

QUESTION 6 HAS THREE PARTS FOR A TOTAL OF 9 MINUTES

Alan Carroll, CFA, is an analyst for MacroFund, a global macro hedge fund. Carroll has been asked to value the national stock market index for Mantrovia, a small developing nation, to determine whether the fund should take a position in the market.

Carroll begins his valuation by analyzing Mantrovia's growth rate. Over the last five years, the average real GDP growth rate has been 9.25%. Carroll estimates that the real growth rate will remain the same for next year, but will decrease at a steady rate over the next ten years to what will be the country's long-term sustainable growth rate. Carroll forecasts the components of the sustainable growth rate provided in the following table:

	Estimated Sustainable Rates
Growth in total factor productivity	1.0%
Growth in capital stock	4.0%
Growth in labor input	0.7%
Output elasticity of capital	0.3

Mantrovia's aggregate stock market index is currently at 645, and the most recent aggregate dividend was 31. Carroll estimates that the real required rate of return is 9%.

A.   For each of the three following factors, **identify** the direction of the change in the factor that would be consistent with a *decrease* in the real economic growth rate.
         i.   Production efficiency
        ii.   Environmental controls
       iii.   Children per household

Answer Question 6-A in the template provided.

(3 minutes)

Template for Question 6-A

Factor	Factor Change (circle direction)
Production efficiency	Increase / Decrease
Environmental controls	Increase / Decrease
Children per household	Increase / Decrease

B.   Using the components of the sustainable growth rate provided in the table,
        calculate Mantrovia's expected sustainable growth rate in real GDP.

(2 minutes)

C.   **Estimate** the intrinsic value of Mantrovia's equity market and **determine**
        if it is overvalued, fairly valued, or undervalued.

(4 minutes)

QUESTION 7 HAS THREE PARTS FOR A TOTAL OF 24 MINUTES

The Sterling Foundation is evaluating its equity portfolio performance over the past year. For the third consecutive year, the portfolio has posted a double digit overall return. Still, the trustees of the foundation would like a more detailed analysis of their returns. The portfolio is allocated into three segments—domestic large capitalization stocks, domestic small capitalization stocks, and international stocks. The Rawls Group, a consulting firm, makes the asset allocation decision among the three segments at the beginning of each year. The segment weights and returns for the past year are provided in the following table.

	Weights		Returns	
Asset Class	Portfolio	Benchmark	Portfolio	Benchmark
Large cap stocks	0.60	0.50	12.5%	10.0%
Small cap stocks	0.25	0.30	16.0%	18.5%
International stocks	0.15	0.20	10.0%	9.0%
	1.00	1.00		

In order to help evaluate the foundation's equity performance, the trustees have asked for an attribution analysis.

A.   **Calculate** the overall returns over the past year for both the Sterling Foundation equity portfolio and the benchmark portfolio, and **state** whether Sterling has outperformed or underperformed the benchmark.

Answer Question 7-A in the template provided.

(10 minutes)

B.   **Calculate** both the pure sector allocation effect and the within-sector selection effect of Sterling's performance relative to the benchmark.

Answer Question 7-B in the template provided.

(8 minutes)

Template for Question 7-A

Portfolio	Calculation	Return
Sterling		
Benchmark		
Circle One		
Outperform		
Underperform		

Template for Question 7-B

Effect	Calculation	Final Answer
Pure sector allocation effect		
Within-sector selection effect		

C.   Based on your answers to Parts A and B, **evaluate** Sterling's performance relative to the benchmark.

(6 minutes)

Questions 8 and 9 relate to Smith Hospital Corporation. A total of 25 minutes is allocated to these questions. *Candidates should answer these questions in the order presented.*

Smith Hospital Corporation (SHC) is a publicly traded company that operates acute care hospitals across the United States. A national nursing shortage has hindered SHC's ability to take full advantage of growth opportunities. To attract and retain qualified nurses, SHC offers a variety of benefits including a defined benefit pension plan. The defined benefit pension plan was created 15 years ago and its assets are currently valued at $100 million. At present, 80% of plan assets are held in publicly traded equities, with the remaining 20% invested in bonds. Benefit payments are fixed at the date the employee retires and do not provide annual cost of living adjustments. Exhibit 1 provides details about the SHC Pension Plan.

Exhibit 1: SHC Pension Plan for 2011

	2011
Average active participants' age	31 years old
Ratio of active to inactive participants	8 to 1
Actuarial value of plan liabilities	$100 million
Average employment service	5.5 years
Average beta of pension plan (equity) assets	0.75

Sarah Weekly, CFA, is the chief financial officer for SHC and oversees the company's pension plan. Weekly believes that the SHC Pension Plan's asset allocation affects the overall company's risk profile, and she created Exhibits 2 and 3 to evaluate it. In addition, stating that the plan's portfolio allocation should more closely reflect plan liabilities, Weekly proposed the following revised asset allocation for the pension plan portfolio:

- Nominal Bonds—85%
- Real Rate Bonds (TIPS)—5%
- Equities—10%

In a meeting with upper management, Weekly also proposed that the company begin a defined contribution plan to assist in the nurse recruiting process by increasing employee benefits. Exhibit 2 provides data to calculate the company's weighted average cost of capital (WACC).

Exhibit 2: SHC WACC Data

	2011
Market value of operating assets	$500 million
Market value of debt	$200 million
Market value of equity	$300 million
Risk-free rate	4.0%
Market risk premium (equity)	7.0%
Smith Hospital's equity beta	1.00
Estimated Core* WACC	8.2%

*Based on operating assets

Exhibit 3 provides a risk analysis for various pension plan asset mixes.

Exhibit 3: Risk analysis of SHC Pension Plan

Equity Percentage	Pension Asset Beta	Total Asset Beta	Smith Equity Beta
0%	0.00	0.400	0.80
80%	?	0.500	1.00
100%	0.75	0.525	1.05

QUESTION 8 HAS THREE PARTS FOR A TOTAL OF 15 MINUTES

A.   Using information in Exhibit 1, **provide** three reasons, one for each asset class allocation, why Weekly's proposed asset allocation is inappropriate for the SHC Pension Plan portfolio.

(6 minutes)

Answer Question 8-A in the template provided.

B.   Using the data provided in Exhibits 1 and 2, **calculate** SHC's estimated overall WACC, which would include SHC's operating and pension plan assets.

(5 minutes)

Answer Question 8-B in the template provided.

C.   **Discuss** *four* effects of using SHC's core WACC (given in Exhibit 2) rather than the estimated WACC adjusted for the company's pension plan (calculated in Part B) in the capital budgeting process.

(4 minutes)

Answer Question 8-C in the space provided below.

Template for Question 8-A

Proposed asset allocation discussion
1.
2.
3.

Template for Question 8-B

Assets ($ Million)		Beta	Liabilities and Equity ($ Million)	
Operating assets	500		Firm liabilities	200
Pension assets	100		Pension liabilities	100
Total	600	0.5	Equity	300
			Total	600

Firm's operating WACC: (Show your calculations)

QUESTION 9 HAS TWO PARTS (A, B) FOR A TOTAL OF 10 MINUTES

A.   Referring to Exhibit 3 in the previous question and assuming the SHC pension plan assets are currently allocated 50/50 to equity and fixed income securities, **explain** the potential effect on SHC of changing the plan asset allocation to 100% equity or to 100% fixed income. For each potential change in the pension plan asset allocation, **explain** (1) the likely impact on SHC's equity beta and WACC, and (2) the required change in SHC's capital structure (i.e., debt/equity ratio), assuming management wants to maintain the firm's current equity risk (i.e., equity beta).

(6 minutes)

Answer Question 9-A in the template provided.

Template for Question 9-A

Pension plan asset allocation	Impact on SHC's equity beta and WACC; change in D/E to maintain current equity beta
100% equity	Impact on equity beta: Impact on WACC: Required change in D/E:
100% fixed income	Impact on equity beta: Impact on WACC: Required change in D/E:

B.   In reference to the defined contribution plan suggested by Weekly, **list** *two* responsibilities of the plan sponsor and *two* responsibilities of the participant.

(4 minutes)

Answer Question 9-B in the template provided.

Template for Question 9-B

Defined contribution pension plan	List two responsibilities for each
Plan sponsor	1. 2.
Participant	1. 2.

QUESTION 10 HAS TWO PARTS FOR A TOTAL OF 9 MINUTES

Hugo Gamez, CFA, manages portfolios for high net worth investors. Gamez established an aggressive asset mix that includes a 10% allocation to international investments for those of his clients who are willing to accept greater risk. However, Gamez's international equity investments are only in developed markets, with no exposure to emerging markets. The recent strong performance produced by emerging market equities has sparked client interest in the investment class. Gamez is impressed with the fact that emerging market countries account for 85% of the world's population and 48% of the global economic output. However, Gamez is concerned about the high risk level of emerging market investments and whether they would be suitable for his clients. After reviewing Exhibits 1 and 2, Gamez states that as a result of the lack of diversification benefits, the rationale for investing in emerging markets no longer holds and thus precludes adding any emerging market equities to client portfolios.

Exhibit 1: Data from 2001 through 2005

	Correlation				Annualized Returns	Standard Deviation
	MSCI Emerging	MSCI World ex-U.S.	U.S. Large Cap	U.S. Small Cap		
MSCI Emerging	1.00				19.3%	21.0%
MSCI World ex-U.S.	0.87	1.00			4.9%	15.6%
U.S. Large Cap	0.81	0.88	1.00		0.5%	14.9%
U.S. Small Cap	0.83	0.83	0.84	1.00	8.2%	19.2%

Exhibit 2: Data from 1996 through 2000

	Correlation				Annualized Returns	Standard Deviation
	MSCI Emerging	MSCI World ex-U.S.	U.S. Large Cap	U.S. Small Cap		
MSCI Emerging	1.00				−4.2%	27.2%
MSCI World ex-U.S.	0.82	1.00			7.5%	15.1%
U.S. Large Cap	0.71	0.78	1.00		18.3%	16.0%
U.S. Small Cap	0.67	0.67	0.65	1.00	10.3%	21.3%

A.   **Identify** *four* reasons for the increased correlation between emerging market and developed market investment returns over the 1996 through 2005 period. (Refer to Exhibits 1 and 2.)

(4 minutes)

B. **State** whether you agree or disagree with Gamez's statement that the rationale for investing in emerging markets no longer holds and **justify** your selection with *two* reasons. (Refer to Exhibits 1 and 2.) No calculations required.

(5 minutes)

Answer Question 10-B in the template provided.

Template for Question 10-B

Circle one	Justify with two reasons
Agree Disagree	

QUESTION 11 HAS THREE PARTS FOR A TOTAL OF 26 MINUTES

Great Northern Company, a U.S.-based global manufacturer of consumer products, recently established a foundation to provide financial and leadership support for nonprofit organizations dedicated to improving the quality of life in the communities where Great Northern Company operates. The foundation will contribute to the global social concerns found in their home communities through grants, volunteerism and leadership. The foundation has been established in the country of Grik. Great Northern selected Grik for both the amount of business conducted in the country and the fact that Grik levies no taxes on foundations, unlike some other countries.

Great Northern funded the foundation with $1.5 billion in cash and will make annual contributions based on the company's profitability. The board of directors has determined that the foundation should be viewed as a perpetual institution. The foundation's investments must pass a socially responsible investing (SRI) screen developed by its board of trustees. In addition, the board requires that the portfolio invest 60% of its assets in non-U.S. investments to meet the constraint of investing in communities where Great Northern operates. The foundation expects to fund annual grants totaling 5.0% of total assets. In addition to the spending requirement, there is an annual expense ratio of 2%.

The board of trustees hired a consulting firm, which has provided five possible asset allocations including eight potential asset classes. The consultant provided Exhibit 1 below highlighting the return expectations for each portfolio, along with a Sharpe ratio for each. The expected inflation rate is 2.75%. The board established a guideline that a minimum of 5% is required to be invested in any one asset class.

Exhibit 1: Great Northern Foundation's Strategic Asset Allocation

Asset Class (U.S. unless noted otherwise)	Alternative Portfolios Asset Allocation Percentages				
	A	B	C	D	E
Stocks	5.0	5.0	5.0	5.0	5.0
International stocks	30.0	5.0	15.0	20.0	20.0
Fixed income	5.0	5.0	5.0	5.0	20.0
International fixed income	30.0	55.0	45.0	20.0	40.0
Private equity	7.0	5.0	5.0	15.0	5.0
Real estate	13.0	15.0	15.0	20.0	5.0
Hedge funds	5.0	5.0	5.0	10.0	5.0
Natural resources	5.0	5.0	5.0	5.0	0.0
Current income (%)	4.0	5.3	5.1	3.5	5.0
Total return (%)	10.8	9.8	10.3	12.9	10.0
Sharpe ratio	0.6	1.0	0.9	1.1	0.9

A. **Prepare** an investment policy statement using the objectives and constraints format for the Great Northern Foundation's portfolio.

Answer Question 11-A in the template provided.

(12 minutes)

Template for Question 11-A

Objectives	Comments
1. Return	
2. Risk tolerance	

Constraints	Comments
1. Liquidity	
2. Time horizon	
3. Taxes	
4. Unique circumstances	

B.   Based on Exhibit 1 and the objectives and constraints determined in Part A, **select** the best asset allocation for Great Northern Foundation's portfolio. **Support** your conclusion with *three* reasons.

(8 minutes)

C.   **Discuss** *three* potential problems with Great Northern Foundation's policy allocation selected in Part B.

(6 minutes)

QUESTION 12 HAS THREE PARTS FOR A TOTAL OF 12 MINUTES

The board of directors for Shark Mutual Funds is conducting its scheduled annual meeting. An agenda item for the meeting is the discussion of best execution. The board hired an outside consultant to review the mutual funds' trading execution. The board is hoping the consultant will help Shark comply with guidelines established in their last SEC audit.

In attendance are John Sullivan, CFA, Shark's head equity trader, and Susan Ullom, CFA, head of equities for Shark. The consultant's presentation praised the company's trading effort. She stated that for 92% of the buy tickets, the purchase price for the security was less than the value-weighted average price (VWAP) and that for 95% of the sell tickets, the selling price for the security was greater than the VWAP. Sullivan was happy with the results, especially in light of the fact that Shark's mutual funds range in style from momentum investing to value investing. However, these results are in direct conflict with Ullom's perceptions of Shark's trading efficiency. Ullom and her portfolio management staff have criticized the trading effort for the poor execution prices. Ullom believes that poor trading has contributed to the Funds' underperformance with respect to their benchmarks.

A.   **Discuss** *two* problems with the consultant's use of the VWAP benchmark as the correct pricing benchmark for Shark's mutual funds.

(4 minutes)

B.   Trades can be motivated by value or by news (i.e., information). **Describe** each of these motivations, and **identify** the *most* appropriate order type for each.

(4 minutes)

C.   A board member questions the consultant as to how best execution can be determined. **Identify** *four* characteristics of best execution.

(4 minutes)

QUESTION 13 HAS ONE PART FOR A TOTAL OF 9 MINUTES

Bill Thacker, CFA, is a portfolio manager for Andrews Advisors, a U.S.-based firm. Thacker is discussing with junior employees how to construct and revise investment policy statements. During their meeting, Thacker makes the following comments:

"Many of our investors use a mental accounting or pyramiding approach to investment planning. Even though this approach might help them achieve a degree of self-control, it is a form of emotional bias that must be overcome for clients to effectively meet their long-term goals."

"An investment policy statement should be reviewed and considered for possible revision when an investor experiences a change in personal circumstances or when external conditions change significantly. For example, a change in tax laws may trigger an investment policy statement review."

"We have a lot of clients I would classify as independent individualists. Due to their tendency toward emotional decisions, they can be very difficult to advise."

State whether *each* of these comments is correct or incorrect. If incorrect, **explain** why.

Answer Question 13 in the template provided.

(9 minutes)

Template for Question 13

Comment	Is the statement correct or incorrect? (circle one)	Explanation, if incorrect
"Many of our investors use a mental accounting or pyramiding approach to investment planning. Even though this approach might help them achieve a degree of self-control, it is a form of emotional bias that must be overcome for clients to effectively meet their long-term goals."	Correct Incorrect	
"An investment policy statement should be reviewed and considered for possible revision when an investor experiences a change in personal circumstances or when external conditions change significantly. For example, a change in tax laws may trigger an investment policy statement review."	Correct Incorrect	
"We have a lot of clients I would classify as independent individualists. Due to their tendency toward emotional decisions, they can be very difficult to advise."	Correct Incorrect	

END OF MORNING SESSION

Exam 3 Afternoon Session Topic Breakdown

Question	Topic	Minutes
1–6	Performance Evaluation and Attribution	18
7–12	Ethics and Professional Standards	18
13–18	Capital Market Expectations/Equity Portfolio Management	18
19–24	Management of Active and Passive Fixed Income Portfolios	18
25–30	Asset Allocation, Global Bonds and Fixed Income Derivatives, Risk Management, and Risk Management Applications of Derivatives	18
31–36	Fixed Income Portfolio Management	18
37–42	Economic Concepts, Global Bonds and Fixed Income Derivatives, Risk Management, and Risk Management Applications of Derivatives	18
43–48	Risk Management and Performance Evaluation and Attribution	18
49–54	Fixed Income Derivatives and Risk Management Applications of Derivatives	18
55–60	Ethics and Professional Standards	18
	Total	180

EXAM 3 SELECTED RESPONSE ITEM SET ANSWER SHEET

The afternoon session of the Level III exam contains 10 Selected Response Item Sets, each with six questions, and you must answer them by filling in a bubble sheet with a number 2 or HB pencil. For realism, we suggest that you use this answer sheet and darken the bubbles corresponding to your answers. This sheet will also facilitate entering your answers into our online Performance Tracker. You have 180 minutes for this session of the exam. That equates to 3 minutes per item set question, so budget your time well.

#					#			
1.	A	B	C		31.	A	B	C
2.	A	B	C		32.	A	B	C
3.	A	B	C		33.	A	B	C
4.	A	B	C		34.	A	B	C
5.	A	B	C		35.	A	B	C
6.	A	B	C		36.	A	B	C
7.	A	B	C		37.	A	B	C
8.	A	B	C		38.	A	B	C
9.	A	B	C		39.	A	B	C
10.	A	B	C		40.	A	B	C
11.	A	B	C		41.	A	B	C
12.	A	B	C		42.	A	B	C
13.	A	B	C		43.	A	B	C
14.	A	B	C		44.	A	B	C
15.	A	B	C		45.	A	B	C
16.	A	B	C		46.	A	B	C
17.	A	B	C		47.	A	B	C
18.	A	B	C		48.	A	B	C
19.	A	B	C		49.	A	B	C
20.	A	B	C		50.	A	B	C
21.	A	B	C		51.	A	B	C
22.	A	B	C		52.	A	B	C
23.	A	B	C		53.	A	B	C
24.	A	B	C		54.	A	B	C
25.	A	B	C		55.	A	B	C
26.	A	B	C		56.	A	B	C
27.	A	B	C		57.	A	B	C
28.	A	B	C		58.	A	B	C
29.	A	B	C		59.	A	B	C
30.	A	B	C		60.	A	B	C

Exam 3
Afternoon Session

Powerful Performance Presenters (PPP) is a performance attribution and evaluation firm for pension consulting firms and has recently been hired by Stober and Robertson to conduct a performance attribution analysis for TopTech. Tom Harrison and Wendy Powell are the principals for PPP. Although performance attribution has come under fire lately because of its shortcomings, Stober believes PPP provides a needed service to its clients. Robertson shares Stober's view of performance attribution analysis.

Stober and Robertson request that Harrison and Powell provide a discussion of performance measures. During a conversation on complements to attribution analysis, Harrison notes the uses of the Treynor ratio. He states that the Treynor ratio is appropriate only when the investor's portfolio is well diversified. Powell states that the Sharpe ratio is useful when you want to find out how the systematic risk of the portfolio is affected when changing its asset allocation.

Stober requests that PPP do some performance attribution calculations on TopTech's managers. In order to facilitate the analysis, Stober provides the information in the following table:

Composite	Weighting		Return	
	TopTech	Benchmark	TopTech	Benchmark
Small-cap value	50%	60%	18.7%	28.6%
Large-cap value	30%	25%	15.8%	12.4%
Financials	20%	15%	12.5%	8.85%

Harrison states one of PPP's services is that it will determine whether TopTech uses valid benchmarks. Stober describes the composition of the benchmarks:

- TopTech uses the top 10% of U.S. portfolio managers each year in each asset class and/or strategy as benchmarks for TopTech managers;

- TopTech is very careful to make sure that its managers are familiar with the securities in each benchmark asset class or category;
- Whenever possible, the identities and weights of securities in the TopTech benchmarks are clearly defined.

During a presentation to Stober, Robertson, and other TopTech executives, Harrison and Powell describe how macro attribution analysis can decompose an entire fund's excess returns into various levels. In his introduction, Robertson delineates the six levels as net contributions, risk-free return, asset categories, benchmarks, investment managers, and allocations effects.

Robertson states that TopTech has performed impressively at the investment managers level for three years in a row. Harrison and Powell then describe the levels in greater detail. Harrison describes the benchmark level as the difference between active managers' returns and their benchmark returns. Powell states that the investment managers' level reflects the returns to active management on the part of the fund's managers, weighted by the amount actually allocated to each manager.

At the request of Stober, Harrison and Powell explore alternatives to the benchmark TopTech is currently using for its small-cap value manager. After some investigation of the small-cap value manager's emphasis, Harrison and Powell derive four potential custom benchmarks and calculate two measures to evaluate the benchmarks: (1) the return to the manager's active management, or A = portfolio return – benchmark return; and (2) the return to the manager's style, or S = benchmark return – broad market return.

The following characteristics are presented below for each benchmark:
(1) the beta between the benchmark and the small-cap value portfolio;
(2) the tracking error (i.e., the standard deviation of A); (3) the turnover of the benchmark; and (4) the correlation between A and S.

	Benchmark A	Benchmark B	Benchmark C
Beta	1.23	1.08	1.53
Tracking error	12%	10%	11%
Benchmark turnover	8%	7%	8%
Correlation between A and S	0.52	0.09	0.33

Harrison and Powell evaluate the benchmarks based on the four measures.

1. Regarding their statements concerning the Sharpe and the Treynor ratios, are Harrison and Powell correct or incorrect?
   A. Only Harrison is correct.
   B. Only Powell is correct.
   C. Both are incorrect.

2. Based on an overall attribution analysis, does TopTech demonstrate superior ability to select sectors?
    A. No, the pure sector allocation effect is –1.8%.
    B. Yes, the pure sector allocation effect is 1.8%.
    C. Yes, the pure sector allocation effect is 3.2%.

3. Based on an overall attribution analysis, does TopTech demonstrate superior ability to select stocks?
    A. No, the within-sector selection effect is –4.5%.
    B. No, the within-sector selection effect is –3.2%.
    C. Yes, the within-sector selection effect is 1.3%.

4. Of those listed, the only characteristic of a valid benchmark that the TopTech benchmarks *likely* possess is:
    A. they are investable.
    B. they are unambiguous.
    C. they are reflective of current investment opinion.

5. Regarding their statements concerning macro attribution analysis, determine whether Harrison and Powell are correct or incorrect.
    A. Only Harrison is correct.
    B. Only Powell is correct.
    C. Both Harrison and Powell are incorrect.

6. Of the three benchmarks, determine which would be *most* appropriate for the small cap value manager.
    A. Benchmark A.
    B. Benchmark B.
    C. Benchmark C.

Questions 7–12 relate to Ethical and Professional Standards.

Jacques Lepage, CFA, is a portfolio manager for Mountain View Securities and holds 4 million shares of AirCon in client portfolios. Lepage issues periodic research reports on AirCon to both discretionary and nondiscretionary accounts. In his October investment report, Lepage stated, "In my opinion, AirCon is entering a phase which could put it "in play" as a takeover target. Nonetheless, this possibility appears to be fully reflected in the market value of the stock."

One month has passed since Lepage's October report and AirCon has just announced the firm's executive compensation packages, which include stock options (50% of which expire in one year), personal use of corporate aircraft (which can be used in conjunction with paid vacation days), and a modest base salary that constitutes a small proportion of the overall package. While he has not asked, he believes that the directors of Mountain View will find the compensation excessive and sells the entire position immediately after the news. Unbeknownst to Lepage, three days earlier an announcement was made via Reuters and other financial news services that AirCon had produced record results that were far beyond expectations. Moreover, the firm has established a dominant position in a promising new market that is expected to generate above-average firm growth for the next five years.

A few weeks after selling the AirCon holdings, Lepage bought 2.5 million shares of Spectra Vision over a period of four days. The typical trading volume of this security is about 1.3 million shares per day, and his purchases drove the price up 9% over the 4-day period. These trades were designated as appropriate for 13 accounts of differing sizes, including performance-based accounts, charitable trusts, and private accounts. The shares were allocated to the accounts on a pro rata basis at the end of each day at the average price for the day.

One of the investment criteria used in evaluating equity holdings is the corporate governance structure of the issuing company. Because Lepage has dealt with this topic extensively, he has been asked to present a talk on corporate governance issues to the firm's portfolio managers and analysts at the next monthly meeting. At the meeting, Lepage makes the following comments:

"When evaluating the corporate governance policies of a company, you should begin by assessing the responsibilities of the company's board of directors. In general, the board should have the responsibility to set long-term objectives that are consistent with shareholders' interests. In addition, the board must be responsible for hiring the CEO and setting his or her compensation package such that the CEO's interests are aligned with those of the shareholders. In that way the board can spend its time on matters other than monitoring the CEO. A firm with good corporate governance policies should also have an audit committee made up of independent board members that are experienced in auditing and related legal matters. The audit committee should have full access to the firm's financial statements and the ability to question auditors hired by the committee."

7.   According to the CFA Institute Standards, Lepage's statement that AirCon could be put "in play" is:
    A. permissible.
    B. not permissible because it blurs the distinction between opinion and fact.
    C. permissible under the mosaic theory, which allows combining nonpublic information with material information.

8.   Which of the following is a correct assessment of Lepage's decision to sell the shares of AirCon? Lepage's decision to sell the shares was:
    A. an inappropriate discharge of his duties as portfolio manager.
    B. an appropriate discharge of his duties as portfolio manager if the details of the compensation structure had not previously been made public.
    C. an appropriate discharge of his duties as portfolio manager only if the details of the compensation structure had previously been made public.

9.   Was Lepage's purchase of the Spectra Vision shares a violation of the CFA Institute Code and Standards?
    A. Yes, he violated the Standard pertaining to market manipulation.
    B. No, because there was no evidence of intent to distort market prices.
    C. Yes, because he overwhelmed the liquidity of Spectra Vision, artificially affecting its price.

10.   Which of the following statements *correctly* characterizes Lepage's method of distributing the shares of Spectra Vision to the 13 relevant accounts? Lepage's allocation method:
    A. does not violate CFA Institute Standard III(B) Fair Dealing.
    B. violates CFA Institute Standard II(B) Market Manipulation.
    C. is a violation of the Code and Standards because he allocated shares to nondiscretionary accounts.

11.   Which of the following statements regarding the compensation packages given to executives at AirCon is *most* correct?
    A. The base salary should make up a larger portion of the compensation package.
    B. The use of the corporate aircraft does not pose any problems for shareholder interests.
    C. The stock options cause a potential misalignment between management and shareholder interests.

12. Determine whether Lepage's statements in his presentation to Mountain View's portfolio managers and analysts regarding the responsibilities of the board of directors and the audit committee are correct or incorrect.
    A. Only the statement regarding the board is correct.
    B. Only the statement regarding the audit committee is correct.
    C. Both statements are incorrect.

Questions 13–18 relate to Capital Market Expectations and Equity Portfolio Management.

Security analysts Andrew Tian, CFA, and Cameron Wong, CFA, are attending an investment symposium at the Singapore Investment Analyst Society. The focus of the symposium is capital market expectations and relative asset valuations across markets. Many highly-respected practitioners and academics from across the Asia-Pacific region are on hand to make presentations and participate in panel discussions.

The first presenter, Lillian So, President of the Society, speaks on market expectations and tools for estimating intrinsic values. She notes that analysts attempting to gauge expectations are often subject to various pitfalls that subjectively skew their estimates. She also points out that there are potential problems relating to a choice of models, not all of which describe risk the same way. She then provides the following data to illustrate how analysts might go about generating expectations and estimating intrinsic values.

Index	Value	D_0	$\hat{g}$	Risk-Free	Expected Risk Premium
Singapore	3,750	90	6.0%	2.4%	?
Taiwan	?	450	4.5%	2.7%	1.10 × Singapore's E(Risk premium)

The next speaker, Clive Smyth, is a member of the exchange rate committee at the Bank of New Zealand. His presentation concerns the links between spot currency rates and forecasted exchange rates. He states that foreign exchange rates are linked by several forces including purchasing power parity (PPP) and interest rate parity (IRP). He tells his audience that the relationship between exchange rates and PPP is strongest in the short run, while the relationship between exchange rates and IRP is strongest in the long run. Smyth goes on to say that when a country's economy becomes more integrated with the larger world economy, this can have a profound impact on the cost of capital and asset valuations in that country.

The final speaker in the session directed his discussion toward emerging market investments. This discussion, by Hector Ruiz, head of emerging market investment for the Chilean Investment Board, was primarily concerned with how emerging market risk differs from that in developed markets and how to evaluate the potential of emerging market investments. He noted that sometimes an economic crisis in one country can spread to other countries in the area, and that asset returns often exhibit a greater degree of non-normality than in developed markets.

Ruiz concluded his presentation with the data in the tables below to illustrate factors that should be considered during the decision-making process for portfolio managers who are evaluating investments in emerging markets.

Characteristics for Russia and Brazil

Characteristic	Brazil	Russia
Foreign exchange to short-term debt	93%	182%
Debt as a percentage of GDP	86%	38%

Characteristics for China and India

Characteristic	China	India
Population growth	0.8%	1.3%
Labor force participation growth	1.8%	0.5%
Growth on spending on new capital inputs	1.3%	1.4%
Growth in total factor productivity	0.9%	0.4%
Expected savings relative to investment	Surplus	Deficit

13. When the first presenter refers to skewed estimates and problems with a choice of models, she is referring to:
    A. selection bias and risk specification error.
    B. psychological traps and risk specification error.
    C. psychological traps and model and input uncertainty.

14. Based upon the information provided by So, the equity risk premium in Singapore and the intrinsic value of the Taiwan index are *closest* to:

	Singapore E(risk premium)	Taiwan Index Value
A.	6.0%	9,800
B.	6.1%	9,500
C.	8.4%	7,125

15. Regarding Smyth's statements concerning exchange rate links:
    A. both statements are incorrect.
    B. only the statement regarding PPP is correct.
    C. only the statement regarding IRSP is correct.

16.   Determine which of the following characteristics of emerging market debt investing presents the global fixed income portfolio manager with the best potential to generate enhanced returns.
        A. Increasing quality of emerging market sovereign debt coupled with the ability of emerging market governments to access global capital.
        B. The Emerging Markets Bond Index Plus (EMBI+) index is dominated by Latin American debt securities.
        C. Emerging market debt can be highly volatile with negatively skewed returns distributions.

17.   With regard to Ruiz's statements concerning emerging market risk, when an economic crisis spreads from one country to other countries in the area, this is known as:
        A. contagion, and non-normality of returns precludes the use of non-parametric models to estimate risk.
        B. contagion, and non-normality of returns makes it more difficult to estimate risk using parametric models.
        C. macro transmission, and non-normality of returns makes it more difficult to estimate risk using parametric models.

18.   Based upon the data provided, which of the following statements is *most* correct?
        A. Brazil would be favored for equity investment.
        B. China would be favored for both equity and bond investment.
        C. Russia would be favored for bond investment.

Questions 19–24 relate to Management of Active and Passive Fixed Income Portfolios.

Eugene Price, CFA, a portfolio manager for the American Universal Fund (AUF), has been directed to pursue a contingent immunization strategy for a portfolio with a current market value of $100 million. AUF's trustees are not willing to accept a rate of return less than 6% over the next five years, the length of time before the liability must be paid. The trustees have also stated that they believe an immunization rate of 8% is attainable in today's market. Price has decided to implement this strategy by initially purchasing $100 million in 10-year bonds with an annual coupon rate of 8.0%, paid semiannually.

Price forecasts that the prevailing immunization rate and market rate for the bonds will both rise from 8% to 9% in one year.

While Price is conducting his immunization strategy he is approached by April Banks, a newly hired junior analyst at AUF. Banks is wondering what steps need to be taken to immunize a portfolio with multiple liabilities. Price states that the concept of single liability immunization can fortunately be extended to address the issue of immunizing a portfolio with multiple liabilities. He further states that there are two methods for managing multiple liabilities. The first method is cash flow matching which involves finding a bond with a maturity date equal to the longest liability, buying enough in par value of that bond so that the principal and final coupon fully fund the liability, and continuing this process until all liabilities are matched. The second method is horizon matching which ensures that the assets and liabilities have the same present values and durations.

Price warns Banks about the dangers of immunization risk. He states that it is usually impossible to have a portfolio with zero immunization risk because of reinvestment risk. Price tells Banks, "Be cognizant of the dispersion of cash flows when conducting an immunization strategy. When there is a high dispersion of cash flows about the horizon date, immunization risk is high. It is better to have cash flows concentrated around the investment horizon, since immunization risk is reduced."

19. The initial cushion spread for Price's strategy is *closest* to:
    A. 100 bps.
    B. 200 bps.
    C. 300 bps.

20. The initial dollar safety margin is *closest* to:
    A. $9.21 million.
    B. $34.39 million.
    C. $42.74 million.

21.   If Price's forecast for interest rates in one year is correct, the dollar safety margin, assuming coupons are reinvested at 8% semiannually, will be *closest* to:
       A. $3.10 million.
       B. $7.58 million.
       C. $31.29 million.

22.   Assuming an immediate (today) increase in the immunized rate to 11%, the portfolio required return that would most likely make Price turn to an immunization strategy is *closest* to:
       A. 11.0%.
       B. 11.7%.
       C. 12.5%.

23.   Regarding Price's statements on the two methods for managing multiple liabilities, determine whether his descriptions of cash flow matching and horizon matching are correct.
       A. Both statements are correct.
       B. Only his statement about horizon matching is correct.
       C. Only his statement about cash flow matching is correct.

24.   Price has stated that, because of the need to reinvest coupons, it is usually impossible to totally eliminate immunization risk with coupon-paying bonds. He has also stated that an increased dispersion of asset maturities around the horizon date increases immunization risk. Determine which of these statements is (are) correct.
       A. Both statements are correct.
       B. Only the statement about the dispersion of cash flows is correct.
       C. Only the statement about totally eliminating immunization risk is correct.

Questions 25–30 relate to Asset Allocation, Global Bonds, Risk Management, and Risk Management Applications of Derivatives.

Mary Rolle and Betty Sims are portfolio managers for RS Global Investments, located in Toronto, Canada. RS specializes in seeking undervalued stocks and bonds throughout the North American, Asian, and European markets. RS has clients throughout North America, however, the majority are Canadian institutional investors. RS has traditionally managed currency risk in their portfolios by assigning it to their portfolio managers. The manager is allowed discretion for hedging currency risk within the confines of the investor's investment policy statement.

Rolle and Sims are currently deciding whether to hedge the currency risk of a portfolio of Japanese stocks. Rolle explores the possibility of using three different currency hedges. Each is an option contract on the yen-Canadian dollar exchange rate.

Hedge A	Buy Yen Puts
Hedge B	Sell Dollar Puts
Hedge C	Sell Yen Calls

RS has a portfolio of European stocks and would like to change its equity risk. They can enter into futures contracts on the Eurostoxx index of large European stocks. The information below provides the characteristics of the futures contract and the portfolio.

Portfolio value in euros	2,000,000
Desired beta value	1.80
Current portfolio beta	0.60
Beta of futures contract	1.02
Value of one futures contract in euros	110,000

RS is also invested in British and Argentine stocks. RS has taken a position in two main sectors of the British economy. The first sector consists of manufacturers who derive a great deal of their business from exporting to the United States and Canada. The other sector consists of British service firms who are largely immune from international competition, because most of their business is localized and cannot be provided by foreign firms. The main investment in the Argentine stocks consists of firms who provide cellular phone service to Argentine consumers. Rolle and Sims discuss which currency positions RS should hedge.

RS occasionally invests in mortgage-backed securities sold in the United States. The growth in these securities has increased tremendously over the past three decades as firms have used securitization to remove the risk of these securities from their balance sheet. RS holds a mortgage security issued by CWC International. This mortgage security has a coupon rate higher than newly issued mortgage securities. Sims discusses the return for this security when hedged with a short position in Treasury bond futures.

Rolle and Sims further discuss how to hedge the risk of mortgage securities. Rolle states that two Treasury bond futures contracts are typically used instead of just one. Sims states that a hedge becomes more important if the volatility of interest rates increases.

25. Which of following *best* describes the approach used by RS to manage currency risk?
   A. Currency overlay.
   B. Balanced Mandate.
   C. Currency as a separate asset allocation.

26. Regarding hedging the currency risk of the Japanese stock portfolio, which hedge would be *most* appropriate?
   A. Hedge A.
   B. Hedge B.
   C. Hedge C.

27. For RS to change the equity risk of their European stocks, the *most* appropriate strategy is to:
   A. buy 4 equity futures contracts.
   B. buy 18 equity futures contracts.
   C. buy 21 equity futures contracts.

28. Regarding the currency hedge of the British and Argentine stocks, which of the following would RS *least likely* hedge?
   A. The British service firms.
   B. The British manufacturers.
   C. The Argentine cellular phone service firms.

29. Assuming interest rates fall, what is the *most likely* performance for the CWC International mortgage when hedged with a short position in Treasury bond futures?
   A. The return will be weakened.
   B. The return will be the risk-free rate.
   C. The return will be high due to the high coupon on the MBS.

30. Regarding their statements about hedging mortgage-backed securities, are Rolle and Sims correct or incorrect?
   A. Only Rolle is correct.
   B. Only Sims is correct.
   C. Both Rolle and Sims are correct.

Questions 31–36 relate to Fixed Income Portfolio Management.

John Rawlins is a bond portfolio manager for Waimea Management, a U.S.-based portfolio management firm. Waimea specializes in the management of equity and fixed income portfolios for large institutional investors such as pension funds, insurance companies, and endowments. Rawlins uses bond futures contracts for both hedging and speculative positions. He frequently uses futures contracts for tactical asset allocation because, relative to cash instruments, futures have lower transactions costs and margin requirements. They also allow for short positions and longer duration positions that are not available with cash market instruments. Rawlins has a total of approximately $750 million of assets under management.

In one of his client portfolios, Rawlins currently holds the following positions:

Bond	Face Amount	Price	Duration Today	Duration in 1 Year
Q	$10m	104.98	10.32	9.46
R	$25m	98.36	8.67	7.83
S	$15m	101.21	7.38	6.51

The dollar duration of the cheapest to deliver bond (CTD) is $13,245.46 and the conversion factor is 1.3698.

In a discussion of this bond hedge, Rawlins confers with John Tejada, his assistant. Tejada states that he has regressed the corporate bond's yield against the yield for the CTD and has found that the slope coefficient for this regression is 1.0. He states his results confirm the assumptions made by Rawlins for his hedging calculations. Rawlins states that had Tejada found a slope coefficient greater than one, the number of futures contracts needed to hedge a position would decrease (relative to the regression coefficient being equal to one).

In addition to hedging specific bond positions, Rawlins tends to be quite active in individual bond management by moving in and out of specific issues to take advantage of temporary mispricing. Although the turnover in his portfolio is sometimes quite high, he believes that by using his gut instincts he can outperform a buy-and-hold strategy. Tejada on the other hand prefers using statistical software and simulation to help him find undervalued bond issues. Although Tejada has recently graduated from a prestigious university with a master's degree in finance, Rawlins has not given Tejada full rein in decision-making because he believes that Tejada's approach needs further evaluation over a period of both falling and rising interest rates, as well as in different credit environments.

Rawlins and Tejada are evaluating two individual bonds for purchase. The first bond was issued by Dynacom, a U.S. telecommunications firm. This bond is denominated in dollars. The second bond was issued by Bergamo Metals, an Italian based mining and metal fabrication firm. The Bergamo bond is denominated in euros. The holding period for either bond is three months.

The characteristics of the bonds are as follows:

	Yield on Annual Basis	Modified Duration	Maturity	Current Price	Semiannual Coupon Payment
Dynacom Bond	5.00%	5.13	6.0	100	$2.50
Bergamo Bond	9.00%	2.62	3.0	100	$4.50

Three-month cash interest rates are 1% in the United States and 2.5% in the European Union. Rawlins and Tejada will hedge the receipt of euro interest and principal from the Bergamo bond using a forward contract on euros.

Rawlins evaluates these two bonds and decides that over the next three months, he will invest in the Dynacom bond. He notes that although the Bergamo bond has a yield advantage of 1% over the next quarter, the euro is at a three month forward discount of approximately 1.5%. Therefore, he favors the Dynacom bond because the net return advantage for the Dynacom bond is 0.5% over the next three months.

Tejada does his own analysis and states that, although he agrees with Rawlins that the Dynacom bond has a yield advantage, he is concerned about the credit quality of the Dynacom bond. Specifically, he has heard rumors that the chief executive and the chairman of the board at Dynacom are both being investigated by the U.S. Securities and Exchange Commission for possible manipulation of Dynacom's stock price, just prior to the exercise of their options in the firm's stock. He believes that the resulting fallout from this alleged incident could be damaging to Dynacom's bond price.

Tejada analyzes the potential impact on Dynacom's bond price using breakeven analysis. He believes that news of the incident could increase the yield on Dynacom's bond by 75 basis points. Under this scenario, he states that he would favor the Bergamo bond over the next three months, assuming that the yield on the Bergamo bond stays constant. Rawlins reviews Tejada's breakeven analysis and states that though he is appreciative of Tejada's efforts, the analysis relies on an approximation.

31. The manager wants to completely hedge Bond Q for an expected change in interest rates. The number of futures contracts required is *closest* to:
   A. 82.
   B. 99.
   C. 112.

32. The portfolio's dollar duration today is *closest* to:
   A. $2,964,708.
   B. $4,335,741.
   C. $5,235,741.

33. Suppose that the original dollar duration of the portfolio was $4,901,106 and that the bond prices remain constant during the year. Based on the durations one year from today, and assuming a proportionate investment in each of the three bonds, the amount of cash that will need to be invested to restore the average dollar duration to the original level is *closest* to:
   A. $5,885,167.
   B. $10,888,662.
   C. $12,793,588.

34. Regarding their statements concerning Tejada's regression results, determine if Rawlins and Tejada are correct or incorrect.
   A. Only Rawlins is correct.
   B. Only Tejada is correct.
   C. Both are correct.

35. In their analysis of the Dynacom and Bergamo bonds, the *most likely* basis for the trading of Rawlins and Tejada are:

	Rawlins	Tejada
A.	Yield pickup	Total return approach
B.	Sector rotation	Sector rotation
C.	Total return approach	Yield pickup

36. Regarding Tejada's choice of the Bergamo bond and Rawlins's statement concerning breakeven analysis, determine which statement(s) is (are) correct.
   A. Only Rawlins is correct.
   B. Only Tejada is correct.
   C. Both are correct -OR- both are incorrect.

Questions 37–42 relate to Economic Concepts, Fixed Income Derivatives, Risk Management, and Risk Management Applications of Derivatives.

International Opportunity Investors (IOI) manages substantial euro-priced equity portfolios for two U.S.-based investors, Mark Taylor and Cindy Amsler. Taylor and Amsler have invested in European stocks because of recent media reports suggesting that, due to continued interest rate increases in the United States, European stocks will outperform U.S. stocks over the next few years. Their portfolios are well diversified and similar to the local index portfolio in capitalization weightings.

Ted Tavinsky, IOI's portfolio manager asks his assistant, Tim Treblehorn, to review the relationship between international asset returns and the level of currency risk assumed when investing in foreign securities. The findings, Tavinsky believes, will prove useful in marketing the fund to North American investors. Treblehorn relays two fundamental conclusions to Taylor. First, correlations between international markets have been increasing, and the result has been reduced diversification benefits for international investors. Second, currency risk is typically less than half that of foreign stock risk, but the actual risk assumed is much lower because currency returns and stock returns are not perfectly positively correlated.

Taylor however is very concerned that the U.S. downturn may spread to the global economy. He states that he would like to explore the possibility of investing in the BRIC countries (Brazil, Russia, India, and China). Tavinsky replies that the prospects for the BRIC countries are quite good. Relative to the current G6 countries (U.S., Japan, U.K., Germany, France, and Italy), the stronger economic growth for emerging markets should result in higher stock returns. Furthermore, the increased growth in these markets will increase the demand for capital, which should strengthen their currency values.

Amsler is a novice investor and has hesitantly invested in the overseas markets. In order to calm her fears, Tavinsky and Treblehorn investigate the possibility of hedging using futures contracts on an equity index as well as a euro forward contract. They have chosen futures contracts written on the Eurostoxx equity index for her portfolio because the price changes of the contract have a high correlation with the returns on Amsler's equity portfolio. Amsler's equity portfolio has a market value of €15,000,000 and a beta of 1.15 relative to the local underlying index.

Tavinsky and Treblehorn collect data for spot exchange rates, futures contract prices and betas, as well as U.S. and European interest rates. Tavinsky and Treblehorn are bearish on the European stock market over the next year as noted by their forecasted return for it.

Relevant values are shown in the table below:

Spot U.S. dollar / euro exchange rate	$1.05
One year risk-free rate in Europe	2%
One year risk-free rate in the United States	4%
Price of futures contract written on the Eurostoxx equity index	€120,000
Beta of futures contract written on the Eurostoxx equity index, relative to the local underlying index	0.975
Forecasted return of the local underlying index over one year	−12%
Forecasted spot U.S. dollar / euro exchange rate in one year	$1.12

Tavinsky has told Amsler that he and Treblehorn will calculate the value of her portfolio in hedged and unhedged scenarios. Tavinsky states that if, at the beginning of the year, he were to fully hedge the systematic risk of Amsler's equity portfolio using the index futures, the appropriate futures position to accomplish this would be 125 contracts. Treblehorn states that if they decide to hedge the currency risk of the portfolio as well, the principal for the forward contract that will hedge the currency risk of the hedged equity position will be €15,000,000, using a "hedging the principal" strategy.

Lastly, Tavinsky and Treblehorn calculate the forecasted return on the portfolio assuming that currency risk is hedged. Assuming that both equity and currency risk are hedged, Tavinsky calculates that the dollar return would be 8.8%. Treblehorn states that the forecasted spot U.S. dollar / euro exchange rate in one year of $1.12 should be used for the forward contract rate.

37. Which of the following is *least* accurate regarding the BRIC countries?
    A. An increase in investment capital will result in a relatively high level of output.
    B. Per capita income in most BRIC countries is expected to surpass that of G6 countries.
    C. The BRIC countries will experience a decline in their working age population later than that in the G6 countries.

38. If IOI wants to hedge the portfolios of Amsler as indicated, Tavinsky should go:
    A. short the equity index futures contract to hedge equity risk and go long a euro forward contract.
    B. long the equity index futures contract to hedge equity risk and go short a euro forward contract.
    C. short the equity index futures contract to hedge equity risk and go short a euro forward contract.

39. Regarding their statements on the amounts needed to hedge the equity and currency risk of Amsler's portfolio, determine whether Tavinsky and Treblehorn are correct or not.
    A. Only Tavinski is correct.
    B. Only Treblehorn is correct.
    C. Both are correct.

40. Determine which of the following is *closest* to the dollar return on the unhedged Amsler equity portfolio (if equity futures and currency forwards are not used).
    A. An 8% loss.
    B. A 12% loss.
    C. A 7% gain.

41. Assuming a futures position based on the expected index value in one year turns out to be a perfect hedge and the currency risk is not hedged, the dollar return on the Amsler equity portfolio is *closest* to:
    A. a 9% gain.
    B. an 11% gain.
    C. a 7% loss.

42. Regarding Tavinsky's forecasted dollar returns on Amsler's portfolio (assuming equity and currency risk are both hedged) and Treblehorn's statement about the appropriate forward rate:
    A. only Tavinski is correct.
    B. only Treblehorn is correct.
    C. neither is correct.

Questions 43–48 relate to Risk Management.

Maurice Taylor, CFA, FRM, is responsible for managing risk in his firm's commodity portfolios. Taylor has extensive experience in the risk management field and as a result has been appointed the task of mentoring entry-level employees. Steven Jacobs is a newly hired Financial Analyst who has been assigned to research the company's risk management process. To verify the accuracy of his findings he consults Taylor. Taylor agrees to thoroughly review Jacobs's findings and volunteers to contribute his knowledge to enhance any part of the report that mentions Taylor's department.

A week later, Jacobs submits his report to his supervisor without reading Taylor's suggestions. Some excerpts from the report are as follows:

1. "Many portfolio managers use a ratio that compares the average alpha to the standard deviation of alpha to measure risk-adjusted performance. This ratio can be used to rank their ability to generate excess returns on a consistent basis."

2. "The main difference between risk governance and risk budgeting is that risk governance is concerned with policies and standards, whereas risk budgeting is concerned with allocating risk."

3. "In an ERM system individual portfolio managers are charged with measuring, managing, and monitoring their portfolio risk as well as determining their optimal amount of capital at risk relative to the overall firm. With this information upper management gains a better overall picture of the firm's risk."

4. "The two general categories of risk are financial and non-financial risks. Financial risks include market risk and credit risk. Non-financial risks include settlement risk, regulatory risk, model risk, liquidity risk, operations risk, and political risk."

Jacobs's supervisor thanks him for the report and assigns him the next task of researching the firm's VAR calculation methodologies. His supervisor is wondering if the firm should switch to the Monte Carlo Method from the Historical Method. Jacobs again decides to consult Taylor for his expertise. Taylor agrees that using the Monte Carlo Method would be useful since it incorporates returns distributions rather than single point estimates of risk and return. This may be appropriate for Taylor's portfolios since commodity returns can exhibit skewed distributions. Taylor, however, informs Jacobs that there are also advantages to using historical VAR including that it is based on modern portfolio theory (MPT).

Jacobs uses the firm's small cap value portfolio to illustrate the calculation of VAR. The value of the portfolio is $140 million and it has an annual expected return of 12.10%. The annual standard deviation of returns is 18.20%. Assuming a normal distribution, 5% of the potential portfolio values are more than 1.65 standard deviations below the expected return.

Jacobs completes his research report on VAR by adding an appendix section on extensions of VAR. He states that one extension that can be particularly valuable in risk management measures the impact of a single asset on the portfolio VAR. This measure captures the effects of the correlations of the individual assets on the overall portfolio VAR.

43. In the first statement in his research report, Jacobs is *most likely* describing the:
     A. Sortino ratio.
     B. RoMAD ratio.
     C. information ratio.

44. Are Taylor's second and third statements on the differences between risk governance and risk budgeting and ERM systems correct?
     A. Only Taylor's third statement is correct.
     B. Taylor is correct regarding both statements.
     C. Only Taylor's second statement is correct.

45. In Jacobs's list of non-financial risks in his fourth statement, all are non-financial *except*:
     A. settlement risk.
     B. operations risk.
     C. liquidity risk.

46. Are Taylor's statements on the advantages of the Monte Carlo Method and the Historical VAR correct?
     A. Only the statement about the Monte Carlo method is correct.
     B. Only the statement about Historical VAR is correct.
     C. Both are correct.

47. Assuming its returns are normally distributed and 250 trading days in the year, the daily VAR Jacobs will calculate for the small cap value portfolio is *closest* to:
     A. $2.59 million.
     B. $25.10 million.
     C. $27.88 million.

48. In the Appendix to his research report, the extension to VAR that Jacobs describes is *most likely*:
     A. portfolio VAR.
     B. incremental VAR.
     C. correlation VAR.

Questions 49–54 relate to Fixed Income Derivatives and Risk Management Applications of Derivatives.

Smiler Industries is a U.S. manufacturer of machine tools and other capital goods. Dat Ng, the CFO of Smiler, feels strongly that Smiler has a competitive advantage in its risk management practices. With this in mind, Ng hedges many of the risks associated with Smiler's financial transactions, which include those of a financial subsidiary. Ng's knowledge of derivatives is extensive, and he often uses them for hedging and in managing Smiler's considerable investment portfolio.

Smiler has recently completed a sale to Frexa in Italy, and the receivable is denominated in euros. The receivable is €10 million to be received in 90 days. Smiler's bank provides the following information:

	Spot	30 days	60 days	90 days	120 days
$/€	1.42	1.43	1.44	1.45	1.46

Smiler borrows short-term funds to meet expenses on a temporary basis and typically makes semiannual interest payments based on 180-day LIBOR plus a spread of 150 bp. Smiler will need to borrow $25 million in 90 days to invest in new equipment. To hedge the interest rate risk on the loan, Ng is considering the purchase of a call option on 180-day LIBOR with a term to expiration of 90 days, an exercise rate of 4.8%, and a premium of 0.000943443 of the loan amount. Current 90-day LIBOR is 4.8%.

Smiler also has a diversified portfolio of large cap stocks with a current value of $52,750,000, and Ng wants to lower the beta of the portfolio from its current level of 1.25 to 0.9 using S&P 500 futures which have a multiplier of 250. The S&P 500 is currently 1,050, and the futures contract exhibits a beta of 0.98 to the underlying.

Because Ng intends to replace the short-term LIBOR-based loan with long-term financing, he wants to hedge the risk of an increase in interest rates for the 20-year bond Smiler will issue in 270 days. The current spread to Treasuries for Smiler's corporate debt is 2.4%. He will use a 270-day, 20-year Treasury bond futures contract ($100,000 face value) currently priced at 108.5 for the hedge. The CTD bond for the contract has a conversion factor of 1.259 and a dollar duration of $6,932.53. The corporate bond, if issued today, would have an effective duration of 9.94 and, based on yield assumptions, has an expected effective duration at issuance of 9.90. A regression of the historical yields on 20-year corporate bonds with a rating the same as Smiler's on the yields of the CTD bond yields a beta of 1.05.

49.   The type of exchange rate exposure generated by the sale to Frexa is:
       A. economic, and the proceeds from a forward contract would be
           $6.9 million.
       B. economic, and the proceeds from a forward contract would be
           $14.5 million.
       C. transaction, and the proceeds from a forward contract would be
           $14.5 million.

50.   If Ng purchases the interest rate call, and 180-day LIBOR at option
       expiration is 5.73%, the annualized effective rate for the 180-day loan is
       closest to:
       A. 6.6982%.
       B. 6.5346%.
       C. 6.3785%.

51.   What position should Smiler take to alter the beta of the equity portfolio?
       A. Long 72 futures contracts.
       B. Short 72 futures contracts.
       C. Long 70 futures contracts.

52.   Determine the strategy in Treasury bond futures contracts that Ng should
       take to hedge the interest rate risk of the bond Smiler will issue.
       A. Short 244 contracts.
       B. Short 449 contracts.
       C. Short 472 contracts.

53.   When hedging the interest rate risk of the bond Smiler will issue, which of
       the following is *not* a likely source of hedging error?
       A. The dollar duration for the corporate bond was incorrect.
       B. Interest rates changed more than expected.
       C. The projected basis of the futures contract at the date the hedge is to be
           removed.

54.   Ng is thinking about hedging several foreign exchange positions. Which of
       the following positions would be the *most* difficult to fully hedge?
       A. Smiler has a loan due in two years that is denominated in yen.
       B. Smiler has an order for German machine parts due in three months,
           payable in euros.
       C. Ng has an investment in British stocks, which he will be converting to
           U.S. dollars in one year.

Questions 55–60 relate to Ethical and Professional Standards.

Shirley Riley, CFA, has just been promoted from vice president of trading to chief investment officer (CIO) at Crane & Associates, LLC (CA), a large investment management firm. Riley has been with CA for eight years, but she has much to learn as she assumes her new duties as CIO. Riley has decided to hire Denny Simpson, CFA, as the new compliance officer for CA. Riley and Simpson have been reviewing procedures and policies throughout the firm and have discovered several potential issues.

Communications with Clients

Portfolio managers are encouraged to communicate with clients on a regular basis. At a minimum, managers are expected to contact clients on a quarterly basis to review portfolio performance. Each client must have an investment policy statement (IPS) created when their account is opened, specifying the objectives and constraints for their portfolio. IPSs are reviewed at client request at any time. When market conditions or client circumstances dictate a change in the investment style or strategy of a client portfolio, the client is notified immediately by phone or email and the client's IPS is revised as necessary before any changes are made.

Employee Incentive Program

CA offers several incentive programs to employees. One of the most popular of these programs is the CA IPO program. Whenever CA is involved in an initial public offering (IPO), portfolio managers are allowed to participate. The structure is simple—for every 100 shares purchased on behalf of a client, the manager is awarded five shares for his own account. The manager is thus rewarded for getting an IPO sold and at the same time is able to share in the results of the IPO. Any time shares are remaining 72 hours before the IPO goes public, other employees are allowed to participate on a first-come, first-serve basis. Employees seem to appreciate this opportunity, but CA does not have exact numbers on employee participation in the program.

Private Equity Fund

CA has a private equity fund that is internally managed. This fund is made available only to clients with more than $5 million in assets managed by CA, a policy that is fully disclosed in CA's marketing materials. Roughly one-third of the fund's assets are invested in companies that are either very small capitalization or thinly traded (or both). The pricing of these securities for monthly account statements is often difficult. CA support staff get information from different sources—sometimes using third party services, sometimes using CA valuation models. In some instances, a manager of the private equity fund will enter an order during the last trading hour of the month to purchase 100 shares of one of these small securities at a modest premium to the last trade price. If the trade gets executed, that price can then be used on the account statements. The small size of these trades does not significantly affect the fund's overall position in any particular company holding, which is typically several thousand shares.

Soft Dollar Usage

Several different managers at CA use independent research in developing investment ideas. One of the more popular research services among CA managers is "Beneath the Numbers (BTN)," which focuses on potential accounting abuses at prominent companies. This service often provides early warnings of problems with a stock, allowing CA managers the opportunity to sell their clients' positions before a negative surprise lowers the price. Stocks covered by BTN are typically widely held in CA client accounts. Managers at CA have been so happy with BTN that they have also subscribed to a new research product provided by the same authors—"Beneath the Radar (BTR)." BTR recommends small capitalization securities that are not large enough to attract much attention from large institutional investors. The results of BTR's recommendations are mixed thus far, but CA managers are willing to be patient.

As they discuss these issues, Riley informs Simpson that she is determined to bring CA into full compliance with the CFA Institute's "Asset Manager Code of Professional Conduct." The following questions should be answered with the Asset Manager Code as a guide.

55. Indicate whether CA's policies related to investment policy statement (IPS) reviews and notification of changes in investment style/strategy are consistent with the Asset Manager Code of Professional Conduct.
    A. Both policies are inadequate.
    B. Both policies are consistent with the Asset Manager Code of Professional Conduct.
    C. The IPS review policy is inadequate, but the policy on communicating changes in style/strategy is adequate.

56. Indicate whether CA's policies related to its IPO program, specifically allowing portfolio manager participation and employee participation, are consistent with the Asset Manager Code of Professional Conduct.
    A. Policies on both portfolio manager and employee participation in IPOs are not consistent with the Asset Manager Code of Professional Conduct.
    B. The employee participation in IPOs policy is consistent with the Asset Manager Code, as is the portfolio manager's policy on participation in IPOs.
    C. The portfolio manager's policy on IPOs is not consistent with the Asset Manager Cod; however, the employee policy on IPOs is consistent with the Asset Manager Code.

57. Participation in CA's private equity fund is limited to clients with $5 million under management. This policy:
    A. does not violate the Asset Manager Code of Professional Conduct.
    B. would be acceptable so long as a similar investment vehicle was made available to all clients.
    C. is not consistent with the Asset Manager Code of Professional Conduct.

58. In discussing the pricing of thinly traded securities in the private equity fund, Riley suggested that CA should choose one pricing method and apply it consistently, thus avoiding the need to disclose specific pricing methods to clients. Simpson responded that using third party sources or internal valuation models was acceptable, so long as the pricing sources are fully disclosed to clients. Indicate whether Riley's comment and/or Simpson's responses are *correct* or *incorrect*.
    A. Both Riley's comment and Simpson's response are correct.
    B. Riley's comment is not correct; however, Simpson's response is correct.
    C. Riley is correct, while Simpson is not correct.

59. Trading stocks during the last trading hour of a month to establish a fair market price:
    A. does not violate the Asset Manager Code of Professional Conduct.
    B. is acceptable so long as the trade is not material relative to the overall CA position in the security.
    C. is not consistent with the Asset Manager Code of Professional Conduct.

60. Simpson has verified that CA has adequate disclosures of its soft dollar usage. Given that full disclosure is made to clients, indicate whether CA's use of soft dollars for BTN and BTR are consistent with the Asset Manager Code of Professional Conduct.
    A. Given the adequate disclosures, use of soft dollars for both BTN and BTR is acceptable.
    B. Use of soft dollars for BTN is acceptable, but not for BTR.
    C. Neither of these publications provide direct benefit to the client; thus, neither may be paid for with soft dollars.

END OF AFTERNOON SESSION

EXAM 1
MORNING SESSION ANSWERS

QUESTION 1

Source: Study Session 4, LOS 10.j,k, 14.c,d
Study Session 8, LOS 21.g
Study Session 17, LOS 41.p

Answer for Question 1-A

		Investment Policy Statement for the Marks
Objectives	Risk Objective	**For the Exam:** Willingness: Below average. Ability: Average. Overall: Below average. **Discussion:** Willingness is below average because Marks states he does not want to lose more than 2% in any year. This statement indicates that Marks's focus is on risk and a desire for stability. Ability is average. Marks's fairly substantial portfolio and fairly low required return indicate above-average ability to take risk. The portfolio must meet all living expenses for the Marks family, however, and that indicates below-average risk tolerance. Considering the two indicators together, we can say Marks has average ability to take risk. Overall risk tolerance is below average, because willingness to take risk is less than ability to take risk and we honor the lesser (i.e., more risk-averse) of the two. Note: On the exam you could see a client with above-average ability to take risk due to a very large portfolio (> $10 million or so) and very small required return (< 2% to 3%), but the client has below-average willingness to take risk. In that case, you would be safe averaging the two and saying the client has average overall risk tolerance. As justification, state that significant wealth and low required return mean the portfolio has the ability to sustain considerable reduction in value before the client's goals are placed in jeopardy. Any time there is a difference between willingness and ability to take risk, you should recommend counseling to reconcile the difference.

Objectives	Risk Objective	Here are a few rules of thumb for determining risk tolerance for an individual:
		Willingness:
		1. Remember, willingness to take risk is psychological.
		2. Always start out at average and then look for statements or actions that might indicate the need to move up or down a notch (i.e., to above average or below average).
		3. If the client makes specific statements about risk, this usually indicates that the client is concerned with risk and you should drop willingness a notch.
		4. Look at the client's past investments and strategies for indications of risk tolerance. The client might make a statement like, "I have average risk tolerance." When you look at the client's past investments, however, you see emerging market equities, commodities, derivatives, etc. In this case actions speak far louder than words. "Average" to this client is above average for others, so move up a notch. The bottom line is that you can usually ignore client statements about risk aversion. The client's actions are usually more relevant.
		Ability:
		1. The client's ability to take risk depends on the portfolio's ability to take risk without putting the client's liquidity needs in jeopardy. This will be determined jointly by the size of the portfolio relative to liquidity needs and the time horizon. (Remember, *liquidity needs* refers to expenditures that must be met by the portfolio; expenditures that are not covered by the client's salary or other income sources.)
		Holding **portfolio size** constant: • As time horizon increases → ability to take risk increases. • As liquidity needs increase → ability to take risk decreases.
		Holding **liquidity needs** constant: • As wealth (portfolio size) increases → ability to take risk increases.
		2. Starting at average ability to take risk, look for reasons to move up or down a notch: • If the client's salary covers all living and other required expenditures, the client's ability to take risk is usually average or above average, depending on the size of the portfolio and the time horizon. • Having to take living or other expenses out of the portfolio decreases the typical client's ability to take risk. If the client is quite wealthy, however, the expenditures might have no affect. The key is the size of the required expenditure(s) relative to the client's portfolio. Even if the portfolio must meet all living expenses (e.g., retired client), if they amount to less than 1% or 2% of the portfolio, the client's ability to take risk is probably unaffected.

Examples: These examples include discussions of ability to take risk as well as demand for life insurance, based solely on the data provided. In determining life insurance demand on the exam you should also look for indications of the individual's willingness to take risk as well as statements about dependents. You will probably be asked to determine whether or not the individual will demand life insurance, not the dollar amount of life insurance. Since life insurance is a hedge against dying and the accompanying loss of human capital, however, the typical amount of life insurance would be the present value of human capital.

1. Retired individual; 15-year time horizon; $50 million portfolio; $500,000 annual expenses are met by portfolio; little or no desire for bequest → *above-average ability*.
   - Not concerned with value of portfolio at death, and expenditures amount to only 1% of the portfolio per year. Overall risk tolerance will depend on the client's willingness to take risk.
      - If willingness is below average, go with average overall and recommend counseling to reconcile the difference.
      - If willingness is average, go with average overall and recommend counseling to reconcile the difference.
      - If willingness is above average, go with above average overall.

   Life insurance. Probably no demand for life insurance because of high wealth and low utility derived from leaving an estate.

2. Retired individual; 15-year time horizon; $50 million portfolio; $500,000 annual expenses are met by portfolio; desire for maximum bequest → *average ability*.
   - This one is somewhat vague, but seems to imply the client wants to leave at least $50 million. An important consideration is the inability of the client to make further contributions to the portfolio. Since the portfolio must meet all expenses and the client wants to maintain or grow the value of the portfolio, we would probably conclude that the client has average ability to take risk. If the client had a time horizon of five years or so, we would no doubt conclude that ability is below average. In this case the client's willingness to take risk will have a somewhat smaller impact on overall risk tolerance.
      - If willingness is below average, go with average overall and recommend counseling to reconcile the difference.
      - If willingness is average, go with average overall.
      - If willingness is above average, go with average overall and recommend counseling to reconcile the difference.

   Life insurance: Based on wealth, little or no demand for life insurance. Since strong desire to maximize bequest, however, this investor probably wants life insurance.

3. Working individual; 30 years until retirement; $1 million portfolio; $150,000 annual expenses are approximately equal to after-tax salary; bequest desire uncertain → *above-average ability*.
   - This is one of those dream scenarios that you hope shows up on the exam, because everything points to above-average ability to take risk. Note that in cases like this, the individual's willingness is often above average, also, which makes your choice very easy.
      - If willingness is below average, go with below average overall and recommend counseling to reconcile the difference.
      - If willingness is average, go with average overall and recommend counseling to reconcile the difference.
      - If willingness is above average, go with above average overall.

   Life insurance. Uncertain from data provided, but probably some demand for life insurance. Because of long time horizon, the correlation of human and financial capital is important as well as whether the client has dependents to protect, especially considering that life insurance replaces lost human capital. Also determine the client's utility from leaving an estate and willingness to take risk.

4. Working individual; 5 years until retirement; $1 million portfolio; $150,000 annual expenses are approximately equal to after-tax salary; wishes to maintain current lifestyle in retirement; bequest desire uncertain → *average ability*.
   - The shortened time horizon changes the scenario dramatically. The individual has made no comments about a desired bequest, so we only assume he wishes to maintain the size of the portfolio (typical assumption for any morning case). However, the shortened time horizon reduces the individual's ability to take risk, even though current expenses are being met by the salary. If the client was using the portfolio to meet part of his living expenses, the ability would be below average.
     - If willingness is below average, go with below average overall. Probably no need to recommend counseling to reconcile the difference, because of the very short time horizon. (You should state that in the risk objective.)
     - If willingness is average, go with average overall.
     - If willingness is above average, go with average overall and recommend counseling to reconcile the difference.

   Life insurance. With short time horizon, the demand for life insurance is uncertain, so look for correlation of human and financial capital as well as whether the client has dependents to protect. Look for statements about the client's utility from leaving an estate and willingness to take risk.

5. Working individual; 15 years until retirement; $1 million portfolio; $150,000 annual expenses approximately equal to after-tax salary; wishes to maintain current lifestyle in retirement; strong bequest desire → *average ability*.
   - The individual now has a strong desire to leave a bequest, so we assume he wishes at a minimum to maintain the size of the portfolio. The lengthened time horizon reinforces the individual's ability to take risk. If the client was using the portfolio to meet any or all living expenses, ability would probably be below average.
     - If willingness is below average, go with below average overall and recommend counseling to reconcile the difference.
     - If willingness is average, go with average overall.
     - If willingness is above average, go with average overall and recommend counseling to reconcile the difference.

   Life insurance. Probably has a strong demand for life insurance, because of the strong bequest desire, long time horizon, and modest wealth.

6. Working individual; 15 years until retirement; $20 million portfolio; $200,000 annual expenses approximately equal to after-tax salary; wishes to maintain current lifestyle in retirement; strong bequest desire → *above average ability*.
   - This is similar to the third example, because everything points to above average ability to take risk. Even if current expenses were being met by the portfolio, this client's ability would be no worse than average, because total expenses amount to less than 1.5% of the portfolio (this considers taxes at 30%, so total before-tax dollar return would have to be $200,000 / 0.7 = $285,714 or 1.429% of portfolio).
     - Because of considerable portfolio size, if willingness is below average, go with average overall and recommend counseling to reconcile the difference. Notice that when the client has significant wealth, we can adopt an overall risk tolerance that is an average of the individual's willingness and ability.
     - If willingness is average, go with average overall and recommend counseling to reconcile the difference.
     - If willingness is above average, go with above average overall.

   Life insurance. Probably some demand for life insurance, because of the long time horizon and strong bequest desire.

7. Working individual; 15 years until retirement; $2 million portfolio; $150,000 annual expenses with $50,000 met by portfolio; will not reduce current lifestyle and wishes to maintain current lifestyle in retirement; strong bequest desire → *below-average ability.*
   - The long time horizon and fairly large portfolio do not compensate for the liquidity needs and the desire to maintain the current lifestyle. The strong bequest desire only reinforces the decision of below average.
     - If willingness is below average, go with below average.
     - If willingness is average, go with below average overall and recommend counseling to reconcile the difference.
     - If willingness is above average, go with below average overall and recommend counseling to reconcile the difference.

   Life insurance. Probably some demand for life insurance, because of the long time horizon and strong bequest desire.

We could go on and on dreaming up new and different scenarios, but this makes a great topic for group discussion. Meet with two or three fellow Level III candidates and think up possible exam scenarios. Make some of them complicated and others more straightforward with changing time horizons, liquidity needs, bequest desires, portfolio sizes, salaries, and amounts of liquidity needs met by the portfolio.

Objectives	Return Objective	
		For the Exam: Cash inflows for the coming year: Salary $150,000 Cash outflows: Taxes on salary $49,500 (150,000 × 0.33) Living expenses 100,000 Allison's care 102,000 (100,000 × 1.02) Ernie Jr. stipend <u>50,000</u> Total outflows: $301,500 Net ($151,500) Required after-tax **real** rate of return = $151,500 / $5,000,000 = 0.0303 = 3.03% Required after-tax real rate of return = 3.03% Plus: Annual inflation rate = 2.0% Required after-tax **nominal** rate of return = **5.03%** **Discussion:** Over the coming year, Marks will draw a salary of $150,000 and pay $49,500 in income taxes. Living expenses are given to us at $100,000 for the coming year, but the $100,000 cost of Allison's care was for the previous year. That means the cost of Allison's care for the coming year will be 2% higher ($102,000). This is the first year of Ernie Jr.'s stipend, so we use $50,000. Total outflows for the coming year, including taxes, are estimated at $301,500 with the only inflow the $150,000 salary Ernie Sr. will draw. This leaves a shortfall of $151,500 that must be made up by the portfolio. To pay the $151,500, the $5,000,000 portfolio must earn 3.03% after-tax. To maintain the purchasing power of the portfolio principal (the $5,000,000), we must add inflation for a total after-tax nominal return of 5.03%. Note 1: Alternatively, you could have compounded by the rate of inflation and arrived at a required after-tax nominal return of (1.0303)(1.02) − 1 = 5.09%. Unless you are directed to present the answer in a specific form, either way would be acceptable on the exam. Note 2: The vignette may or may not state that you must protect the principal (i.e., maintain purchasing power). To stress the point, I deliberately left out the statement in this case. On the exam, always assume you are to protect the principal unless you are specifically told otherwise.

Answer for Question 1-B

Constraints	Time Horizon	**For the Exam:** Long term consisting of two stages: (1) three years until retirement; (2) retirement years. A possible third stage relates to the daughter, Allison, whose care is to be funded by the portfolio as long as she lives. **Discussion:** Individuals usually have a two-stage time horizon; the years until retirement and the years of retirement. Note that unless stated otherwise, the estate becomes someone else's concern upon the death of the client. That is, the client's IPS, including time horizon, stops at death. In this case, the time horizon is somewhat uncertain, because Allison might outlive both parents and her care is to be paid by the portfolio. The portion of the estate that goes to Ernie Jr., however, becomes his portfolio with all constraints and objectives associated with his needs. Note: On the exam, you don't necessarily have to state whether a time horizon is long-term, intermediate-term, or short-term. If you can figure out the number of years, state that. For example, you could say the three years until retirement represents a short-term first stage of the time horizon, and that would be fine. Trouble starts, however, when you have stages of uncertain classification (e.g., eight years).
	Liquidity	**For the Exam:** In first year, portfolio must provide $151,500. After the first year, any expenses that exceed salary. **Discussion:** Under liquidity include only those expenses that must be met by the portfolio. These are expenses above salaries or any other sources of income such as pensions. When you are not specifically asked for the liquidity for a given year, such as the first year of retirement, include all expenses that are known or anticipated, including negative liquidity events, such as inheritances.
	Legal/Regulatory	**For the Exam:** Seek legal counsel to create a trust to care for Allison. **Discussion:** Legal and regulatory can be minimal or non-existent for individual investors. In this case we should include mention of legal counsel for protecting the daughter, should she outlive the clients.

Constraints	Taxes	**For the Exam:** The average tax rate is 33%, so tax aspects of investments should be considered. **Discussion:** The Marks are taxable investors. Tax aspects of investments should always be considered for individuals.
	Unique Circumstances	**For the Exam:** Support of the daughter and son. **Discussion:** Allison's care will presumably continue after the death of both parents and must be provided. There is some desire to leave 50% of the estate to the son, although no minimum amount is specified. Given their below-average risk tolerance, Ernie and Ellie probably hold some life insurance.

C. **For the Exam:**

For the calculation part of the question, your objective would be to simply provide the calculations as shown below. You should show your work on the exam in case you make a mathematical mistake. This provides you with the potential for receiving partial credit as long as your process for calculating the answer is correct.

The question also asks you to explain the information provided by the ratio, for which you would state: "The safety first ratio is the number of standard deviations by which the expected return exceeds the minimum acceptable return."

Discussion:

Roy's Safety First Ratio (RSF) is a measure of downside risk. The manager calculates the expected return and standard deviation of returns for the portfolio. Employing the empirical rule:

- ≈ 68% of all returns will fall within one standard deviation of the mean.
- ≈ 95% of all returns will fall within two standard deviations of the mean.
- ≈ 98% will fall within three standard deviations.

A safety first ratio is the number of standard deviations the portfolio expected return exceeds the minimum acceptable return. For example, with an expected return of 14%, a standard deviation of 8%, and a minimum acceptable return of zero, the safety first measure

is $\dfrac{0.14 - 0}{0.08} = 1.75$, indicating that the minimum acceptable return lies 1.75 standard deviations below the portfolio expected return.

Professor's Note: Safety first rules were first introduced in the Level I curriculum, Investment Tools, Quantitative Methods section, and are in the Level III Portfolio Management material as Roy's Safety First measure. Basically, they tell us the probability of experiencing a return below some minimum desired return. You're looking at the left hand side of the distribution, so a higher safety first ratio means that there is a smaller chance of a return less than the desired minimum.

In order to calculate Roy's Safety First Ratio (RSF) for the portfolios, we must first determine the portfolios' expected standard deviations. Recall that the Sharpe and RSF ratios are calculated as:

$$\text{Sharpe}_P = \frac{\hat{R}_P - R_F}{\sigma_P}$$

$$\text{RSF}_P = \frac{\hat{R}_P - \text{MAR}}{\sigma_P}; \text{ MAR} = -2\% \text{ (given)}$$

We are provided with Sharpe ratios, expected returns, and the risk free rate, so we can utilize the Sharpe ratios to calculate the portfolio standard deviations to be used in the RSF calculations. Note that the table provides after-tax returns (R_{AT}), so we first gross them up for taxes to obtain before-tax returns (R_{BT}) before estimating standard deviations and RSF:

$$\hat{R}_{A,BT} = \frac{\hat{R}_{A,AT}}{1 - 0.33} = \frac{0.08}{0.67} = 0.1194$$

$$\hat{R}_{B,BT} = \frac{0.072}{0.67} = 0.1075$$

$$\hat{R}_{C,BT} = \frac{0.063}{0.67} = 0.0940$$

$$\hat{R}_{D,BT} = \frac{0.052}{0.67} = 0.0776$$

We now use the Sharpe ratios provided to estimate each standard deviation:

$$\text{Sharpe}_P = \frac{\hat{R}_P - R_F}{\sigma_P} \Rightarrow \sigma_P = \frac{\hat{R}_P - R_F}{\text{Sharpe}_P}$$

$$\sigma_A = \frac{\hat{R}_A - R_F}{\text{Sharpe}_A} = \frac{\dfrac{0.080}{(1 - 0.33)} - 0.02}{0.66} = \frac{0.1194 - 0.02}{0.66} = 0.1506$$

$$\sigma_B = \frac{\hat{R}_B - R_F}{\text{Sharpe}_B} = \frac{0.1075 - 0.02}{0.70} = 0.1250$$

$$\sigma_C = \frac{\hat{R}_C - R_F}{\text{Sharpe}_C} = \frac{0.0940 - 0.02}{0.77} = 0.0961$$

$$\sigma_D = \frac{\hat{R}_D - R_F}{\text{Sharpe}_D} = \frac{0.0776 - 0.02}{1.17} = 0.0492$$

We use the standard deviations, minimum acceptable return, and expected returns to calculate the RSF ratios:

$$\text{RSF}_P = \frac{\hat{R}_P - \text{MAR}}{\sigma_P}$$

$$\text{RSF}_A = \frac{0.1194 - (-0.02)}{0.1506} = 0.9256$$

$$\text{RSF}_B = \frac{0.1075 - (-0.02)}{0.1250} = 1.0200$$

$$\text{RSF}_C = \frac{0.0940 - (-0.02)}{0.0961} = 1.1863$$

$$\text{RSF}_D = \frac{0.0776 - (-0.02)}{0.0492} = 1.9837$$

D. **For the Exam:**

Portfolio D is best:
- Return exceeds the required return.
- Highest safety first criterion.

Discussion:

Portfolio D is the most appropriate portfolio for the Marks.

Return: The expected portfolio total return is 5.2%, which exceeds the return required (5.03%) to meet the liquidity needs of the Marks and the expected rate of inflation.

Risk: The ability of Marks to take risk is average, but his willingness is low and he does not want the portfolio value to decline more than 2% in any year, thus overall both his ability and willingness are below average. This is clearly the portfolio that best meets the client's safety first criterion. The safety-first ratio indicates that there is less than a 3% chance that returns will be worse than –2%, assuming portfolio returns are normally distributed.

 Professor's Note: How did we arrive at less than a 3% chance? Using a one-tailed test (we're only worried about the downside here), at a critical value of 1.98 (RSF = 1.9837), less than 3% of the distribution lies to the left. Or if you want to be more precise, look up 1.98 in a z-table and you will find that only 2.39% lies in the tail.

Overall: There is no reason given in the case to take more risk or seek a higher return than that generated by Portfolio D. The Marks state no other bequest motive other than what we have addressed. Do not misinterpret the issues here—the Marks' needs are covered by a good margin, and the bequest to the son is a maximum, not a minimum, and is not defined in dollar terms.

Sample Scoring Key:
A. 6 points each for addressing the two objectives.
B. 3 points each for time horizon and liquidity, 2 points for addressing the unique considerations, 1 point each for tax and legal.
C. 2 points for ratio formula, 2 points for interpretation, 2 points for correct calculations.
D. 4 points for selecting and justifying the correct portfolio.

QUESTION 2

Source: Study Session 5, LOS 15.i,j,l

Answer for Question 2-A

	Investment Policy Statement for Unilife Portfolio Segments
Objectives	**Return Objectives** **For the Exam:** Short-term portfolio: return should meet the return for 90-day high-grade commercial paper. Long-term bond portfolio: return should exceed the crediting rate + operating expenses = 7% (5% + 2%). Stock portfolio: returns should meet or exceed the returns for the benchmarks S&P midcap and S&P 500 to grow the surplus. **Discussion:** Short-term portfolio: Returns of the short-term portfolio should meet the returns for Moody's or Standard and Poor's 90-day benchmark commercial paper. Investment returns from U.S. Treasuries are acceptable, but somewhat higher returns are desirable for competitive positioning. Long-term bond portfolio: Since the purpose of this portfolio is to cover crediting rates and operating expenses, the required return of this segment is 7% plus the desired spread (i.e., 5% + 2% + spread). Attention to opportunities in 10-year or longer A-rated corporate instruments should be directed to attaining the required after-tax return. Stock portfolio: Returns to the stock portfolio should meet or exceed the total returns to the designated benchmarks, the S&P MidCap and S&P 500. The focus should be on growing the surplus and providing a competitive advantage. *Professor's Note: This answer is a good example of situations where you should not be afraid to state the obvious, even when it means more or less repeating what is stated in the vignette.*
	Risk Tolerance **For the Exam:** Short-term portfolio: risk should not exceed the risk for 90-day high-grade commercial paper. Long-term bond portfolio: risk should not exceed that for A1-rated corporate bonds. Stock portfolio: can accept market to above market levels of risk. The portfolio should be well diversified including the maximum 5% international allocation. **Discussion:** Short-term portfolio: The quality of commercial paper instruments should not be sacrificed. The minimum acceptable quality for this portfolio is that at 90-day high-grade commercial paper. Long-term bond portfolio: A1-rating is the lowest quality corporate instruments that can be held in this portfolio. Although UniLife seeks higher return from extending maturity, minimum acceptable credit quality instruments are required to meet the liability structure.

	Stock portfolio: The stock portfolio can accept market to above market levels of risk. Growing the surplus is the focus. Maintaining a well-diversified portfolio is required, including the maximum 5% international allocation, because adding international equities to a diversified holding of domestic equities has been shown to shift the efficient frontier upward (i.e., increased return for given risk). Notice that the investment portfolio is effectively segmented into three separate portfolios, each with a specific goal. The goals for the three portfolios, as stated in the statements by UniLife management, are typical.

Answer for Question 2-B

Constraints	**Time Horizon** **For the Exam:** Short-term portfolio: 30 days to 1 year. Long-term bond portfolio: 10 to 20 years. A laddered maturity portfolio is appropriate. Stock portfolio: Perpetual due to capital gains (i.e., growth) preference. **Discussion:** Since the investment portfolio is segmented according to goals, each segment has its own time horizon. Short-term portfolio: Very liquid, low-risk, low-return assets. The targeted time horizon for the short-term portfolio is as short as 30 days and no longer than one year. Long-term bond portfolio: The targeted time horizon for the long-term portfolio is 10 to 20 years. To minimize sensitivity to interest rates, a laddered maturity portfolio is appropriate. This laddered maturity structure represents a pseudo-cash flow matching strategy, in that bonds sequentially mature to meet liquidity needs. Maturing short term bonds are replaced with bonds of maximum maturity within the IPS guidelines. Stock portfolio: The time horizon for the stock portfolio is perpetual. Insurance companies are taxable entities, so attention to dividends versus capital gains is encouraged.
	Liquidity **For the Exam:** Short-term portfolio: Liquidity requirements are high to provide cash as needed to cover liability payments. Long-term bond portfolio: Liquidity required to meet credited rates and net interest margin and can be met from the laddered maturities. Stock portfolio: Liquidity requirements are low and focus is on long-term growth. **Discussion:** Short-term portfolio: Liquidity requirements for this portfolio are high. Access to cash when needed to cover liability payments is paramount. Long-term bond portfolio: Liquidity requirements (i.e., the credited rates and net interest margin) of the long-term portfolio are expected to be met from the laddered maturity schedule inherent in the instruments selected. Periodic income payments generated by instruments in the portfolio can be used to meet shorter term liquidity needs. Stock portfolio: The liquidity requirements for the stock portfolio are low. Liquidity will be provided by the short term portfolio and to a lesser extent, the long-term bond portfolio.

Constraints	**Legal/Regulatory** **For the Exam:** State and NAIC regulations should be considered. **Discussion:** Numerous state regulations and general provisions of the NAIC govern the activities of insurance companies. Therefore, operating divisions should meet with appropriate counsel for advice on regulatory matters. Exam questions are getting more specific; they tend to ask for parts of the objectives and constraints. If asked for the legal/regulatory constraint for an insurance company, this "canned" answer will suffice in addition to anything specifically mentioned in the case (e.g., outstanding lawsuits).
	Taxes **For the Exam:** State and federal taxes apply so investments should be considered on an after-tax basis. **Discussion:** Operations are taxable at both the state and federal level. Within risk objectives, investments in instruments that generate the highest after-tax total return are encouraged.
	Unique Considerations **For the Exam:** None. **Discussion:** *Professor's Note: No unique circumstances are apparent in the case. An answer of "none" would suffice because even though UniLife finds itself facing steep competition, this is not unique to UniLife. Had UniLife faced a large, uncertain loss due to pending litigation, however, that would be considered specific to UniLife and should be listed as a unique circumstance.*

Sample Scoring Key:
A. 2 points for each of the three portfolio segment return objectives and 2 points for each of the three portfolio segment risk objectives.
B. 2 points for each of the three time horizons, 2 points for each of the three liquidity constraints, and 2 points each for the legal, tax, and unique consideration statements.

QUESTION 3

Source: Study Session 3, LOS 8.c., 8.d, and 9.d

Answer for Question 3

Statement	Behavioral Concept	Explanation
Meriwether: "One of our clients has experienced a change in management and is now willing to accept more risk in hopes of generating higher returns. They want to start thinking outside the box and are now open to strategies they haven't used before, such as short selling. Specifically, they want to short sell a large, popular foreign equity index. I suggested that they wait for a short period of time, because the index's weekly returns for the last four weeks have been below the long-run average weekly return, and I am expecting a correction before the index starts falling again."	Gambler's fallacy	For the Exam: Expects short-term reversion to mean based on small amount of data.
Allen: "One of my pension clients has well over 1,000 employees participating in their defined contribution plan. I have been trying over the last year to get them to educate their employees about the need to reallocate their portfolios as circumstances change. Some of the employees have had their plan portfolios for over two decades, and they have not made any significant changes to the portfolio allocation or even the way they want new contributions allocated."	Status quo bias	For the Exam: Do nothing strategy.
Parker: "One of my clients is exactly the opposite. He is quite young and has inherited a large sum of money. Even though he has little investment experience and doesn't know much about portfolio theory, he is quite willing to make investments or even change his allocation based on small amounts of information. I can't tell you how many times he has said that he heard a Wall Street talk show person say this or that and it really resonated with him, so it made sense."	Availability bias	For the Exam: Basing decisions on resonating information.

Discussion:

Gambler's fallacy is the expectation of reversion to the mean more frequently than would be expected, based on short-term information. In other words, the index should not be expected to revert to its mean performance simply based on a few months' data. This can be related to the gambler who has experienced a run of "bad cards" and feels that he is due to receive a good hand. Rather than quit and accept his losses, he continues to play and even increases his bets. Another example is tossing a coin, for which the odds of heads or tails on any given toss is 50%. Over a very large number of tosses, we would expect to see heads and tails split about evenly. If in the short run, ten to twenty tosses for example, we see a run of 90% tails, that does not imply that the probability of heads on the next toss is greater than 50%.

Status quo bias is often exhibited by participants in defined contribution pension plans. Their failure to make changes to the portfolio allocation or even to the allocation of new contributions can result from a lack of investment knowledge or simply laziness. Perceiving the cognitive cost too high, participants might not evaluate their changing personal circumstances or the even different funds in the plan. The result is that they tend to make an initial allocation and then do nothing. The result is changing portfolio risk and return characteristics and not making potentially value-enhancing decisions.

The *availability bias* refers to individuals basing decisions on the available information. It can be caused by retrievability, categorization, a narrow range of experiences, and resonance. Retrievability refers to the ease that an experience or idea can be retrieved from memory. Individuals tend to classify information based on their own experiences and how easily the experiences can be recalled. Categorization is similar. Individuals are more likely to categorize information into categories with which they are most familiar. Narrow range of experience is exactly what it says. The narrower the individual's range of experiences, the fewer the number of categories into which new information can be classified. Resonance (specifically mentioned here) refers to classifying information or investments according to what resonates with your way of thinking. Individuals will be more likely to react to information that resonates with their thinking. If they are bullish on a sector (for whatever personal reason) and an analyst recommends that sector, they will be likely to follow the analyst's recommendation even though several others recommend against the sector.

Sample Scoring Key: 3 points for discussing each behavioral concept.
1 point for proper identification of each behavioral concept.
2 points for explaining each behavioral concept, but only if identification is correct.
0 points possible if identification is wrong.

QUESTION 4

Source: Study Session 18, LOS 43.d,e,g,h,i,l

Answer for Question 4

Knight's statements	Accurate/inaccurate representation of CFA Institute GIPS (circle one)	Reason(s) for inaccuracy
"All composites will have the same beginning and ending annual dates. We will apply accrual accounting to all interest accruing assets in our portfolios. Starting 2010 we will calculate time-weighted returns on the date of all large external cash flows. All discretionary, fee-paying portfolios will be included in at least one composite and composites will be defined according to investment strategy, mandate, and/or objectives."	Accurate	**For the Exam:** Not required. **Discussion:** These statements come directly from the GIPS standards. Starting January 1, 2005, until January 1, 2010, time-weighted returns that approximate the daily cash flows are acceptable. Starting January 1, 2010, time-weighted returns based on the date of all large external cash flows are required.
"My firm is approximately seven years old. Since GIPS only requires five years of annual investment performance, I can easily meet that requirement. Since my reporting systems are so effective, I also will have no problem maintaining the 5-year reporting requirement into the future."	Inaccurate	**For the Exam:** Five years is minimum report (unless the firm is less than five years old). Must add additional year each year until at least ten compliant years reported. **Discussion:** GIPS requires at least five years of compliance, or from firm inception. Each year the firm must add an additional year until at least ten compliant years are reported.

"My effective electronic systems will have no trouble capturing and maintaining cost and market values for portfolio valuations. My system automatically generates return information every quarter and, for my international composites, uses the same exchange rate sources for the portfolios and the benchmark."	Inaccurate	**For the Exam:** Portfolio returns must be calculated monthly. **Discussion:** Beginning January 1, 2001, portfolios must be valued at least monthly. Beginning January 1, 2010, at least monthly and on the date of all large external cash flows. Beginning January 1, 2006, composite returns must be calculated at least quarterly using asset-weighted portfolio returns. Beginning January 1, 2010, composite returns must be calculated at least monthly. Beginning January 1, 2011, firms must utilize *fair value* concepts in valuing composites, where fair value is defined as the price at which an asset would be exchanged between willing, knowledgeable participants in an arm's length transaction. If fair value is not available, firms should use the observed price of an identical asset in an active market on the transaction day. Otherwise, the value must represent the firm's best estimate. Firms must also comply with local laws and regulations pertaining to valuation, and disclose the presence and nature of any conflict with GIPS valuation principles. Beginning January 1, 2011, firms must state if they use subjective portfolio value inputs, if the portfolio is material to the overall value of the composite, and must disclose any material changes in the composite valuation methodology. The valuation methodology, including the hierarchy, should be applied on a composite-specific basis, as appropriate.
"All of my fee-paying portfolios will be included in at least one composite. When clients decide they no longer need my services, my system automatically recalculates previous portfolio performance to reflect the removal of the portfolios from relevant historical performance presentations."	Inaccurate	**For the Exam:** Composite performance should reflect the historical performance of removed portfolios. **Discussion:** All fee-paying discretionary portfolios need to be included in at least one composite. When clients ask for their funds, however, prior portfolio performance should not be adjusted for the removal of the portfolio.

Sample Scoring Key:
1 point for proper selection of accurate or inaccurate.
2 points for reason(s) provided, but only if accurate/inaccurate choice is correct.
0 points possible if accurate/inaccurate decision is wrong.

QUESTION 5

Source: Study Session 11, LOS 27.i,l,r,s,u

A. **For the Exam:**

Your objective in this type of question would be to provide the calculations as shown below (without our accompanying verbiage). You should show your work on the exam in case you make a mathematical mistake. This provides you with the potential for receiving partial credit if your process for calculating the answer is correct.

Discussion:

The expected active return and risk for this subset of managers is determined using the allocations to the managers. Note that to calculate the portfolio active risk, we assume that the correlations between the managers' active returns are zero. Note that active return and active risk are labeled alpha and tracking risk in the table.

The expected active return is calculated as a weighted average:

expected active portfolio return = $(0.10 \times 2.8\%) + (0.20 \times 0\%) + (0.25 \times 2\%) +$
$(0.05 \times 3.5\%) + (0.40 \times 1.1\%) = 1.40\%$

The expected active risk is calculated as:

portfolio active risk
$$= \sqrt{(0.10)^2(0.052)^2 + (0.20)^2(0)^2 + (0.25)^2(0.031)^2 + (0.05)^2(0.068)^2 + (0.40)^2(0.0162)^2}$$
$$= \sqrt{0.000141} = 0.01187 = 1.19\%$$

The investor's expected information ratio is 1.40% / 1.19% = 1.18.

Sample Scoring Key:
3 points for the calculation of the expected active return.
4 points for the calculation of the expected active risk.
2 points for the calculation of the information ratio.

Answer for Question 5-B

Comment	Correct or incorrect? (circle one)	Explanation
"From your data it appears that your core investment is Hoke associates. Hoke should mitigate the overall risk of your strategy, while the four satellites should provide an active return component."	Incorrect	**For the Exam:** Hoke Associates and Wrightsville Managers constitute the 60% core. **Discussion:** Hoke's expected 0% active return indicates a passive indexing style. Wrightsville Managers utilizes an enhanced indexing style, which is not classified as active management, so Wrightsville is also part of the core. The strategy behind a core and satellite approach entails using indexed and/or enhanced indexed portfolios as a core to generate a fairly stable return. The satellites are actively managed portfolios and can have both a true active return (alpha) and risk (tracking error) and misfit active return and risk. The strategy in a core-satellite approach is attaining a fairly stable return (managed within desired risk parameters) and adding potential for added return through active management of the satellites.
"The portfolio of Diamond Management is likely weighted towards utility and financial stocks."	Correct	**For the Exam:** Value managers tend to have greater representation in the utility and financial industries. **Discussion:** Because Diamond Management is value-oriented, it is likely to have greater representation in the utility and financial industries. These industries typically have higher dividend yields and lower valuations. Growth managers tend to have higher weights in the technology and health care industries because these industries often have higher growth.

"I expect that investors who pursue an investment approach similar to Hoke Associates will generally have higher information ratios than other investment approaches."	**Incorrect**	**For the Exam:** Enhanced indexing usually has the highest information ratios. Hoke Associates is using a passive investment strategy. **Discussion:** Hoke Associates is using a passive investment strategy approach, Wrightsville is using an enhanced indexing (also known as semiactive) approach, and the other managers are using active approaches. Generally, semiactive managers have the highest information ratios. That is also the case in this specific example. The expected information ratio (active return divided by active risk) for Wrightsville is $1.10 / 1.62 = 0.68$, the highest of the managers.
"We should carefully monitor the style of SRI Advisors because they likely have a bias towards value stocks, given their investment emphasis."	**Incorrect**	**For the Exam:** SRI uses a socially responsible investing approach, which is usually tilted towards growth and small-cap stocks. **Discussion:** SRI Advisors uses a socially responsible investing approach, which typically excludes basic industries and energy companies. These industries tend toward value stocks, so socially responsible portfolios are usually tilted toward growth stocks. They also usually have a bias towards small-cap stocks. Investors should, however, monitor style biases from socially responsible investing so the appropriate benchmark can be chosen and so that unintended style biases can be curtailed.

Sample Scoring Key:
1 point for identifying whether the statement is correct or incorrect.
2 points for the explanation of why each is correct or incorrect.

Answer for Question 5-C

Comment	Correct or incorrect? (circle one)	Explanation
"Our proposed plan should contain high water mark provisions. These provisions state that managers will be paid no less than a certain amount during bear markets. This will prevent us from losing good managers during market downturns and, at the same time, help us avoid paying excess performance fees."	Incorrect	**For the Exam:** High water mark provisions require a manager to recoup underperformance in previous years before they receive future performance-based fees. **Discussion:** Dumas is inaccurate regarding her description of high water mark provisions. High water mark provisions require a manager to generate excess returns above underperformance in previous years before they receive their performance-based fee this year. The inclusion of high water mark provisions facilitates symmetric compensation (rewards for good performance and punishment for bad performance), which increases the incentive for the manager to generate excess returns.
"Your proposal to cap performance fees is illogical. The cap would discourage your managers from taking the risks necessary to obtain higher returns. Rather than aligning the managers' goals with your own, this could have a very negative effect."	Incorrect	**For the Exam:** Fee caps are used to discourage managers from taking too much risk and to align the managers' goals with the sponsor (investors). **Discussion:** Performance-based fees are a common component of the total fees paid to portfolio managers. They are usually included as an incentive for managers to pursue alpha-generating strategies, rather than rely solely on an assets-under-management (AUM) fee. AUM fees are based on the size of the portfolio, where performance fees are based on performance. The proportion of total fees represented by the two components depends on the managers' track record and the size of the portfolio (which tend to be highly positively correlated). Generally, the better the track record, the larger the portfolio, and the smaller the AUM fee as a proportion of total fees. That is, the better the track record and the larger the portfolio, the more the manager is willing to accept a small AUM fee and a larger performance-based fee. Note, however, that performance fees provide an incentive for the manager to take greater and greater risks in the hopes of generating larger and larger performance fees. In response, investors and sponsors tend to place caps on the overall performance fee. Since the manager no longer has unbounded fee potential, he will take only the risk necessary to maximize portfolio performance and resulting fees. Since the cap is jointly established by the manager and the sponsor, the cap effectively aligns the interests of the two.

Sample Scoring Key:
1 point for identifying whether the statement is correct or incorrect.
2 points for the explanation of why each is correct or incorrect.
0 points possible if correct/incorrect decision is wrong.

QUESTION 6

Source: Study Session 17, LOS 41.k,l

For the Exam:

A. Pure sector allocation effect:

$$R_{agric,PS} = \left(w_{agric,P} - w_{agric,B}\right)\left(R_{agric,B} - R_B\right)$$
$$= (0.1055 - 0.0645)(0.0135 - 0.0056)$$
$$= (0.041)(0.0079) = 0.000323 = 0.032\%$$

B. Within-sector selection effect:

$$R_{agric,WS} = w_{agric,B}\left(R_{agric,P} - R_{agric,B}\right)$$
$$= 0.0645\left[-0.0082 - (0.0135)\right]$$
$$= 0.0645(-0.0217) = -0.001399 = -0.14\%$$

C. Allocation-selection effect:

$$R_{agric,AS} = \left(w_{agric,P} - w_{agric,B}\right)\left(R_{agric,P} - R_{agric,B}\right)$$
$$= (0.1055 - 0.0645)(-0.0082 - 0.0135)$$
$$= (0.041)(-0.0217) = -0.000889 = -0.09\%$$

Discussion:

The pure sector allocation effect measures the ability of the manager to identify sectors that will out-perform and over-weight them in the portfolio (relative to the benchmark). When the manager over-weights an out-performing sector or under-weights an underperforming sector, the effect is positive. Roberts added 3.2 bps by over-weighting an out-performing sector.

The within-sector selection effect (a.k.a. security selection effect or selection effect) measures the manager's ability to identify and select superior securities (relative to those in the benchmark) to represent each sector. When the manager is able to do this, the sector return in the portfolio is greater than the same sector return in the benchmark. Roberts lost 14 bps by selecting different securities to represent the agriculture sector in his portfolio than those in the benchmark.

The allocation/selection effect (a.k.a. allocation/selection interaction effect) measures the combination of the manager's ability to identify superior securities in each sector and his ability to over- or under-weight sectors according to their expected performance. Note that the weight of a sector in the portfolio is affected by the manager's feelings about the overall sector as well as individual securities in the sector. Over-weighting expected outperformers and under-weighting expected underperformers may not offset each other and hence the portfolio weight for the sector can end up different from the benchmark. In other words, the manager can overweight a sector in the portfolio by simply holding more of the same securities as held by the benchmark or by changing the selection and weighting of individual securities in the sector. The combination of over-weighting the agriculture sector with Roberts' selection of under-performing securities in the agriculture sector produced a negative allocation/selection effect.

When you see a question like this on the exam, look at the numbers quickly to get an overall impression of the how the manager's return relative to the benchmark was produced. For example, by comparing the return for the agriculture sector in the benchmark to the overall benchmark return, you know that agriculture outperformed over the period. Since the manager over-weighted the sector in the portfolio, you know his pure sector allocation effect must be positive. He must have generated excess return (alpha) by over-weighting the agriculture sector.

Likewise, you know by comparing the manager's agriculture sector return (i.e., the agriculture sector return in the portfolio) to the agriculture sector return in the benchmark, that the manager's within-sector selection effect must be negative.

The allocation-selection (AS) interaction effect is harder to judge by simply looking at the data. This return measures the overall impact on the portfolio return of changing the weights of the sectors and selecting different securities to represent the sectors. The AS effect is positive only when the two effects have the same sign. For example, if he over-weights a sector in which he has selected out-performers, the AS effect is positive. Likewise, if he under-weights a sector in which he selects poorly, the AS effect is positive. Anytime the signs are different, as in this case, the effect is negative. Roberts over-weighted the sector but selected poorly (i.e., negative selection effect).

Sample Scoring Key:
2 points for each correct equation.
2 points for each successful calculation.
2 points for each correct explanation.

QUESTION 7

Source: Study Session 5, LOS 16.c
Study Session 9, LOS 23.j
Study Session 10, LOS 25.d,e
Study Session 15, LOS 37.c

A. **For the Exam:**

    i.   Buy the interest rate puts.

    ii.   A decrease in interest rates results in higher values of the puts, which helps offset the higher value of the liabilities.

    iii.   The present value of the liabilities (pension obligations) is based on long-term rates while interest rate puts are written on short-term rates, so this is probably not the preferred strategy.

Discussion:

The present value of plan liabilities increases as interest rates decrease. Exchange-traded interest rate put options will increase in value if rates decline below the put strike rate. The increased value of the put will offset to some extent an increase in plan liabilities.

The payoff to an interest rate put is calculated as:

payoff = notional principal [max (0, strike rate – LIBOR)(D/360)]

As interest rates (e.g., LIBOR) fall, the payoff increases.

The premium paid to purchase the interest rate put could be thought of as an insurance premium. The insurance (i.e., payoff from the put) offers protection against even greater funding requirements from the plan sponsor if interest rates fall in the future.

Note: Some might argue for the sale of interest rate call options to generate income (i.e., premiums). If interest rates should increase, however, the calls would go in the money at the same time that liabilities (inflation-indexed pension payments) increase.

The main disadvantage to the put strategy, and the reason it is not recommended, is that exchange-traded interest rate options are on short-term interest rates, whereas the liabilities of the plan have a long duration. If the short end of the yield curve does not fall, while the long end does, the strategy provides no protection, and they are out the premium. For this reason, they will not necessarily achieve the stated goals. In other words, the potential remains for the underfunding of the plan to worsen.

B. **For the Exam:**

    i.   Buy call options on Treasury bonds.

    ii.   A decrease in interest rates results in a higher value of the calls which helps offset the higher present value of the liabilities.

    iii.   The duration of the liabilities should be similar to that of the hedge and unlike going long in Treasury bond futures, the option does not result in losses if interest rates increase as expected, so this is the preferred hedge.

Discussion:

Purchasing call options on Treasury bonds is the strategy that will most likely achieve the stated goals. Call options on long maturity bonds will spread the cash flows on the underlying over the yield curve to best match the liability cash flows, and the duration of the bonds can be matched to the duration of the liabilities. This should offer a fairly good hedge against future funding requirements arising from a downward shift of the yield curve. This strategy provides the best protection against further underfunding of the plan, because it also does not result in losses (except for the cost of the option premium) if interest rates increase as expected.

Since exchange-traded Treasury bond options are thinly traded, these call options will likely be OTC options so counterparty risk is a concern. If exchange traded options are used, the terms will not be as flexible as OTC options, and they may have to be rolled over. OTC options are less liquid and more expensive. American style options would offer some flexibility.

C.   **For the Exam:**

i.   Go long Treasury bond futures.

ii.   A decrease in interest rates results in a higher value of the Treasury bond futures, which helps offset the higher value of the liabilities.

iii. However, an increase in interest rates would produce losses, so this is not the preferred hedge. The option in Part B provides flexibility that the Treasury bond futures does not.

Discussion:

A long position in Treasury bond futures will hedge the risk of increasing liabilities due to interest rate decreases, and the duration and cash flow arguments from above support this. The use of futures, however, is inappropriate because they also hedge upward shifts in the yield curve. If rates rise (as they expect), Matrix will have losses (and negative cash flows from marking to market) on the futures position.

In other words, Matrix prefers an asymmetric hedge, (i.e., one that only hedges against falling interest rates). With the option in Part B, an asymmetric hedge, the put provides protection when interest rates fall. If interest rates rise as expected, however, Matrix lets the option expire worthless.

Sample Scoring Key:
A. 3 points for describing the purchase of puts, 3 points for rejecting the strategy because the puts are on short term rates.
B. 3 points for buying call options on Treasury bonds, 3 points for recommending the strategy because a good duration/cash flow match is possible.
C. 3 points for buying the futures and the duration match argument, 3 points for rejecting the strategy because of the poor outcome if their expectation of rising rates turns out to be true.

QUESTION 8

Source: Study Session 4, LOS 10.n

Answer for Question 8

Statement	Agree or disagree (circle one)	Explanation
"Since all has gone according to plan since our first meeting a year ago, I think it is time we focus efforts on your retirement. The most important objective is to determine an exact future value goal for your portfolio, integrating an expected rate of return, inflation, and your tax position to produce your retirement profile."	Disagree	**For the Exam:** • Single estimates do not account for the range of potential outcomes. • Investors need to see the range of potential outcomes so that they understand the risks involved. **Discussion:** Although single (deterministic) estimates of retirement portfolio value are useful as a starting point, they are not the most important objective in retirement planning because they do not account for the probabilistic nature of future outcomes. Portfolio values generated by the deterministic procedures do not allow either the investor or professional to see the range of outcomes that can potentially occur. Hence, single values are not the most informative retirement profile figure. Investors need to see the range of potential outcomes so that they understand the risks involved in retirement planning.

"Once we have generated the single point estimate for the value of your retirement portfolio, we can apply some Monte Carlo techniques to see various other outcomes. Monte Carlo techniques will generate various portfolio values at retirement but, unfortunately, will not account for the risks inherent in our investment decisions. So, we will just have to pay a little more attention to the various portfolio levels."	Disagree	**For the Exam:** Monte Carlo techniques allow managers to use various return and risk assumptions as inputs. **Discussion:** Monte Carlo techniques allow managers to incorporate not only return expectations, but also risk factors such as inflation, changes in interest rates, and the correlation between portfolio assets. Because of the dynamic nature of Monte Carlo simulations, investors not only see potential portfolio values, they also see potential risk situations along the path to retirement. For example, the investment advisor can run a Monte Carlo simulation analysis using a 60/40 allocation to stocks/bonds. The advisor can run it again using a 70/30 allocation. Each simulation will produce its own distribution of returns, given the inputted model assumptions. By comparing the distributions and the associated probabilities of meeting some retirement goal, the Monte Carlo simulations provide a more complete picture of the risk involved with investment decisions.
"Think of the various portfolio levels as a range of potential outcomes your portfolio can achieve in ten years. The primary focus when evaluating those outcomes, however, will still be on the risks you wish to avoid in the present, and not necessarily any risks that may occur along the way."	Disagree	**For the Exam:** Monte Carlo shows the tradeoff between short-term and long-term risk exposures. **Discussion:** One of the most beneficial outcomes of using Monte Carlo in retirement planning is having the ability to see the tradeoff of short-term risk with the risk of not meeting retirement objectives. Although one can focus on short-term risk, seeing the ultimate risk of not meeting retirement goals as well as potential value paths the portfolio could take on the way to retirement are two of the primary benefits of using Monte Carlo. For example, clients may say that they only want to invest in bonds because they think that stocks are too risky. The investment advisor can use Monte Carlo analysis to show the clients that a focus on bonds increases their risk of falling short of the long-term retirement objective.

"Although we can incorporate taxes in our Monte Carlo techniques, the compounding assumptions we made when we calculated the single point estimate of portfolio value are just fine. Compounding does not play that much of a role with Monte Carlo, which simplifies the application of the procedure."	Disagree	**For the Exam:** Monte Carlo does a better job of incorporating the compounding effects of reinvestment, which can have a large impact on future portfolio values. **Discussion:** The compounding assumptions used in the deterministic approach to retirement planning are too simplistic. Monte Carlo does a much better job of incorporating the compounding effects of reinvestment, which can have a large impact on future portfolio values. For example, using an assumed reinvestment rate of 3% will lead to much different terminal values than a 5% reinvestment rate assumption. Or a client who starts using portfolio income for living expenses at age 62 will have a much lower portfolio value to work with than another who waits until age 70.

Professor's Note: This material is drawn from the discussion of Monte Carlo analysis in Study Session 4, Private Wealth Management. Be aware, however, that Monte Carlo analysis is also discussed in Study Session 8, Reading 21, Asset Allocation; and Study Session 14, Reading 34, Risk Management. You should be ready to answer a question on it given its frequency of appearance in the curriculum.

Sample Scoring Key:
1 point for correctly agreeing or disagreeing.
2 points for justification.
0 points possible if agree/disagree decision is wrong.

QUESTION 9

Source: Study Session 6, LOS 18.h,o,p,q
Study Session 7, LOS 19.e,g

Answer for Question 9-A

Comment	Correct or incorrect? (circle one)	Explanation, if incorrect
"Using the Taylor rule, I expect the Canadian central bank to target an interest rate of about 6.0%."	Incorrect	**For the Exam:** Your objective in this type of question would be to provide the calculations as shown below (without our accompanying verbiage). You should show your work on the exam in case you make a mathematical mistake. This provides you with the potential for receiving partial credit if your process for calculating the answer is correct. **Discussion:** Given this information, the interest rate the central bank should target using the Taylor rule is: $r_{target} = 4.0\% + [0.5 \times (6.5\% - 4.5\%) + 0.5 \times (7.5\% - 3.5\%)]$ $= 4.0\% + [1.0\% + 2.0\%] = 7.0\%$ The higher than targeted growth and higher than targeted inflation argue for a targeted interest rate of 7%. This rate is intended to slow down the economy and inflation.
"Based on the information I have gathered, we should be advising clients interested in the Canadian economy to invest in Canadian cash instruments, rather than stocks or bonds."	Correct	**For the Exam:** Not required. **Discussion:** Hoey's advice is correct because when expected inflation is high (here 7.5%), the return on cash instruments increases and it is likely that the central bank will raise rates to curb inflation. The return on cash instruments will increase as the bank's targeted rate increases. Although stocks can sometimes provide an inflation hedge, prices often fall when the central bank raises rates, as is predicted here. Inflation above 3% can be negative for stocks, because it increases the likelihood that the central bank will raise rates. Bonds are a poor inflation hedge and are adversely affected by increases in interest rates.

Sample Scoring Key:
1 point for identifying whether the statement is correct or incorrect.
2 points for the explanation if incorrect.
0 points possible if correct/incorrect decision is wrong.

Answer for Question 9-B

Comment	Correct or incorrect? (circle one)	Explanation, if incorrect
"The European Central Bank has been cutting interest rates. One potential impact on the euro is to decrease its value because investors will seek higher returns elsewhere. Unlike most analysts, however, I use a capital flows approach which projects that the euro will actually increase in value."	**Correct**	**For the Exam:** Not required. **Discussion:** Nurnberg is correct in stating that in a capital flows approach, the euro would actually increase in value. In this approach, it is the flow of long-term funds that influences the value of a currency. Under this approach, a cut in interest rates could stimulate the European economy, which would result in higher stock returns, thus making Europe a more attractive place to invest. This process would increase the value of the euro.
"Short-term interest rates on government bonds in Great Britain are 3.2% and 10-year rates are 5.9%. This indicates that, for an investor considering investing in Britain, British corporate bonds would be a better investment than British stocks."	**Incorrect**	**For the Exam:** The yield curve is upward sloping, indicating that the economy will expand. This is more favorable for stock investments. **Discussion:** Nurnberg is incorrect. Given the stated interest rates, the yield curve in Britain is upward sloping, and the upward-sloping yield curve indicates that the British economy is likely to expand in the future. When an economy expands, stocks are typically better investments than bonds. Stocks benefit from the increased business activity. Inflation and interest rates often increase in an expansion, resulting in decreased bond prices. Relationships between asset prices and returns, inflation, stages of the business cycle, and shapes of the yield curve are important for the exam.

"Mexico's largest trading partner is the United States. Given that the United States is in the early stages of an economic expansion, Mexican stocks would be attractive investments."	**Correct**	**For the Exam:** Not required. **Discussion:** Nurnberg is correct. The returns for emerging market stocks are positively correlated with the business cycles of developed economies. The correlation is due to trade and capital flows between countries. If the United States is in an early expansion, Mexican businesses and stocks should benefit from the increased economic activity.
"Economists project that in the coming months, business confidence in Japan will increase. The Bank of Japan will continue to accommodate growth by keeping interest rates low. Japanese government spending will increase as Japan puts a renewed emphasis on defense spending. Inflation in Japan will fall or remain stable. Given this outlook, I suggest that for an investor with a time horizon of a few years, an allocation to Japanese bonds is warranted."	**Incorrect**	**For the Exam:** Japan is in the initial recovery phase, which is followed by the early expansion phase with rising interest rates. Bonds are poor investments while stocks do better in these phases. **Discussion:** Nurnberg is incorrect. The scenario of increasing business confidence, low interest rates, increased government spending, and falling inflation is consistent with the initial recovery phase of an economy. This phase of the economy usually lasts a few months and is typically followed by the early expansion phase, which usually lasts a year to several years. In both these phases, stock prices increase while bonds are stagnant or falling in price. Thus, an investor with a time horizon of a few years should be invested in Japanese stocks.

Sample Scoring Key:
1 point for identifying whether the statement is correct or incorrect.
2 points for the explanation if incorrect.
0 points possible if correct/incorrect decision is wrong.

C.   Using the Cobb-Douglas production function restated in terms of percentage change:

$$\%\Delta Y = \%\Delta A + \alpha(\%\Delta K) + (1-\alpha)(\%\Delta L) = 2.0\% + 0.35(1.0\%) + 0.65(3.5\%) = 4.625\%$$

> Sample Scoring Key: 3 points for correct answer or 1 point each for up to two correct components of the formula.

D.   The Solow residual is the estimate of the change in total factor productivity, TFP, given the expected growth in labor and capital as well as the expected rate of change in economic output:

$$\%\Delta Y = \%\Delta A + \alpha(\%\Delta K) + (1-\alpha)(\%\Delta L)$$

$$\text{Solow residual} = \%\Delta TFP = \%\Delta Y - \alpha(\%\Delta K) - (1-\alpha)\%\Delta L$$
$$= 3.5\% - 0.6(1.5\%) - 0.4(2.5\%) = 1.60\%$$

> Sample Scoring Key: 3 points for correct answer or 1 point each for up to two correct components of the formula.

E.   Use the constant growth dividend discount model to estimate the intrinsic level of the market index:

$$P_0 = \frac{D_1}{r-g} = \frac{D_0(1+g)}{r-g} = \frac{100(1.021)}{0.075-0.021} = \frac{102.10}{0.054} = 1{,}890.7$$

The estimated intrinsic level of the index is 1,891. At its current level of 2,050 the index is overvalued. Nurnberg appears to be correct.

> Sample Scoring Key: 3 points for correct index level and 1 point for agreeing with Nurnberg.

Exam 1
Afternoon Session Answers

To get detailed answer explanations with references to specific LOS and SchweserNotes content, and to get valuable feedback on how your score compares to those of other Level III candidates, use your Username and Password to gain Online Access at *www.schweser.com* and choose the left-hand menu item "Practice Exams Vol. 2."

1.	B	25.	A	49.	B
2.	B	26.	C	50.	C
3.	A	27.	A	51.	C
4.	B	28.	A	52.	A
5.	C	29.	B	53.	B
6.	A	30.	C	54.	B
7.	A	31.	B	55.	C
8.	C	32.	B	56.	B
9.	A	33.	B	57.	C
10.	A	34.	C	58.	C
11.	C	35.	A	59.	C
12.	C	36.	B	60.	B
13.	C	37.	B		
14.	C	38.	B		
15.	B	39.	A		
16.	C	40.	C		
17.	B	41.	A		
18.	C	42.	C		
19.	B	43.	A		
20.	C	44.	B		
21.	B	45.	C		
22.	C	46.	B		
23.	C	47.	B		
24.	C	48.	A		

Exam 1
Afternoon Session Answers

QUESTIONS 1–6

Source: Study Session 1

1. **B** Standard II(B) Market Manipulation prohibits members and candidates from misleading investors through manipulated securities prices or volume. BIC's principals have suggested to Bair that she artificially inflate the Horizon Fund's price to alter the market's perception of demand for the fund and mislead investors. A "pump priming" strategy is one that is intended to increase trading volume due to some other action taken, such as temporarily lowering commission costs. This is not a violation of the Code and Standards as long as it is fully disclosed to investors. Even though Blair may delegate supervisory duties to a compliance officer, it does not relieve Blair of making sure laws, rules, regulations, firm policies, and the Code and Standards are being followed. (Study Session 1, LOS 1.b)

2. **B** Standard I(A) Knowledge of the Law requires members and candidates to know and comply with rules, laws, and regulations that apply to their professional activities. If there is a conflict, members and candidates are expected to adhere to the stricter of applicable laws, rules, and regulations or the Code and Standards. Because the Horizon Fund is located in Holland, which does not allow crossing trades (a law that is stricter than the Code and Standards), the fund is not allowed to utilize such a practice even for clients that live in countries with less strict regulations. Thus, the policy for clients in Norway violates Standard I(A). In the case of the policy for clients located in Denmark, no violation has occurred since the fund is going to comply with Denmark's law, which is stricter than the Code and Standards. (Study Session 1, LOS 1.b)

3. **A** According to Standard III(B) Fair Dealing, members and candidates are allowed to offer different levels of service but must offer all levels of service to all clients and must disclose the existence of different levels of service to all clients and prospects. By not disclosing the levels of service to Swedish investors, Bair is adhering to local law, which is less strict than the Code and Standards and thus is in violation of Standard I(A) Knowledge of the Law, which requires she adhere to the stricter of the two. She also violated Standard III(B) by not disclosing the service levels. (Study Session 1, LOS 1.b)

4. **B** According to Standard II(A) Material Nonpublic Information, it is appropriate procedure for the member or candidate who possesses material nonpublic information to first attempt to have the subject company disclose the information publicly themselves. If this is not possible, then the appropriate supervisor and/or compliance officer should be made aware of the situation. (Study Session 1, LOS 1.b)

5. **C** Standard II(A) Material Nonpublic Information prohibits trading on material nonpublic information in all situations. The investment bankers should have known that the information was material and nonpublic and have thus violated Standard II(A) by trading on the information. (Study Session 1, LOS 1.b)

6. A   The large earnings restatement is certainly material information. Disclosing the
        information before the conference call does not make the information public even if
        several analysts overheard the information. Disclosing the information to her compliance
        officer also does not make the information public. Therefore, Bair has traded on the
        basis of material nonpublic information and is in violation of Standard II(A).
        (Study Session 1, LOS 1.b)

Sample Scoring Key: 3 points for each correct response.

QUESTIONS 7–12

Source: Study Session 1

7.   **A**   Mackley has appropriately disclosed the referral arrangement to clients and prospects but the nature of the arrangement itself is a violation of Standard VII(A) Conduct as Members and Candidates in the CFA Program. According to this Standard, members and candidates are prohibited from activities that compromise the integrity of CFA Institute. Mackley has misused her authority to select companies to make presentations to her local society. She only selects Kern & Associates to make presentations and excludes their competitors in order to generate referrals for her business. This reflects poorly on the local society and CFA Institute. Mackley may have also violated Standard I(D) Misconduct by engaging in behavior that reflects poorly on her professional reputation. (Study Session 1, LOS 1.b)

8.   **C**   Welch violated Standard V(C) Record Retention by failing to maintain adequate records to support his investment recommendations. In the absence of other regulation, CFA Institute recommends keeping such records for a minimum of seven years. Certainly, one week is not an adequate record retention policy. Mackley violated Standard III(C) Suitability by purchasing the stock for all clients with a net worth greater than $6 million. It does not matter that the clients are later happy with the stock performance. Mackley should have evaluated the stock purchase for all of her accounts, not just the larger ones, in terms of each account's objectives and constraints as stated in their investment policy statements. (Study Session 1, LOS 1.b)

9.   **A**   According to Standard IV(B) Additional Compensation Arrangements, members and candidates are not to accept additional compensation (monetary or non-monetary) unless they obtain written consent from all parties, including their employer. The promised future use of the condo creates a conflict of interest because it represents an incentive for Mackley to place undue focus on that client's account. Thus, it must be disclosed to the employer and written consent must be obtained from the employer. Standard I(B) Independence and Objectivity notes that client gifts must be disclosed to the employer and should be disclosed before being accepted. (Study Session 1, LOS 1.b)

10. **A**   According to Standard VII(B) Reference to CFA Institute, the CFA Designation, and the CFA Program, proper use of the designation would stipulate that CFA and Chartered Financial Analyst always be used as adjectives. Also, the designation may not be written in bold type, so that it is more prominent than the rest of the name.
(Study Session 1, LOS 1.b)

11. **C**   Mackley violated Standard VII(B) Reference to CFA Institute, the CFA Designation, and the CFA Program by linking her future investment performance to her status as a CFA charterholder. Mackley has not, however, violated the standard with her references to the CFA program and the examinations. Mackley also violated Standard V(B), which requires separating fact from opinion, with her statement about client satisfaction. (Study Session 1, LOS 1.b)

12. **C**   According to Standard III(E) Preservation of Confidentiality, Mackley has a duty to keep information about her clients confidential, unless it involves illegal activities, in which case she may need to disclose the information to her supervisor, compliance officer, or regulatory authorities as is appropriate. She should not have divulged the inheritance to an outside contractor, especially since that individual has contacts with other management firms. (Study Session 1, LOS 1.b)

> Sample Scoring Key: 3 points for each correct response.

QUESTIONS 13–18

Source: Study Sessions 5 and 18

13. **C** Firm B and Firm C both have a plan surplus. Both Firm A and Firm D are underfunded by $160 million, which represents 11% for A and over 18% for D.

    Pension plan liabilities are similar to debt securities in that their present values fluctuate with interest rates. Plan D has only 25% of assets invested in fixed income securities. (75% in equities), so the plan assets of Firm D are sensitive to the systematic risk of equity markets to a greater degree than those of the other firms. (Study Session 5, LOS 17.a)

14. **C** Both of the statements have correct and incorrect portions, so the answer is C, neither is correct. Rose starts off with a correct statement, when he says that pension assets should be included in the firm's overall weighted average cost of capital (WACC). Since we use asset betas, however, the WACC usually decreases when we calculate the firm's overall WACC. The equity securities held as assets by the pension plan can have an average beta that is higher than the beta of the sponsoring firm's assets. However, the weighted average asset beta for the plan, assuming debt securities have zero betas, is usually less than that for the sponsoring firm's operating assets, so combining the firm's and plan's assets usually produces a lower WACC.

    Boatman also starts out with a true statement when he says that pension plans usually hold long term bonds to match their pension liabilities. However, it is the proportion of equity securities in the plan's assets that drives the risk of the plan assets, not the proportion of debt (fixed income). The rest of his statements are correct. (Study Session 5, LOS 17.b)

15. **B** Scenario B is the most likely scenario. Using an expanded balance sheet format, it can be seen that as pension plan risk increases, so does the total asset beta.

    Under the assumption that the firm would like to keep its cost of equity capital constant, the firm must make changes in its capital structure on the right hand side of the balance sheet to accommodate the pension plan's increased allocation to equity. More specifically, to keep the equity beta constant, the firm must reduce its risk to its shareholders by reducing its financial leverage (debt). Thus it must use more equity capital, thereby decreasing its debt-to-equity ratio. (Study Session 5, LOS 17.c)

16. **C** To obtain the capital and income return, we must first calculate the capital employed (C_E), which utilizes the capital at the beginning of the period (C_0), the capital contribution, and the capital disbursement. If the capital contribution came at 0.52 into the quarter, then the manager had use of those funds for 0.48 of the quarter. We weight the capital contribution of $2,300,000 by this portion.

    If the capital disbursement came at 0.74 into the quarter, then the manager lost use of these funds for 0.26 of the quarter. We weight the capital disbursement of $850,000 by 0.26 and subtract it as follows.

    $$C_E = C_0 + \sum_{i=1}^{n}(CF_i \times w_i)$$

    $$C_E = \$18,000,000 + \$2,300,000(0.48) - \$850,000(0.26) = \$18,883,000$$

©2011 Kaplan, Inc.

To determine the capital return (R_C), we examine the capital gain or loss, capital expenditures, and sale of properties. Capital expenditures (E_C) are those used for improving a property and are subtracted because they will be reflected in the property's ending value and the manager should not receive credit for this additional value.

The proceeds from the sale of properties (S) are added in because the drop in ending property value from a sale should not be counted against a manager.

Using the provided figures:

$$R_C = \frac{MV_1 - MV_0 - E_C + S}{C_E}$$

$$R_C = \frac{\$20,200,000 - \$19,100,000 - \$1,000,000 + \$1,820,000}{\$18,883,000} = 10.2\%$$

To determine the income return (R_i), we use the investment income (INC) minus the non-recoverable expenses (E_{NR}) minus debt interest (INT_D) minus property taxes (T_P). Essentially we subtract the cost of doing business on a periodic basis from investment income as below.

$$R_i = \frac{INC - E_{NR} - INT_D - T_P}{C_E}$$

$$= \frac{\$58,000 - \$178,000 - \$152,000 - \$219,000}{\$18,883,000} = -2.6\%$$

The total return for the quarter is the sum of the capital return and the income return:

$$R_T = R_C + R_i = 10.2\% - 2.6\% = 7.6\% \text{ (Study Session 18, LOS 43.p)}$$

17. **B**   Statement 2 is correct. Statement 1 is incorrect. Beginning January 1, 2008, real estate portfolios must be valued at least quarterly. However, for periods prior to January 1, 2012, external real estate valuations must be performed at least every 36 months. Beginning 2012, external valuations must be performed at least annually, unless the client agrees to a less frequent valuation, but in no case less frequently than every 36 months. (Study Session 18, LOS 43.p)

18. **C**   Both statements 3 and 4 are correct. (Study Session 18, LOS 43.v)

Sample Scoring Key: 3 points for each correct response.

QUESTIONS 19–24

Source: Study Sessions 9, 10, and 15

19. **B**   Price of bond in one year: N = 19 × 2 = 38; PMT = 7 / 2 = 3.5; I/Y = 8 / 2 = 4; FV = 100; CPT → PV = –90.32

        Value of coupons at end of one year: N = 1 × 2 = 2; PMT = 7 / 2 = 3.5; I/Y = 8 / 2 = 4; PV = 0; CPT → FV = –7.14

        The semiannual return is the rate of return between today and the accumulated value one year from now:

        N = 2; PMT = 0; PV = –100; FV = (90.32 + 7.14) = 97.46; CPT → I/Y = –1.28%

        The bond equivalent yield is –1.28% × 2 = –2.56%. (Study Session 9, LOS 23.e)

20. **C**   In the first sentence of the first statement, two of the three statements are correct. The repo rate is directly related to the maturity of the repo (the repo term) and inversely related to the quality of the collateral. The longer the repo term, the higher the repo rate and as the quality of the collateral increases, the repo rate decreases. Although the maturity of the collateral is considered in determining the quality of the collateral, however, it does not act as a separate factor in determining the repo rate. The last part of the first statement is correct.

        The first sentence in the second statement is correct, but the second sentence is incorrect. If the availability of the collateral is limited, the repo rate will be lower, not higher. Limited availability makes the collateral more valuable due to its scarcity (e.g., callable bonds, long maturity bullets). (Study Session 10, LOS 25.b)

21. **B**   The gross profit on the portfolio is: $200 million × 8% = $16 million.

        The cost of borrowed funds is: $60 million × 3% = $1.8 million.

        The net profit on the portfolio is: $16 million – $1.8 million = $14.2 million.

        The return on the equity invested (i.e., the portfolio) is thus: $14.2 / $140 = 10.14%.

        Alternatively, the problem can be solved using:

$$R_p = R_i + [(B / E) \times (R_i - c)]$$

        where:
        R_p = return on portfolio
        R_i = return on invested assets
        B = amount of leverage
        E = amount of equity invested
        c = cost of borrowed funds

        Using the figures above: 8% + [(60 / 140) × (8% – 3%)] = 10.14%.
        (Study Session 10, LOS 25.a)

22. **C**   The duration is calculated with the following formula:

$$D_p = \frac{D_i I - D_B B}{E}$$

where:
D_p = duration of portfolio
D_i = duration of invested assets
I   = amount of invested funds
B   = amount of leverage
E   = amount of equity invested

Using the values in the problem:

$$D_p = \frac{(7.2)200 - (0.8)60}{140} = 9.9$$

(Study Session 10, LOS 25.a)

23. **C**   Both statements are incorrect. It is true that portfolio managers, especially active managers, complain that using variance and standard deviation to calculate Sharpe ratios biases the results, because the variance includes returns in excess of the hurdle rate (i.e., positive outcomes). The only false part of the first statement is that semi-variance is easy to calculate. Because of the difficulties of calculating all the variances and correlations, neither regular variance nor semi-variance is easily calculated for large bond portfolios.

Although much of the second statement is true, shortfall risk is effectively the flip side of VAR. The output from a VAR calculation is the maximum loss at a given probability. In other words, you specify the probability and VAR provides the amount of loss. With shortfall risk, you provide the amount of loss (or other target amount or return) and shortfall risk provides the probability. They are both deficient in that they do not provide a measure of the magnitude of potential catastrophic losses. To help compensate for this deficiency in VAR, managers sometimes calculate tail value at risk (TVAR) which is VAR plus the expected value in the lower tail. (Study Session 10, LOS 25.c)

24. **C**   Castillo is incorrect. The name of a swaption refers to the fixed arm in the underlying swap. A payer swaption, for example, gives the holder the option of entering a swap as the fixed rate payer. To synthetically refinance Shaifer's fixed rate euro debt of 9.5%, Shaifer should buy a receiver swaption which would give Shaifer the option to enter a swap as pay-floating, receive fixed. If Euribor falls below the swap fixed rate of 7.60%, Shaifer will exercise the swaption and pay the lower floating rate while receiving 7.60%. In net, they would pay Euribor plus 1.9% (9.5% + Euribor − 7.6%). In net, they would pay a floating rate, which would be 7.8% in one year, given the projected Euribor of 5.9% in one year. Note: The terms "receiver" and "payer" refer to the pay fixed arm of the swap. A receiver swaption, therefore, is an option to enter a swap as the receive-fixed counterparty.

So Diaz is incorrect because the effective rate is not 7.5% in one year. In essence, Shaifer has called in the old debt at 9.5% and synthetically refinanced its debt to a floating rate, which will be 7.8% in one year. (Study Session 15, LOS 38.h)

> Sample Scoring Key: 3 points for each correct response.

QUESTIONS 25–30

Source: Study Sessions 9 and 10

25. **A** Truxel is correct as international bond portfolio duration management has been made easier through the increasing availability of fixed income derivatives. Timberlake is also correct in saying that the European Monetary Union has made it easier to rotate across sectors, because there are now more non-governmental bonds available internationally. (Study Session 10, LOS 25.h)

26. **C** Any duration mismatch is considered a large factor mismatch, so Truxel is incorrect. Timberlake is correct as credit analysis is the most important determinant of relative bond performance. (Study Session 9, LOS 23.b)

27. **A** If there is a parallel shift in the yield curve of 60 basis points for Treasury yields, the approximate percent change is the modified duration of the portfolio times 0.6%. The modified duration of the portfolio is a weighted average of the individual sector durations: $(0.12 \times 5.3) + (0.3 \times 5.4) + (0.3 \times 5.5) + (0.28 \times 5.0) = 5.3$. The modified duration of $5.3 \times 0.6\% = 3.2\%$ change in the portfolio value. (Study Session 9, LOS 23.g)

28. **A** The spread durations for non-Treasuries are the same as their effective durations. The calculation and resulting change from a uniform widening of 60 bps in all spreads is the same as if the yield curve had shifted 60 bps with no change in the spreads. (Study Session 9, LOS 23.h)

29. **B** To determine which sector could generate the greatest tracking error, calculate the contribution to the portfolio's duration for each sector and do the same for the index. The sector whose duration contribution deviates the most from the benchmark will contribute the most to potential tracking error. The contribution to duration is the proportion invested in each sector times the sector's duration. For example, for AAA bonds in the portfolio, it is $0.12 \times 5.3 = 0.636$. For AAA bonds in the index, it is $0.35 \times 5.3 = 1.855$. The discrepancy between the portfolio and the index for this sector is $0.636 - 1.855 = -1.219$. This is the largest absolute difference of all the sectors. The calculations for all the sectors are as follows:

	Contribution to Effective Duration		
	Portfolio	Index	Difference
AAA	0.636	1.855	−1.219
AA	1.620	1.620	0.000
A	1.650	1.375	0.275
BBB	1.400	0.500	0.900
TOTAL	5.306	5.350	

(Study Session 9, LOS 23.h)

30. **C**   The following are rationales for trading in the secondary bond market:
    - Yield/spread pickup trades.
    - Credit-upside trades.
    - Credit-defense trades.
    - New issue swaps.
    - Sector-rotation trades.
    - Curve-adjustment trades.
    - Structure trades.
    - Cash flow reinvestment.

    Seasonality is a secondary trading constraint (i.e., reason for not trading).
    (Study Session 10, LOS 24.e)

    Sample Grading Key: 3 points for correct response.

QUESTIONS 31–36

Source: Study Session 10

31. **B** Because interest rates are higher in Great Britain, we know by covered interest rate parity that its currency must trade at a forward discount. To determine the exact forward discount, we calculate a simple percentage change using the formula:

$$f_{d,f} = \frac{F - S_0}{S_0}$$

where:
$f_{d,f}$ = forward premium or discount for currency f relative to d
F = forward rate
S_0 = spot rate

In the formula, be sure to put the currency that you want to make a statement about (whether it is at a premium or discount) in the denominator. Here we are discussing the £.

$$f_{d,f} = \frac{C\$1.60 - C\$1.75}{C\$1.75} = -8.57\%$$

So the British pound is trading at an 8.57% forward discount relative to the Canadian dollar. Note: Since the current 1-year rates in Great Britain and Canada are 11% and 4%, respectively, we would expect the £ to depreciate relative to the \$C.
(Study Session 10, LOS 25.j)

32. **B** Based on current interest rates, the no-arbitrage forward exchange rate (C\$/£) is:

$$F = S_0 \left(\frac{1 + c_d}{1 + c_f} \right) = 1.75 \, C\$/£ \left(\frac{1.04}{1.11} \right) = 1.6396 \, C\$/£$$

where:
F = forward exchange rate, $F_{C\$,£}$
S_0 = spot exchange rate, $S_{C\$,£}$
c_d = the domestic cash rate (Canadian dollar)
c_f = the foreign cash rate (British pound)

Considering the current spot rate and the no-arbitrage forward rate, the correct forward discount for the British pound relative to the Canadian dollar is:

$$f_{d,f} = \frac{1.6396 - 1.75}{1.75} = -0.063086 \cong -6.31\%$$

This forward differential indicates that the Canadian dollar should appreciate only 6.31% relative to the pound. Using spot and forward rates in question 15.1, we calculated a forward differential of –8.57%. That is based on the current forward price the Canadian dollar should gain 8.57% against the pound. Thus the current spot rate (1.75 C\$/£) and forward rate (1.60 C\$/£) indicate that the pound will depreciate too much (the forward Canadian dollar is too expensive relative to the pound). An arbitrageur could simultaneously buy Canadian dollars and sell them forward for pounds at the inflated forward price. Possible arbitrage transactions are shown in the following table.

We work with £1000 to simplify the numbers:

(The spot rate is 1.75 C$/£ and the 1-year forward rate is 1.60 C$/£)

Today	In One Year
Borrow £1000 at 11%	
Repay in one year	−£1100.00
Buy £1,000 × 1.75 $C/£ = $C1,750 in the spot market	
Invest the $C1,750 at 4% → C$1,820 in one year	
Sell the C$1,820 forward for £ at 1.60 C$/£	£1137.50
Net	+£37.50

We see that, because the forward Canadian dollar is too expensive (alternatively the pound is too cheap), we can profit by simultaneously buying the spot Canadian dollar and selling it forward. (Study Session 10, LOS 25.j)

33. **B**   Rolle should recommend investment in the Tatehiki bond if a hedged position will be taken. The easiest way to make this determination is to examine their excess returns, which is the bond return minus the risk-free rate in the foreign country.

The Knauff company bond return: 8.0% − 5.0% = 3.0%.

The Tatehiki company bond return: 6.0% − 2.0% = 4.0%.

Note that we assume both bonds have similar risk and maturities, and any currency risk is hedged, so the decision is based solely on the excess returns.
(Study Session 10, LOS 25.j)

34. **C**   The Knauf bond promises a return of 8% in euros. Since you hedge using current forward rates, which would incorporate the expected 0.2% depreciation in the euro relative to the dollar (the euro will be trading at a forward discount of 4.8 − 5 = −0.2%), you effectively lock in the current forward discount. The expected return to U.S. investors would be 7.8%, the expected return on the bond (8%) less the forward currency differential (−0.2%).

The unhedged return for the Tatehiki bond is its return in yen of 6.0% plus the expected 2.0% appreciation in the yen geometrically linked which equals (1.06)(1.02) − 1 = 8.1%.
(Study Session 10, LOS 25.j)

35. **A**   The hedge is best described as a currency proxy hedge. In a proxy hedge the manager enters a forward contract between the domestic currency and a second foreign currency that is correlated with the first foreign currency. Proxy hedges are utilized when forward contracts on the first foreign currency are not actively traded or hedging the first foreign currency is relatively expensive.

In a proxy hedge, the manager is long (or short) the first foreign currency and takes the opposite position in the second foreign currency. You can think of it this way; if the manager is long a foreign currency, he would want to short (sell) the currency forward to hedge potential changes in its value. Since forward contracts on the currency are either too expensive or non-existent, the manager shorts a second foreign currency in terms of the domestic currency. The hope is that, since the two currencies are highly correlated, their value changes will be similar and the change in the value of the second foreign currency will compensate for (offset) changes in the first foreign currency.

An important consideration with a proxy hedge is that there is no connection (no contract) between the two foreign currencies. In a cross hedge, however, the manager sells the first foreign currency forward for a second foreign currency. That is, there is a connection, like a bridge, between the two foreign currencies such that you could *cross* between them. (Study Session 10, LOS 25.j)

Proxy hedge:

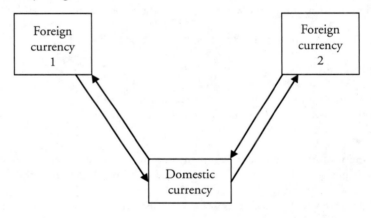

Cross hedge:

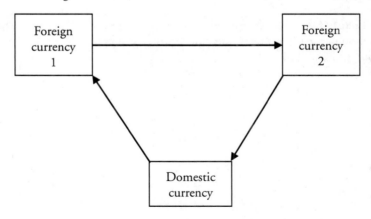

36. **B**   The best hedge of the Crawfordville floating rate CD is an interest rate cap. An interest rate cap is a series of interest rate calls that put a cap on the cost of a liability. If interest rates rise above the cap strike rate, the cap will provide a payment to the bank that mitigates their increased cost of paying out interest on the CD. If interest rates fall, the bank will let the cap expire worthless and benefit from the lower rate. An interest rate floor is a series of interest rate puts that provide a minimum return on an asset if interest rates go below the floor strike rate. An interest rate floor would not hedge the bank's floating rate CD liability.

The best hedge for Ryder's portfolio of fixed coupon rate bonds would be a protective put on the T-bond futures contract. The purchase of a put hedges a bond investment because the put will rise in value when interest rates rise. If interest rates fall, the bond investment will increase in value and the manager will let the put expire worthless. The cost of the put will however reduce the manager's return.

In a covered call, the manager sells a call to earn extra income. If interest rates rise, the loss on the bond will be buffered by the income from the sale of the call. However, the call does not provide downside protection as strong as that from the protective put. (Study Session 10, LOS 25.f)

> Sample Scoring Key: 3 points for each correct response.

QUESTIONS 37–42

Source: Study Session 13

37. **B** A representative set of checkpoints for selecting an alternative investment manager would include assessing the market opportunity, the investment process, the organization, the people, the terms and structure, the ancillary service providers, and the documents. Low market efficiency is a common feature of many alternative investments. In fact, the reason that alternative investments present market opportunities is that their markets are not efficient. (Study Session 13, LOS 31.b)

38. **B** Historically, private equity returns have generally been higher than stock returns over most periods. Since a source of the return is often associated with IPOs and other market activity, the returns tend to be correlated with stock returns. This lowers the amount of diversification private equity can offer a standard stock and bond portfolio. (Study Session 13, LOS 31.d)

39. **A** The portfolio allocation to this class should be 5% or less with a plan to keep the money invested for 7–10 years and not 5 years as stated in the vignette. Five to ten investments is a recommended range to achieve diversification within the private equity investments. Since five investments times $5 million is less than $30 million (5% of the portfolio), the recommended size is appropriate. (Study Session 13, LOS 31.d)

40. **C** They were both correct. It is true that private equity benchmarks suffer from infrequent repricing. It is also true that many private equity investors create their own benchmarks. (Study Session 13, LOS 31.e)

41. **A** In contrast to VC funds, buyout funds usually have higher leverage, earlier and steadier cash flows, less error in the measurement of returns, less frequent losses, and less upside potential. These differences are the natural consequence of the buyout funds purchasing entities in later stages of development or even established companies where the risks and returns are lower. Due to the large number of failures and poor performers, even though venture capital has more upside potential, the average return to venture capital tends to be lower than the returns to buyout funds. (Study Session 13, LOS 31.i)

42. **C** Farmington indicated that the clients have not expressed a concern even when the market and portfolio have not performed well. This indicates that decision risk, the risk of the client irrationally requesting a change in strategy because of recent investment losses, may not be an issue. Tax issues are always important. Since Carnegie will be investing in private equity, he certainly needs to find out about other closely held investments the Lewis family holds. Finally, the horizon is important, and it is especially important because Farmington indicated a five-year horizon for the private equity investments. That is too short for this category of asset. (Study Session 13, LOS 31.c)

Sample Scoring Key: 3 points for each correct response.

QUESTIONS 43–48

Source: Study Session 4

43. **A**   A flat tax structure on income, dividends, and capital gains can be best classified as a flat and heavy tax regime. Note that a common feature of this type of regime is the favorable treatment of interest income. A flat and light regime would extend the favorable treatment to dividends and capital gains. (Study Session 4, LOS 11.a)

44. **B**   Given a pretax return of 7%, an annual tax rate of 25%, and annual compounding (note that the account is taxed annually, so we reduce the annual return for taxes):

$$FV = 1{,}000{,}000\ [1 + 0.07\ (1 - 0.25)]^{15} = 2{,}154{,}426$$

(Study Session 4, LOS 11.b)

45. **C**   The reduction in portfolio risk can be expected to reduce expected returns. Since her investment objective is to accumulate assets that will generate income equal to her wage income, the investment horizon will increase. When taxes are paid periodically during the holding period, a longer investment horizon will increase tax drag, and the tax drag will exceed the applicable tax rate. (Study Session 4, LOS 11.e)

46. **B**   Given a pretax return of 12%, a 10-year holding period, a tax rate of 35%, and a cost basis of $250,000:

$$FV = 250{,}000\ [(1 + 0.12)^{10}\ (1 - 0.35) + 0.35] = 592{,}200$$

$$gain = 592{,}200 - 250{,}000 = 342{,}200$$

Note that solution A is approximately the value that would be derived if the last term in the brackets were left out. Solution C ignores the cost basis in calculating the gain. (Study Session 4, LOS 11.b)

47. **B**   The gross sale proceeds, tax, $ tax drag, and % tax drag are:

$$FV = 250{,}000[(1 + 0.12)^{10}] = 776{,}462$$

$$Tax = (776{,}462 - 250{,}000)0.35 = 184{,}262$$

$$TaxDrag = \left(\frac{184{,}262}{(776{,}462 - 250{,}000)}\right) = 0.35$$

Because this is a (deferred) capital gains tax situation, the tax drag is equal to the capital gains tax rate of 35%. (Study Session 4, LOS 11.b)

48. **A**   The accrual equivalent after tax return is: $R_{AE} = \sqrt[9]{\dfrac{150{,}000}{60{,}000}} - 1 = 0.1071$

Note that 17.7% is the accrual equivalent tax rate [$= 1 - (10.7\ /\ 13.0)$], but this is not the value that we are looking for in the question. (Study Session 4, LOS 11.c)

Sample Scoring Key: 3 points for each correct response.

QUESTIONS 49–54

Source: Study Session 10, 14, and 15

49. **B**   Reneau is correct. Reneau is describing a bull call strategy which profits when the stock market rises. The bull call strategy involves purchasing one call with a low exercise price and selling the other with a high exercise price. The beginning stock price is usually below the two call strike prices. The maximum loss is the price of the low exercise price call minus the price of the high exercise price call.

        Belanger is incorrect. Although a put and call of the same maturity and same exercise price could be used here, the correct strategy would be to sell the two options, not purchase them. Belanger is suggesting a long straddle where the better strategy in a flat market is a short straddle. However, if the stock market does rise, this strategy would have potentially unlimited losses, due to the call that was sold. An alternative strategy to exploit expectations of a stable stock market would be a long butterfly strategy. (Study Session 15, LOS 37.b)

50. **C**   Reneau's intended strategy is a bull call spread. She should buy the 35 call and sell the 40 call for a net cost of $3.00. The maximum loss for a bull call spread is when it expires out of the money. In that case, the investor loses the initial investment, in this case $3.00. The breakeven for a bull call spread can be expressed as $X_L + C_L - C_H = \$35.00 + \$4.50 - \$1.50 = \$38.00$. If the stock closes at $38.00, the investor gains $3.00 on the call with the low exercise price; the call with the higher exercise price expires worthless. The $3.00 profit on the low exercise price call offsets the initial cost of $3.00. (Study Session 15, LOS 37.b)

51. **C**   The option strategy Belanger is describing is a long straddle. Since the stock price will likely increase or decrease by a relatively large amount, the strategy would be to buy a straddle (i.e., a put and a call of the same strike price). The 40 put/calls offer the lowest cost straddle at a total cost of $5. At a stock price of $45, the call payoff is $5 and the strategy breaks even. (Study Session 15, LOS 37.b)

52. **A**   The option strategy Reneau is describing is a butterfly spread. In this case, a butterfly spread is constructed by buying the 35 call and the 45 call, and selling two 40 calls for a net cost of 2.50. The maximum gain is calculated as $X_M - X_L - C_L + 2C_M - C_H = \$40.00 - \$35.00 - \$4.50 + 2(\$1.50) - \$1.00 = \$2.50$. Note that this is when the stock price is equal to the middle exercise price ($40.00). The maximum loss is calculated as $C_L - 2C_M + C_H = \$4.50 - 2(\$1.50) + 1.00 = \$2.50$. The maximum is incurred if the stock price closes below X_L (i.e., $35.00) or above X_H (i.e., $45.00). (Study Session 15, LOS 37.b)

53. **B**   Reneau is correct and Belanger is incorrect. Reneau is describing a binary credit option (not a credit spread option as Belanger states) because it is based on the price of the underlying asset. When the payoff is based on the asset's yield spread, it is referred to as a credit spread option. (Study Session 10, LOS 25.g and Study Session 14, LOS 34.k)

54. **B**   Reneau is correct but Belanger is incorrect. It is true that credit options written on an underlying asset directly protect against declines in the value of the asset and that credit spread options protect against adverse movements of the credit spread over a referenced benchmark. However, credit spread calls have value when the spread widens, and credit spread puts have value when the spread narrows. (Study Session 10, LOS 25.g and Study Session 14, LOS 34.k)

Sample Scoring Key: 3 points for each correct response.

QUESTIONS 55–60

Source: Study Session 16

55. **C**   In a market expected to increase in relatively constant fashion, constant proportion portfolio insurance will outperform the other strategies. In a constant proportion strategy, a fixed proportion (m) of the cushion (= assets – floor value) is invested in stocks. CPPI refers to a constant proportion strategy with m > 1. Buy and hold is equivalent to the constant proportion strategy with m = 1, so its performance would be good, but not as good. A constant-mix strategy (CM) would be the poorest performer, because as the market continually rises, the CM strategy would dictate selling stocks. (Study Session 16, LOS 40.h)

56. **B**   In a market expected to oscillate, constant mix strategies (fixed percentage allocation to stocks) outperform the others, since they involve buying/selling stocks when prices fall/rise. CPPI would perform worst in this scenario, with buy and hold performing better but not as well as CM. (Study Session 16, LOS 40.h)

57. **C**   Although CPPI strategies offer downside protection, it is their convex nature that provides it. Statements A and B are correct. (Study Session 16, LOS 40.h)

58. **C**   The portfolio has increased from $1,000,000 to $1,150,000, representing a 20% increase ($120,000) in equities and a $30,000 increase in debt and cash ($1,150,000 – $720,000 = $430,000). Since equities now represent 62.6% (= 720,000 / 1,150,000) of the portfolio and their strategic allocation is 60%, Tratman should take no action. (Study Session 16, LOS 40.f)

59. **C**   This statement is too general. The need to rebalance is determined by several factors, including the volatility of the assets and the correlations among the classes. For example, if the assets in the portfolio are not overly volatile and are fairly highly correlated, monitoring more frequently than on an annual basis may be a waste of time and money. (Study Session 16, LOS 40.e)

60. **B**   Illiquid assets generally have higher costs associated with buying and selling. In that case, too tight of a tolerance band (i.e., corridor) could require high costs. The investor should always strive for a happy medium between the need to rebalance and the associated costs. Answers A and C would support wider corridors. (Study Session 16, LOS 40.f)

> Sample Scoring Key: 3 points for each correct response.

EXAM 2
MORNING SESSION ANSWERS

QUESTION 1

Source: Study Session 4, LOS 10.j,k

Answer for Question 1

		Investment Policy Statement for the Smythes
Objectives	Risk Tolerance	**For the Exam:** Ability: Average. Willingness: Below average. Overall: Below average. Counseling to reconcile difference. **Discussion:** To determine either willingness or ability to take risk, you should always start at average and then look for client statements or actions or other factors that would reduce or increase risk tolerance. In this case the portfolio must provide a substantial portion of the client's living expenses. As shown in the calculations under required return below, the portfolio must provide $116,438 of their required cash flows of $165,188 in the coming year (for the clients to maintain their current lifestyle). Had these clients been retired, that alone would suffice to reduce the client's ability to take risk to below average. On further analysis of this case, however, we note that Barney and Heather are relatively young (40 and 39) with a long time horizon, and they would appear to have a degree of flexibility. For one thing, Heather could take a job to decrease the annual drag on the portfolio. They could also reduce their living expenses to achieve the same result. In addition, their portfolio is relatively large relative to the annual cash flows. The return required to meet the additional $116,438 of inflation-adjusted living expenses and to maintain the portfolio principal is a moderate 5.1%. Balancing the two factors, the large annual cash flow need (which reduces ability) and their flexibility (which increases ability), the Smythes would be considered to have average ability to take risk. When the client makes statements about risk, regardless of the statement, this usually indicates a focus on risk and below average willingness. This is confirmed by their desire for no debt. Also, if the client makes statements about prior risky investments, this would indicate below average tolerance. Take the client's actions into consideration, however. For example, you can almost totally ignore direct statements about their own risk aversion, because they will often say one thing and do another. You might see them say something like, "I have average risk aversion," but you notice that they have made regular speculative investments in the past. In this case the client's actions speak much louder than his words.

©2011 Kaplan, Inc.

Objectives	Return	**For the Exam:**
		Cash inflows for the coming year: Salary $48,750 **Cash outflows:** Taxes on salary $12,188 Living expenses $153,000 Total outflows: ($165,188) Net ($116,438) Required after-tax **real** rate of return = $116,438 / $3,750,000 = 0.03105 = 3.1% Required after-tax real rate of return = 3.1% Plus: Annual inflation rate = 2.0% Required after-tax **nominal** rate of return = **5.1%** **Discussion:** Over the coming year, Barney will draw a salary of $48,750 and pay $12,188 in income taxes. Living expenses are given to us at $150,000 for the previous year, so for the coming year they should be 2% higher at $153,000. Total outflows for the coming year, including taxes, are estimated at $165,188 and their only inflow is Smythe's $48,750 salary. This leaves a shortfall of $116,438 that must be made up by the portfolio. To pay the $116,438, the $3,750,000 portfolio ($1,250,000 + $2,500,000) must earn 3.1% after-tax. To maintain the purchasing power of the portfolio principal (the $3,750,000), we must add inflation for a total after-tax nominal return of 5.1%. Note 1: Alternatively you could have compounded by the rate of inflation and arrived at a required after-tax nominal return of $(1.031)(1.02) - 1 = 5.16\%$. Unless you are directed to present the answer in a specific form, either way would be acceptable on the exam. Note 2: The vignette may or may not state that you must protect the principal (i.e., maintain purchasing power). To stress the point, I deliberately left out the statement in this case. On the exam, always assume you are to protect the principal unless you are specifically told otherwise.

| Constraints | Time Horizon | **For the Exam:**

Long-term, 2-stage time horizon: pre-retirement 25 years; retirement 15 to 20 years. There could be an intermediate stage consisting of the children's college years.

Discussion:

The most common time horizon statement for individual investors is: "Long-term time horizon consisting of two stages, pre-retirement and retirement." You will probably be able to note the number of pre-retirement years based on the client's current age and desired retirement age. In this case, we are told Barney is 40 and plans to retire at 65, so the pre-retirement stage is 25 years. The number of retirement years is only a guess, so putting a likely range is appropriate by assuming the client will live to 80 or 85.

The children provide a bit of a twist, in that we are not given any costs for college or even the number of college years. It is usually acceptable to state that another stage coinciding with the college years is possible. In our scenario, the children will complete college before the Smythes retire, so their college years will actually divide Barney and Heather's pre-retirement stage into three stages. The first stage lasts about six years until the first child starts college. The second stage consists of about six years until both children have finished college. The third stage consists of about 13 years until retirement. In this way, the children's college years could actually divide the Smythes' overall time horizon into four stages. To avoid this situation, prior exam questions have had the children graduating at the same time as the clients retire. |
| | Liquidity | **For the Exam:**

$116,438 of the Smythes' living expenses in the coming year. Sufficient cash for emergencies.

Discussion:

For the liquidity portion of the IPS, include only those items that the portfolio must pay. Here, the Smythes' portfolio must meet a large portion of their living expenses ($116,438 of $165,188), so you state that. Also, you should probably always mention that an amount equal to 5–6 months salary should be held in cash or cash equivalents to meet emergency needs. (That is obviously more important when the client's salary pays most or all of the annual expenses.)

This would also be the place to mention any charitable gifts the clients would like to pay out during the coming year. (None in this case.) |

Constraints (cont.)	Legal/ Regulatory	**For the Exam:** There are no special legal or regulatory issues. **Discussion:** Even though there are dependents/heirs, there is no indication in the case that the Smythes have a desire to establish trusts or engage in other succession planning issues. Consequently, you do not have to address any. Doing so would be an example of adding material that will not increase your score, and could cost you points if incorrect.
	Taxes	**For the Exam:** The Smythes are taxed as individuals at a rate of 25%, so all investment decisions should consider tax effects. **Discussion:** • It appears that they have to pay taxes on portfolio income and capital gains. • The degree to which the assets are subject to taxes depends upon the extent to which they are held in tax-sheltered accounts. • Any investment actions must take tax status into consideration.
	Unique Circumstances	**For the Exam:** There are no material unique circumstances. **Discussion:** Other than items addressed at other points in this IPS, there are no unique circumstances that warrant consideration from a financial planning standpoint.

Sample Scoring Key:
2 points for each of the three risk components (ability, willingness, overall).
2 points for each of the return components (real = 3.1%, nominal = 5.1%).
2 points for each constraint.

QUESTION 2

Source: Study Session 3, LOS 8.b,c
Study Session 5, LOS 15.b,c

A. i. **For the Exam:**

Elliot is exhibiting overconfidence.

Discussion:

Elliot's over reliance on his personal belief that there is a high probability of interest rate increases ignores historical evidence that interest rate changes are very difficult if not impossible to predict with that degree of accuracy. Elliot is more than likely overestimating the probability that his analysis will prove correct.

ii. **For the Exam:**

The return objective is excessive, relative to the level of risk that is appropriate for the fund.

Discussion:

Elliot's plan to solve the underfunded status of the plan by investing in high return securities is ill-advised. It requires the plan to invest in high-risk securities to obtain the high returns. Given the current plan funding status, retired to active lives ratio, and the demographic profile of the workforce, the plan's ability to bear risk is below average. Also, Elliot is considering only the present value of the liabilities when interest rates increase, where increasing rates can have a dampening effect on equity values. Hence, the return objectives are excessive relative to the level of risk that is appropriate for the fund.

iii. **For the Exam:**

The investment of plan assets for the stated purpose of bolstering profitability is inappropriate, and may constitute a violation of Elliot's fiduciary responsibilities under ERISA.

Discussion:

ERISA requires that pension plan assets be invested in the sole interest of plan beneficiaries. Failure to do so most likely constitutes a breach of fiduciary duty. Moreover, the financial implications of such an objective suggest an increase in the uncertainty about the future funding status of the plan. For both reasons, Elliot's investment plan is inappropriate.

Answer for Question 2-B

	Investment Policy Statement for Matrix Corporation
Objectives	Risk tolerance: **For the Exam:** Below average. • The plan is underfunded. • The age of active employees is high. • The ratio of active to retired lives is low. **Discussion:** All of the factors above suggest the ability to bear risk is below average.
	Return: **For the Exam:** Return sufficient to meet plan obligations on an inflation-adjusted basis. • Given the lower risk tolerance, the return objective would be lower as reflected in a mix of more conservative investments. • Invest in higher-quality nominal bonds of shorter duration to minimize the effect of a projected increase in interest rates. • Invest in real return bonds as a hedge against inflation. • Invest in nonspeculative stocks for the equity part of the portfolio. **Discussion:** The actual return requirement depends on the plan's funded status, the ability of the sponsor to make contributions, characteristics of the workforce, and the accumulation of plan obligations (e.g., growth in firm size with accompanying growth in employment). If the plan is fully funded, the *minimum* return requirement is the discount rate an actuary applies to the plan's obligations (liabilities). The sponsoring firm may wish to set a return requirement above the minimum as insurance against possible future declines in returns or expected increases in pension obligations and to minimize the probability of future firm contributions. For example, if the firm's workforce has an average age that is significantly below the industry average, we would say the plan has a longer than usual time horizon with increased ability to take risk. In that case, management could set a return requirement significantly above the minimum. Likewise, an above-average age translates into a shortened time horizon with accompanying reduced ability to take risk. In that case, the plan would probably only strive to just meet the minimum required return. The bottom line is that the return requirement must be aligned with the plan's ability to take risk. Increasing the required return minimizes the probability that the sponsor will have to make special contributions to the plan, but the higher return requirement could violate the plan's ability to take risk.

Answer for Question 2-C

Time horizon	**For the Exam:** Average employee age > industry average. Time horizon shorter than average. **Discussion:** The principal factor that dictates the time horizon for the pension plan is the average age of active employees. This factor suggests the time horizon is shorter than average. Also, with a low active to retired lives ratio, the firm will probably need to make a special contribution to the plan. This is another indication of a shortened time horizon.
Liquidity	**For the Exam:** Plan liquidity requirements are high. **Discussion:** • The plan funding status and the ratio of active to retired lives suggest that income on plan assets is not far in excess of current benefits, and may be less. • The average age of current employees indicates the income to benefits situation is unlikely to improve dramatically. Plan liquidity requirements are high and will more than likely remain high.
Legal/ Regulatory	**For the Exam:** As a pension plan, significant legal and regulatory requirements apply. **Discussion:** In the vast majority of countries where they exist, pension funds are subject to a legal and regulatory framework. Under U.S. law, Matrix's defined benefit plan must conform to ERISA regulations. • Plan assets must be invested for the sole benefit of plan participants. • Pension fund trustees have fiduciary responsibilities. • Standards of prudence and investment restrictions apply.
Taxes	**For the Exam:** Pension plans in the United States are not subject to taxes on investment income. **Discussion:** • Matrix's defined benefit plan is not taxable under U.S. law, so taxes on securities income and capital gains are not an investment consideration from the plan's perspective. • Retirees may have to pay taxes on benefits received, however.

Unique circumstances	**For the Exam:** High average employee age; low active to retired lives ratio; significantly underfunded. **Discussion:** Unique circumstances are those that are at least somewhat uncommon but have an impact on the clients' risk and/or return objectives and possibly constraints. For example, a university endowment might have to make a large cash outlay to cover costs of a new building. Even if the outlay isn't significant compared to the size of the fund and, therefore, doesn't affect the funds' required return or risk tolerance, it should be stated under liquidity requirements and unique circumstances. Other examples included an underfunded pension plan or a pension plan with a very low active to retired lives ratio, as in this case.

Sample Scoring Key:
A. 2 points for each critique of Elliot's statement.
B. 6 points for identifying relevant return objectives, 6 points for identifying relevant risk arguments.
C. 2 points for each constraint.

QUESTION 3

Source: Study Session 9, LOS 23.b
Study Session 12, LOS 29.a
Study Session 13, LOS 31.e

Answer for Question 3

Comment	Correct or incorrect? (circle one)	Justification
"The popularity bias can cause problems for measuring value-weighted hedge fund benchmark performance. The popularity bias argues that out-performing hedge funds as well as hedge fund styles tend to attract additional funding, so as they grow in popularity their performance tends to have a greater and greater impact on the value-weighted index's measured performance. This creates a double impact on the value-weighted hedge fund index return; the individual funds have good returns, and their increasing size means they have a greater weight in the index. The result is that the index's return has an upward bias. This bias, however, can be counteracted by utilizing two indices, one long and one short. Since most hedge fund managers attempt to generate alpha through both long and short positions, they can have a net zero weight or even a net negative weight. A single, long-only benchmark will not capture the performance of both strategies."	Incorrect	**For the Exam:** Solution to popularity bias is an equally-weighted index. **Discussion:** The discussions of popularity bias and long-short investing and indices are correct, but they are not related. Popularity bias can lead one or a few funds or styles to dominate a value-weighted hedge fund index, and investors must be aware of this. One alternative is using an equally-weighted index, but equally-weighted indices are not usually rebalanced (reconstituted) often and are, therefore, not considered investable. It is also true that hedge fund managers often utilize both long and short trading to generate alpha. One possible solution, since the managers often have zero or even negative net weights, is using two separate indices.

"If an investor is averse to market value risk, the bond benchmark used should have a long maturity so they can lock in a yield to maturity."	Incorrect	**For the Exam:** Long maturity bond portfolios have more market value risk. Should use short maturity. **Discussion:** The market values of long maturity (i.e., long duration) portfolios have more interest rate risk than shorter maturity portfolios, and thus are prone to larger swings in market value. Therefore, the greater the investor's aversion to market risk, the shorter the appropriate maturity of the portfolio and the selected benchmark.
"The recommended solution to the 'free float' problem in international markets is to determine the amount of shares to be floated by an issuer in the upcoming year and use that to recalculate the issuer's weight in market capitalization weighted indices."	Incorrect	**For the Exam:** The free float problem refers to the fact that many firms have shares that are closely held or otherwise not available for public trading. Only the values of firms' freely traded shares should be included in a market value weighted index. **Discussion:** The "free float" problem refers to the fact that many firms have shares that are closely held and not available for public trading. When calculating the capitalization of firms in a cap-weighted index, only those shares that are freely traded should be included. However, the determination of the free float is often difficult. This is particularly problematic in emerging markets.
"For bond investors such as foundations who desire a stable stream of income, long-term bond benchmarks should be used."	Correct	**For the Exam:** No explanation required. **Discussion:** If the client is dependent on cash flows from the portfolio, those cash flows should be dependable. Long term bonds offer the investor a longer and more certain income stream. Investors desiring a stable, long-term cash flow should invest in longer-term bonds and, therefore, utilize long-term benchmarks.

Sample Scoring Key:
1 point for identifying each statement as correct or incorrect.
2 points for justifying why the statement is incorrect.
0 points possible if the correct/incorrect decision is wrong.

QUESTION 4

Source: Study Session 6, LOS 18.b,c

Answer for Question 4-A

Comment	Is the statement susceptible to problems in using economic data to forecast? (circle one)	If yes, identify and describe the problem
"The stock returns in emerging markets are quite impressive. The mean returns are quite high and the risk is lower than many investors expect. Consider the example of the country of Yalewian. An index of Yalewian stocks had high returns for the period January 1, 1995, to December 31, 2006. This includes the period of crisis for emerging market stocks in 1997 and 1998. Yalewian stocks escaped from this crisis unscathed as their returns were positive during these years."	Yes	**For the Exam:** Using ex post data to make statements about ex ante performance—he is underestimating the risk faced by investors during the emerging market crisis of 97 and 98. This results in an overestimation of their risk-adjusted future performance. **Discussion:** Barkley is using ex post (past) data to make statements regarding the ex ante (future) risk and return of emerging market stocks. In 1997 and 1998, the stock prices of Yalewian stocks were probably depressed because investors feared that the emerging market crisis would extend to Yalewian stocks. When the country escaped unscathed from the crisis, stock prices and returns increased. In this case, Barkley has underestimated the risk that investors faced in 1997 and 1998 and perhaps overestimated the future returns that could be expected from Yalewian stocks.
"After extensive research on stock price patterns in 30 developed and emerging markets, I have uncovered a turn of the month effect in the U.S. Specifically, the returns for U.S. stocks are higher in the first half of every month compared to the returns during the latter part of the month. The reason why this pattern is found in the United States and not in the other countries is because U.S. investors tend to invest after they have been paid their wages at the end of the month."	Yes	**For the Exam:** Data mining—if one examines enough data, random return patterns can appear. **Discussion:** Barkley's research findings are probably due to data mining. He has studied the returns for 30 countries and finds one that has a pattern in returns. If he is using a 5% significance level, just by random chance, one out of 20 countries will demonstrate a pattern in returns. In this case (1 / 20) × 30 = 1.5 countries are expected to demonstrate a pattern in returns just by random chance. Although his explanation may have some basis in fact, the analyst must determine whether the observed pattern is just a statistical artifact or if it is real and likely to occur again in the future.

| "U.S. inflation from 1960 to 2006 averaged 3.4%. Because it was measured over such a long period, it would be hard to argue that the rate of U.S. inflation for the next year would be different from this historical average." | Yes | **For the Exam:**
Overreliance on historical data and failure to account for conditioning information.

Discussion:
Although historical data can be used as one input to forecasts, there are at least three potential problems here. First, there are limitations to using historical data when data definitions and methodologies have changed over time. For example, the basket of goods in the U.S. CPI (consumer price index) has changed over time. Second, there are limitations to using historical estimates if the data are no longer relevant. For example, the U.S. Federal Reserve has changed its objectives over time and this might impact the future path of inflation such that historical data are no longer relevant. Third, when forecasts fail to account for conditioning information, they may be inaccurate. Conditioning means that the statistical relationships were determined over a given historical time period and are naturally based on economic conditions at that time, and economic conditions can change over time. For example, perhaps the price of oil is expected to increase due to increased demand from developing economies. This information should be used to help form inflation forecasts. Historical data should not be the sole basis of forecasts. |
| "After evaluating the historical data for the U.S. and European stock markets, I have found that when the central bank is increasing the growth of the money supply, stock returns are higher. When they are restricting the growth, stock returns are lower. In fact, the correlation between the central bank discount rate and stock returns is 0.74 on average, indicating that central bank monetary policy is very influential on stock returns." | Yes | **For the Exam:**
Misinterpretation of the correlation statistic—correlation does not imply causation.

Discussion:
Barkley is misusing the correlation statistic. He is assuming that central bank policies drive stock returns, when in fact there are likely other variables influencing the relationship. For example, perhaps economic activity drives both central bank policy and stock returns. The correlation statistic does not indicate causality. |

Sample Scoring Key:
1 point each for correctly identifying whether there is a potential problem.
2 points for each description of the problem.
0 points possible if yes/no decision is wrong.

B. **For the Exam:**

Your objective in this type of question would be to provide the calculations as shown below (without our accompanying verbiage). You should show your work on the exam in case you make a mathematical mistake. This provides you with the potential for receiving partial credit if your process for calculating the answer is correct, but you make a mathematical error.

Discussion:

In the following equations, we denote Airedale as country A, Bermiese as country B, and the MSCI World index as the global market portfolio, M. To solve for the expected returns, we must calculate the equity risk premiums for both markets assuming full integration and full segmentation. Note that for the emerging market, the illiquidity risk premium is included:

Full integration:

$$ERP_i = \rho_{i,M}\sigma_i \left(\frac{ERP_M}{\sigma_M} \right)$$

$$ERP_A = 0.79(0.11)0.26 = 2.26\%$$

$$ERP_B = 0.58(0.21)0.26 + 0.0260 = 5.77\%$$

Full segmentation:

$$ERP_i = \sigma_i \left(\frac{ERP_M}{\sigma_M} \right)$$
$$ERP_A = (0.11)0.26 = 2.86\%$$
$$ERP_B = (0.21)0.26 + 0.0260 = 8.06\%$$

We then weight the integrated and segmented risk premiums by the degree of integration and segmentation in each market:

$$ERP_A = (0.85 \times 0.0226) + [(1 - 0.85) \times 0.0286] = 2.35\%$$
$$ERP_B = (0.65 \times 0.0577) + [(1 - 0.65) \times 0.0806] = 6.57\%$$

The expected return in each market is the risk-free rate plus the equity risk premium:

$$\hat{R}_A = 3.5\% + 2.35\% = 5.85\%$$
$$\hat{R}_B = 3.5\% + 6.57\% = 10.07\%$$

The betas for the markets, which are needed to calculate the covariance of the two markets, are calculated as:

$$\beta_i = \rho_{i,M}\sigma_i / \sigma_M$$
$$\beta_A = (0.79)(0.11) / 0.10 = 0.87$$
$$\beta_B = (0.58)(0.21) / 0.10 = 1.22$$

Lastly, we calculate the covariance of Airedale and Bermiese:

$$\text{cov}_{i,j} = \beta_i \beta_j \sigma_M^2$$
$$\text{cov}_{A,B} = (0.87)(1.22)(0.10)^2 = 0.0106$$

Your answer may be slightly different depending on the number of digits you used for intermediate calculations.

Sample Scoring Key:
6 points for the calculation of the expected returns (3 points each).
6 points for the calculation of the betas (3 points each).
4 points for the calculation of the covariance.

QUESTION 5

Source: Study Session 11, LOS 27.f,i

A. **For the Exam:**
- Examine manager's portfolio and divide investments into categories.
- Disadvantage: Subjective classification of categories.
- Advantage over returns-based: Detects style drift faster.

Discussion:

Holdings-based style analysis (HB), as its name implies, involves actually examining the portfolio and classifying securities based on characteristics such as capitalization, value, growth, industry, etc. HB requires access to the portfolio, so it is not applicable to hedge funds and other managers who consider their holdings proprietary. Also, the classifications themselves are subjective, as different analysts might consider the same stock as value and growth, for example, so they might not be the same classifications employed by the portfolio manager in constructing the portfolio. HB requires more data than returns-based analysis but picks up style drift faster.

> Sample Scoring Key:
> 4 points possible: 2 points for describing HB; 1 point each for disadvantage and advantage over returns-based style analysis.

B. **For the Exam:**

Regress portfolio returns against style indices' returns:

$$R_P = b_0 + b_1 I_1 + b_2 I_2 + b_3 I_3 + b_4 I_4 + \ldots + b_n I_n + e$$

$$\sum_{i=1}^{n} b_i = 1.0$$

R^2 = degree to which the model explains portfolio returns
b_i = portfolio sensitivity to index i
R_P = portfolio returns
I_i = returns on index i
e = returns to active management
n = number of indices used

Disadvantage: Determining number of and which indices to use.

Advantage over HB: Doesn't require looking at portfolio holdings.

Discussion:

To perform a returns-based style analysis (RB) the analyst regresses the returns on the portfolio against the returns on several style indices. The coefficients are constrained to sum to one, so each coefficient shows the portfolio's proportional exposure (sensitivity) to the respective style index. If a returns-based analysis indicates a coefficient of 0.30 to a large cap growth index, for example, the portfolio is assumed to consist of 30% large cap growth stocks. The analysis requires a significant number of consecutive returns for each index and the portfolio. Rolling regressions can be used to determine style drift over time, but RB does not generally detect style drift as quickly as HB. RB is subject to all the potential difficulties associated with multiple regression analysis, such as asynchronous data, misspecification, multi-colinearity, spurious correlation, etc. A particular limitation of RB is the need to select indices. It is difficult to identify the exact number of indices necessary to describe the returns on the portfolio. R-square identifies the proportion of the variability in the portfolio returns that can be attributed to the model (indices selected), and (1 − R-square) is considered to be the variability resulting from active management.

> Sample Scoring Key:
> 10 points possible: 2 points for describing RB; 2 points for writing the equation; 1 point each for identifying index returns, betas (sensitivities), and error term; 1 point for constraint $\left(\sum_{i=1}^{n} b_i = 1.0 \right)$; 1 point for disadvantage; 1 point for advantage over HB.

C.   **For the Exam:**

Full replication: Hold all securities in index and in same proportions. Use to minimize tracking error.
Disadvantage: Higher costs.

Stratified sampling: Select sample based on capitalization, style, etc. Use when cost is important and some tracking error is OK.
Disadvantage: Increased tracking error.

Optimization: Factor model replicates factor sensitivities. Use when factor sensitivities are more important than actual holdings.
Disadvantage: Based on historical data.

Discussion:

Full replication (FR) is the most costly to employ, as every security in the index must be purchased in the same proportion as in the index. FR produces the lowest tracking error but its return is somewhat lower than that of the index due to initial trading costs. FR can be inappropriate if the index is frequently rebalanced, as it might require many frequent, small trades to rebalance to the index or for smaller investment portfolios. FR picks up style drift quickly, but it requires regular access to the portfolio.

Stratified sampling (SS) involves dividing the securities in the portfolio into groups by style, market cap, etc. A sample from each group is selected to represent that group by its weight in the index. For example, if 25% of the securities in the index fall into a group classified as small cap growth, a sample of the group is selected and purchased in an amount equal to 25% of the manager's portfolio. In that way the portfolio and index have the same 25% sensitivity to small cap growth stocks. Benefits to SS include less initial cost than FR, but increased tracking error. Also, since the manager selects a representative sample from each group of stocks, he can potentially generate alpha by selecting only the best stocks in the group. Note that SS produces the same factor sensitivities as the index and actually holds index securities.

Optimization involves constructing a factor model that replicates the factor sensitivities of the index. The model can be complex and difficult to construct. Optimization usually produces less tracking error than SS but the portfolio can contain different securities than the index. Unlike SS, the factor model method implicitly considers the covariances of the risk factors, but sensitivities are determined from historical data and are subject to change. Optimization may provide a misleading model if the sample of data is skewed by a particular security or time period. Optimization must be updated to reflect changes in risk sensitivities leading to frequent rebalancing.

> Sample Scoring Key:
> 9 points possible: 1 point for each definition; 1 point for properly identifying when each should be used, and 1 point for each disadvantage.

QUESTION 6

Source: Study Session 8, LOS 21.g,n

For the Exam:

For the calculation part of questions A through C, your objective would be to provide the calculations as shown below. You should show your work on the exam in case you make a mathematical mistake. This provides you with the potential for receiving partial credit if your process for calculating the answer is correct.

A.   **Discussion:**

Since the $750,000 will be donated within the next year, the total amount should be subtracted from the portfolio and not considered part of the investable asset base.

Subtract from the asset base = $5,000,000 − $750,000 = $4,250,000.

As a percent of investable assets, the required after-tax **spending rate** is then 150,000 / $4,250,000 = 3.53%. Since the $150,000 is the amount of expected spending, we can assume it already incorporates inflation.

To calculate the investor's before-tax return objective, we factor in taxes first and then expected inflation:

The grossed up required before-tax real rate of return:

3.53 / (1 − .25) = 4.71%

The before-tax nominal rate of return: 4.71 + 3.50 = 8.21%. We add inflation to the before-tax required returns to protect the principal.

Note: Compounding the return components is equally correct but results in slightly different answers for parts B and C.

To obtain Beitia's utility for each of the corner portfolios, use the expected portfolio return, his risk aversion value of 5.0, the variance of the portfolio, and the following formula:

$$U_p = \hat{R}_p - 0.5(A)(\sigma_p^2)$$

Corner Portfolio	Calculation	Utility of Corner Portfolio
1	$0.065 - 0.5(5)0.041^2$	0.0608
2	$0.0775 - 0.5(5)0.058^2$	0.0691
3	$0.097 - 0.5(5)0.078^2$	0.0818
4	$0.135 - 0.5(5)0.106^2$	0.1069

 Professor's Note: The question does not ask you to identify the portfolio with highest utility-adjusted return, but it is Portfolio 4 at 0.1069. Essentially, the utility-adjusted return for a portfolio is the return for the portfolio minus a deduction for risk. The deduction gets larger as risk aversion increases.

B.   **Discussion:**

Given his required return of 8.21% and no borrowing or short selling, we combine corner portfolios 2 and 3. To solve for their weights, we use:

$0.0821 = w_2(0.0775) + (1 - w_2)(0.097)$

$w_2 = 0.764 = 76.4\%; w_3 = 1 - w_2 = 23.6\%$

$\sigma_p = 0.764(5.8\%) + 0.236(7.8\%) = 6.27\%$

Professor's Note: We can check our weight calculations by calculating the expected return from this portfolio:

0.764(7.75%) + 0.236(9.7%) = 8.2%

Also, the approximate expected portfolio standard deviation is a weighted average of the standard deviations of corner portfolios 2 and 3. We assume that the standard deviation is a linear combination of the corner portfolios' standard deviations (we don't use the correlation between them).

As such, the calculated standard deviation represents the maximum standard deviation for the combination of the two corner portfolios in the calculated proportions. If the correlations between the corner portfolios are given, be sure to incorporate them into the standard deviation calculation.

You might be asked on the exam to calculate the resulting weights in assets 1 to 5, given calculated weights for corner portfolios 2 and 3. For example, in our resulting portfolio:

$$\text{weight}_{\text{asset 1}} = 0.764(0\%) + 0.236(60\%) = 14\%$$
$$\text{weight}_{\text{asset 2}} = 0.764(15\%) + 0.236(10\%) = 14\%$$
$$\text{weight}_{\text{asset 3}} = 0.764(85\%) + 0.236(30\%) = 72\%$$
$$\text{weight}_{\text{asset 4}} = \text{weight}_{\text{asset 5}} = 0\%$$

C.   **For the Exam:**

$$0.082 = w_4(0.135) + (1 - w_4)(0.04)$$

$$w_4 = \frac{(0.082 - 0.04)}{(0.135 - 0.04)} = 44\%$$

$$w_{RF} = 1 - w_4 = 56\%$$

$$\text{standard deviation} = 0.44(10.6\%) + 0.56(0\%) = 4.7\%$$

Discussion:

When there is a risk free asset (RF), the investor is always better off combining it with the tangency portfolio, which is the portfolio with the highest Sharpe ratio. Combining the risk free asset with the tangency portfolio creates a capital allocation line (CAL), and the CAL always provides the highest available reward to risk, whether or not the investor borrows (negative weight for RF). The portfolio with the highest Sharpe ratio is portfolio 4 (0.896). Since portfolio 4 has the highest Sharpe ratio and its expected return is higher than Beitia's return requirement, we know we will end up with positive weights for both the risk free asset and portfolio 4.

In this case, the restriction on borrowing turned out not to be a constraint, because the expected return for portfolio 4 is higher than the required return. If you were prohibited from borrowing (i.e., shorting the risk-free asset) and the return on portfolio 4 wasn't sufficient, you would not have been asked to combine the risk free asset with one of the corner portfolios. If the return to portfolio 4 had not been sufficient to cover the required return, the only way to stay on the CAL would be to borrow at the risk free rate and invest more than 100% of your assets in portfolio 4 (leverage the return to portfolio 4). This would move the final portfolio to the right of portfolio 4 on the CAL but would still provide the same reward to risk (Sharpe ratio) as portfolio 4. Remember, the slope of the CAL is the Sharpe ratio of the tangency portfolio, so any portfolio that falls on the CAL provides the same Sharpe ratio. Any portfolio below the CAL will provide less return per unit of risk (i.e., will have a lower Sharpe ratio), so the investor will always try to select a portfolio on the CAL. Exam questions generally follow the form of this practice exam question; combine two corner portfolios or combine the tangency portfolio with the risk-free asset.

Sample Scoring Key:
A. (9 points maximum) 1 point for deducting the $750,000 donation; 2 points for correct portfolio required return; 2 points for correct risk-adjusted utility equation; 1 point for each correct utility adjusted return.
B. (7 points maximum) 1 point for correctly identifying the two corner portfolios to combine; 4 points for correctly determining the corner portfolio weights; 2 points for resulting standard deviation.
C. (6 points maximum) 2 points for selecting portfolio 4; 2 points for weights of RF and portfolio 4; 2 points for the portfolio standard deviation.

QUESTION 7

Source: Study Session 5, LOS 15.i

Answer for Question 7

<table>
<tr>
<td colspan="3">Investment Policy Statement for A1 Casualty</td>
</tr>
<tr>
<td rowspan="2">Objectives</td>
<td>Return</td>
<td>For the Exam:
A1 should follow a total return investment objective that maximizes their ability to maintain a competitive policy pricing, reduce volatility in overall profitability, and achieve a reasonable growth in surplus. (This is a "canned answer" that you can use for most casualty insurance companies' return requirements.)

Discussion:
Casualty companies are plagued by the uncertainties associated with their underlying business. The potential for increasing claims may require shifting some of the asset portfolio into instruments that better match higher liability outflows, but attention to maintaining a reasonable surplus is also required. The overall objective should be to maximize total after-tax return within a prudent asset/liability (ALM) framework that also pays attention to surplus growth.</td>
</tr>
<tr>
<td>Risk</td>
<td>For the Exam:
There are two important factors affecting the risk tolerance of A1 in this case: the uncertain cash flow characteristics of their claims and the stock-to-surplus ratio. The primary objective is to meet policyholder claims, and the overall level of risk tolerance is low.

Discussion:
Not only is A1 apparently near the end of a typical 3-year period of an intensely competitive market environment, the current underwriting cycle also appears coincident with a downturn in the general business cycle. In addition, the recent hurricane may generate substantial claims in the near future due to the "long tail" characteristic of claims submissions. If A1 has approximately 50% of overall homeowner exposure to the region impacted by the hurricane, they should be prepared to see substantially more claims in the near future.
The proportion of A1's investment portfolio in equity instruments seems rather high in an environment where the financial stability required to meet the demands of current policyholders should be increasing. Most casualty companies restrict equity investments to no more than 75% of surplus. Although the willingness of A1 to take risk seems apparent, combining all the above with the general quasi-fiduciary role perceived of casualty insurance companies indicates a limited ability to take risks at this stage.

Professor's Note: The underwriting cycle is also known as the profitability cycle. The typical cycle lasts three to five years for casualty insurance companies. The bottom of the cycle usually coincides with an economic recession and/or a competitive pricing environment during which investments are liquidated to meet claims.</td>
</tr>
</table>

Constraints	Time Horizon	**For the Exam:** The duration of A1's liabilities is relatively short. **Discussion:** The uncertainty associated with A1's liability payments, especially at the end of an underwriting cycle, and the potential for hurricane claims substantially reduces the time horizon pertinent to A1's investment portfolio. Note that the time horizon for casualty insurance companies is usually less than that for life companies.
	Liquidity	**For the Exam:** The timing of the underwriting cycle, combined with the prospect of hurricane-related claims, suggests that liquidity needs are high. **Discussion:** Liquidity is always a concern for casualty companies. The end of the underwriting cycle (which implies fewer new policies and inflows), potential increase in claims due to the hurricane, and a downturn in the general business cycle indicate that a greater than usual level of attention to liquidity is required. A1's portfolio should be positioned to meet higher liquidity demands over the near term.
	Legal/ Regulatory	**For the Exam:** A1 is subject to legal and regulatory requirements that vary from state to state. **Discussion:** Casualty companies are subject to the regulations of the states in which they operate. One specific area of concern is the various state regulations affecting investment and allowable asset classes. Risk-based capital regulations also apply.
	Taxes	**For the Exam:** Casualty companies, such as A1, are taxable entities. **Discussion:** Because investment income is subject to taxes, the portfolio management process should focus on maximizing after-tax returns, consistent with the overall level of risk-tolerance. The use of specialist tax advisers is likely to be required.
	Unique Circumstances	**For the Exam:** Significant claims outstanding and geographical concentration of policies. **Discussion:** A1's location in the underwriting cycle, the potential overhang of hurricane-related claims, the general business cycle, and the common stock to surplus ratio are the main distinguishing factors. These have all been addressed previously in the IPS, but the business cycle is experienced by all firms, so large amount of outstanding claims, geographically concentrated policies, and high stock to surplus ratio are all suitable answers.

Sample Scoring Key:
4 points each for the return and risk components.
2 points for the liquidity component.
1 point each for all other components of the IPS.

©2011 Kaplan, Inc.

QUESTION 8

Source: Study Session 18, LOS 43.c,d,e,f,g,l

Answer for Question 8

Maximum 12 points for any four of the following non-compliant items.
1. For the Exam: Only four years presented. Must present at least five years or since inception if less than 5 years. **Discussion:** Firms claiming GIPS® compliance must present at least five years' data or since inception if less than five years. If less than five years presented, the firm must add an additional year each year until ten years are presented. Since Bailey was in existence for all of 2006, they should have presented all 5 years.
2. For the Exam: Assets in the composite. Must present the amount of assets in the composite and either total firm assets or the percentage of firm assets represented by the composite. **Discussion:** Firms must present not only the number of portfolios in the composite but also the total assets in the composite.
3. For the Exam: Incorrect dispersion measure. Must present the measure used to calculate internal dispersion. **Discussion:** Firms must present the internal dispersion of the composite (i.e., the dispersion of individual portfolio returns around the composite return) and the measurement method used. The following are allowed methods: range of annual returns; high and low annual returns; inter-quartile range; equal-weighted and asset-weighted standard deviation of annual portfolio returns.
4. For the Exam: Incomplete disclosure of fees. Must disclose the presence of and access to a complete fee schedule.
5. For the Exam: Composite information. Disclose the presence of and access to descriptions of all the firm's composites.

6. For the Exam:
Discretionary and non-discretionary portfolios included in composites.

Non-discretionary portfolios must not be included.

Discussion:
All fee-paying discretionary portfolios must be included in at least one composite, but non-discretionary portfolios may not be included. Non-fee paying discretionary portfolios may be included with a disclosure.

7. For the Exam:
Incorrect compliance statement.

Firms must disclose whether verified.

Discussion:
The compliance statement is outdated. The 2010 version of GIPS requires firms to use one of the three allowable compliance statements depending on whether the firm had been verified or not. In addition, there is now a statement that must be included with the compliant presentation for a composite that has had an independent, external performance review.

1. **If the firm has been verified:**

   "(Name of firm) claims compliance with the Global Investment Performance Standards (GIPS®) and has prepared and presented this report in compliance with the GIPS standards. (Firm) has been independently verified for the periods (...-...). The verification report(s) is/are available upon request.

   Verification assesses whether (1) the firm has complied with all the composite construction requirements of the GIPS standards on a firm-wide basis and (2) the firm's policies and procedures are designed to calculate and present performance in compliance with the GIPS standards. Verification does not ensure the accuracy of any specific composite presentation."

2. **For individual composites that have had a performance review:**

   "(Name of firm) claims compliance with the Global Investment Performance Standards (GIPS®) and has prepared and presented this report in compliance with the GIPS standards. (Firm) has been independently verified for the periods (...-...).

   Verification assesses whether (1) the firm has complied with all the composite construction requirements of the GIPS standards on a firm-wide basis and (2) the firm's policies and procedures are designed to calculate and present performance in compliance with the GIPS standards. *The (composite name) composite has been examined for the periods (...-...). The verification and performance examination reports are available upon request.*"

3. **If the firm has not been verified:**

   "(Name of firm) claims compliance with the Global Investment Performance Standards (GIPS®) and has prepared and presented this report in compliance with the GIPS standards. (Name of firm) has NOT been independently verified."

Verification and performance reviews:
Verification is not intended as an assurance that a performance presentation is accurate. It only indicates that the firm has followed its documented policies and procedures for achieving and maintaining GIPS compliance, and a single verification report must be issued for the entire firm; a firm cannot claim that one of its composites has been verified.

The firm may have the performance of an individual composite thoroughly reviewed (audited). The performance review can be conducted simultaneously with or after verification, but a performance review statement cannot be issued unless the firm has been verified. In the performance review statement, the verification firm attests that the composite has been constructed, calculated, and presented in accordance with the GIPS. The GIPS neither require nor recommend performance reviews.

Sample Scoring Key: (12 points maximum)
1 point for stating each non-compliant item.
2 points for each correct recommended change.

For the Exam:

Any of the GIPS® 35 required disclosures that are relevant to the firm itself or to the presentation should be included in the footnotes. Any omitted disclosures would qualify as errors in the presentation. Be sure you know the required disclosures as well as all GIPS requirements for the exam. Remember, they are all provided for your review in the Level III Standards Pack located in the Schweser online library.

These 35 disclosures are found in the footnotes to a GIPS-compliant presentation and must include:

1. The proper GIPS compliance statement.
2. Definition of firm.
3. Composite description.
4. Benchmark description.
5. If gross-of-fees returns, any fees in addition to trading expenses.
6. If net-of-fees, any fees in addition to management fees and trading expenses that are deducted; if model or actual management fees are deducted; if net of any performance-based fees.
7. Currency used to express returns.
8. Internal dispersion and the measure used.
9. Fee schedule.
10. Composite creation date.
11. That a list of composite descriptions is available.
12. That the policies for valuing portfolios, calculating performance, and preparing compliant statements are available.
13. If material, the presence, use, and extent of leverage, derivatives, and short positions, including frequency of use and instruments used.
14. Any significant event that would facilitate understanding the presentation.
15. Any presented periods prior to 2000 that are not GIPS-compliant.
16. If appropriate, the date, description of, and reason for redefining the firm.
17. If appropriate, the date, description of, and reason for redefining a composite.
18. Any changes to the composite's name.
19. Minimum asset level for a portfolio to be included in the composite and any changes to the level.

20. Treatment of withholding taxes if material and whether benchmark returns are net of withholding taxes (if known).
21. Periods beginning on or after January 1, 2011, any known material differences in exchange rates used between the portfolios and the composite and the composite and the benchmark.
22. Any instances where the presentation conforms with local laws or regulations that conflict with the GIPS.
23. If relevant for results prior to January 1, 2010, how cash is allocated to carve-outs.
24. If appropriate the types of fees included in bundled fees.
25. For periods beginning on or after January 1, 2006, the use of sub-advisors and the periods used.
26. For periods prior to January 1, 2010, if any portfolios were not valued at month-end or last business day of the month.
27. If material for periods beginning on or after January 1, 2011, the use of unobservable subjective inputs for portfolio valuation.
28. For periods beginning on or after January 1, 2011, whether the valuation hierarchy used differs from the GIPS suggested hierarchy.
29. If no benchmark is presented, why.
30. If appropriate, the date and reason for changing benchmarks.
31. If a custom benchmark or a combination of benchmarks is used as benchmark, the components of and method for constructing the benchmark.
32. How significant cash flow is defined, if appropriate.
33. Whether a 3-year ex-post standard deviation is not presented because three years of monthly data are not available.
34. If determined that a 3-year ex-post standard deviation is not appropriate, describe why not appropriate, present an alternative ex-post risk measure, and explain why that risk measure is appropriate.
35. Whether past performance from a past firm or affiliate is linked to the presentation.

QUESTION 9

Source: Study Session 17, LOS 41.p

A.   **For the Exam:**

$$\text{Sharpe Ratio} = \frac{\overline{R_P} - \overline{R_F}}{\sigma_P}$$

$$\text{HNW} = \frac{28.2 - 4.4}{45.0} = 0.53$$

$$\text{S\&P 500} = \frac{22.4 - 4.4}{20.0} = 0.90$$

Sharpe → The HNW portfolio significantly underperformed the S&P 500.

$$\text{Treynor Measure} = \frac{\overline{R_P} - \overline{R_F}}{\beta_P}$$

$$\text{HNW} = \frac{28.2 - 4.4}{1.35} = 17.6$$

$$\text{S\&P 500} = \frac{22.4 - 4.4}{1.0} = 18.0$$

Treynor → The HNW portfolio only modestly underperformed the S&P 500.

Discussion:

The Sharpe ratio is the portfolio's excess return over the risk-free rate (R_F) divided by the portfolio standard deviation (σ_P). The greater the Sharpe Ratio, the greater the excess return received per unit of total risk assumed. The HNW portfolio has significantly underperformed the S&P 500 on this basis.

The Treynor Measure is the portfolio's excess return over the risk-free rate (R_F) divided by the portfolio's systematic risk as measured by beta (β_P). The greater the Treynor Measure, the greater the excess return received per unit of systematic risk assumed. The HNW portfolio has modestly underperformed the S&P 500 on this basis.

> Sample Scoring Key:
> 2 points for correctly computing each of the measures.

B.   **For the Exam:**

The Treynor measure uses beta (systematic risk) as a measure of risk, so it underestimates true risk exposure when the portfolio is under-diversified. If the investor is also exposed to unsystematic risk, the Treynor measure will rank individual portfolio performance higher than the Sharpe ratio.

Discussion:

The standard deviation of the portfolio's returns is caused by systematic and unsystematic risk factors or only systematic risk factors, depending on whether it is diversified or not. Whether we use Sharpe or Treynor to measure its risk-adjusted excess return depends on the structure of the portfolio as well as its place in the investor's total holdings. In any case, we want to account for the all of the risk (volatility) faced by the investor, which may or may not be accurately reflected in the portfolio beta.

When comparing the performance of individual portfolios, consider:

If the portfolio comprises a *large part* of the investor's wealth: (i.e., not enough other assets to diversify away any unsystematic risk)
- If it is fully diversified, we can use Sharpe and/or Treynor to measure and rank its risk-adjusted performance.
  - Since the portfolio is fully diversified, its total risk (standard deviation) is comprised of systematic risk only.
  - Both measures accurately capture the risk to which the investor is exposed.
- If it is *not* fully diversified, we should only use *Sharpe*.
  - Treynor captures the systematic risk component only, so it underestimates the risk to which the investor is exposed.
  - Treynor over-states its risk-adjusted performance relative to other portfolios.

If the portfolio is only a *small part* of the investor's total wealth: (i.e., plenty of other assets to diversify away any unsystematic risk).
- If it is fully diversified, we can use Sharpe and/or Treynor to measure and rank its risk-adjusted performance.
  - Since the portfolio is fully diversified, its total risk (standard deviation) is comprised of systematic risk only.
  - Both measures accurately capture the risk to which the investor is exposed.
- If it is *not* fully diversified, we should only use its *Treynor* measure.
  - The individual portfolio's unsystematic risk is diversified away by the investor's other assets.
  - Treynor measures only the systematic risk component, which is the only risk faced by the investor.
  - Sharpe, which uses standard deviation, will in this case measure both systematic and unsystematic risk.
    - Overstates the risk to which the investor is exposed and depresses the portfolio's ranking relative to other portfolios.

Sample Scoring Key:
1 point for differentiating between systematic and unsystematic risk.
1 point for explaining which type of risk is relevant to each measure.
1 point for explaining when each measure is most appropriate.

C. **For the Exam:**

$$M^2 \text{ Measure} = R_F + \left(R_P - R_F\right)\frac{\sigma_M}{\sigma_P}$$

$$\text{HNW} = 4.4 + \left(28.2 - 4.4\right)\frac{20}{45} = 15.0\%$$

The M^2 for any asset will only equal the M^2 for the market if it has the same level of excess return per total risk. That is, they will be the same if the Sharpe ratios are the same.

Discussion:

The M^2 measure evaluates portfolio performance by computing what the portfolio's excess return would have been if the level of total risk was exactly the same as the market. This excess return can be directly compared with the market's excess return in order to determine relative performance for the portfolio.

$$M^2 \text{ Measure} = R_F + \left(R_P - R_F\right)\frac{\sigma_M}{\sigma_P}$$

$$M^2_{HNW} = 4.4 + \left(28.2 - 4.4\right)\frac{20}{45} = 15.0\%$$

Since the M^2 for the market is its return, 22.4%, we can see that HNW has underperformed the market based on this measure. Since the M^2 ranking will always agree with the Sharpe ratio ranking, we already knew that the portfolio had underperformed from our work in parts A and B.

A portfolio will have an M^2 that is exactly the same as the market if it has the same level of excess return per unit of total risk assumed as the market. That is, they will have identical M^2 if the Sharpe ratios are also the same.

Sample Scoring Key:
1 point for computing the measure.
1 point for explaining the relative performance.
1 point for demonstrating the requirements for the portfolio's measure to equal the market.

QUESTION 10

Source: Study Session 5, LOS 15.i
Study Session 11, LOS 27.u

 Professor's Note: The objectives and constraints of the bank's security portfolio will be affected by its particular circumstances. The effect on Opportunity's investment objectives, constraints, and investment policies in the described scenarios (when viewing each separately from the others) is as follows.

Answer for Question 10-A

Scenario	*Affect on bank's policies*
1. Due to pressure from local activists, Opportunity has stepped up lending in low-income areas. Groh expects the default rate on these loans to be higher than the loans currently in their portfolio.	**For the Exam:** • Reduced risk tolerance of security portfolio. • Risk of assets in security portfolio should be reduced. • Note in unique circumstances about new loans with increased default rate. **Discussion:** Because Groh expects the default rate on these loans will be higher than the loans in their current portfolio, Opportunity should invest in less risky securities in its security portfolio to offset the increased risk in its loan portfolio. Although it does not directly pertain to the bank's security portfolio, the increased lending to low-income areas could be noted in the bank's unique circumstances section of its investment policy statement.
2. Opportunity has bought a regional bank with operations in North Carolina, South Carolina, and Georgia. The acquired bank's loan portfolio consists mostly of commercial loans to small, local businesses.	**For the Exam:** • Loan portfolio has better geographical diversification. • Operating assets have less risk, so risk objective of security portfolio can be increased. **Discussion:** Opportunity has bought banks in a different region of the country and with products that differ from their current loan portfolio. Opportunity's loan portfolio is now better diversified. With the acquisition of banks in other geographical and product areas, Opportunity's security portfolio could allow its risk objective to reflect a greater ability to take risk.

Exam 2
Morning Session Answers

3. A recent downturn in interest rates has caused many of Opportunity's variable-rate mortgages to be refinanced to 15- and 30-year fixed rate mortgages. Opportunity has retained the business of most of its customers who have refinanced.	**For the Exam:** • Increased asset duration. • Increase return objective for security portfolio to compensate for reduced returns on assets. • Reduce liquidity constraint for security portfolio. **Discussion:** The refinancing of Opportunity's variable-rate mortgages to fixed-rate mortgages has several effects. First, it extends the duration of Opportunity's assets, which results in a positive leverage-adjusted duration gap. To counterbalance this increase in duration, Opportunity should decrease the duration of its securities portfolio by investing in shorter duration assets. Second, although Opportunity has retained the business of most of its customers who have refinanced, it will have the cash from those who have paid off their mortgages by refinancing with other institutions. This increased liquidity decreases the need for the security portfolio to provide liquidity. Third, the new mortgages that Opportunity makes may have a lower return than Opportunity had forecasted. This may put increased pressure on the security portfolio to generate a higher return.

B.   **For the Exam:**

Advantage: Compensation will be more performance based and should better motivate the manager.

Disadvantages:
- Manager has an incentive to take bigger risks when lagging the benchmark.
- Performance-based fee structures are more complicated to administer.

Discussion:

The advantage of the new fee structure is that the manager's compensation is more heavily dependent on performance. Hence, the trust will not pay as much for poor performance as they would if the compensation was based solely on the amount of assets managed (as was the case for the previous manager). The primary disadvantage of performance-based fees is that they create an incentive for the manager to take bigger risks. If the manager's performance is lagging their benchmark, they have an incentive to take greater risk in order to generate higher returns and compensation. Secondly, performance-based fee structures are more complicated to administer.

Sample Scoring Key: A.   2 points for correctly identifying the influence of *each* scenario. B.   1 point for identifying the advantage of performance-based fee structures and 1 point for identifying *each* disadvantage of performance-based fee structures.

Exam 2
Afternoon Session Answers

To get detailed answer explanations with references to specific LOS and SchweserNotes content, and to get valuable feedback on how your score compares to those of other Level III candidates, use your Username and Password to gain Online Access at *www.schweser.com* and choose the left-hand menu item "Practice Exams Vol. 2."

1.	B	25.	A	49.	B
2.	B	26.	C	50.	C
3.	B	27.	B	51.	C
4.	C	28.	B	52.	B
5.	C	29.	C	53.	A
6.	A	30.	C	54.	A
7.	C	31.	A	55.	C
8.	C	32.	C	56.	C
9.	A	33.	C	57.	C
10.	C	34.	A	58.	A
11.	A	35.	A	59.	C
12.	B	36.	B	60.	C
13.	B	37.	B		
14.	B	38.	A		
15.	B	39.	B		
16.	A	40.	A		
17.	C	41.	C		
18.	B	42.	A		
19.	A	43.	C		
20.	B	44.	C		
21.	B	45.	A		
22.	C	46.	A		
23.	B	47.	B		
24.	B	48.	A		

Exam 2
Afternoon Session Answers

QUESTIONS 1–6

Source: Study Session 1

1. **B** In the meeting with Pavlica's children, King disclosed Pavlica's medical condition. Since King learned this information as a result of his professional relationship with the client, he has a duty to keep it confidential, even from her children. By breaking the confidentiality, King has violated Standard III(E) Preservation of Confidentiality. Remaindermen are the beneficiaries of a trust or anyone who has a claim on the assets of an estate. Pavlica is the only one named as the beneficiary of the trust; thus, technically she is the only remainderman. It could be argued the children have a claim on the remaining assets of the estate but there is nothing mentioned about whether or not Pavlica has a will or how it is worded. (Study Session 1, LOS 1.b)

2. **B** Since the annual meeting between Pavlica and King was only three months before the meeting between King and Pavlica's children, it is safe to assume the portfolio allocation represented Pavlica's investment policy statement. King reallocated the portfolio before meeting with Pavlica to discuss the suggested strategy and then withheld information that he had met with her children. The reallocation (after meeting with the children) was according to the wishes of Pavlica's children, who are not beneficiaries of the trust. King has a responsibility under Standard III(A) Loyalty, Prudence, and Care to act solely in the best interest of his client and maintain loyalty to Pavlica, not her children. He has thus violated the Standard. (Study Session 1, LOS 1.b)

3. **B** King has essentially guaranteed a certain level of portfolio performance by stating that Pavlica's spending requirements will definitely be met by the new strategy. This is a violation of Standard I(C) Misrepresentation, which prohibits misrepresentations in dealing with clients. The investment strategy has some inherent level of uncertainty and by implicitly guaranteeing performance, King has misrepresented the strategy. (Study Session 1, LOS 1.b)

4. **C** Private placement shares are likely to be illiquid and have more risk than publicly traded equity. By not taking any shares for himself and only allocating shares to accounts for which the investment is appropriate, King has complied with the Standards. However, King has violated Standard VI(B) Priority of Transactions by trading his shares ahead of his client's shares. It doesn't matter that in this situation it benefited the client. King must always take investment action first for his clients and act in their best interests. As a member of the ShaleCo board, King must also be careful not to violate Standard II(A) Material Nonpublic Information. (Study Session 1, LOS 1.b)

5. **C** King may accept the directorship even though it may create a potential conflict of interest as long as the conflict is prominently disclosed in understandable language to all clients and prospects as well as to his employer. According to Standard VI(A) Disclosure of Conflicts, such disclosure is necessary so that all related parties can assess the impact the potential conflict will have on King's professional activities. Additionally, the directorship will provide additional compensation that must be approved ahead of his assuming the position. (Study Session 1, LOS 1.b)

6. **A**   Standard VI(A) Disclosure of Conflicts. Performance compensation such as the one in effect at Rowan Brothers encourages portfolio managers to act in their own interests instead of their clients' best interest (a potential conflict of interest) and encourages them to take additional risks to attain the 10% goal. Therefore, this compensation scheme must be totally disclosed to all clients and prospects. By not disclosing the fees to current clients (he only discloses the new fee structure to prospective clients), King has violated the Standard. It is not a violation to have such a compensation program, however, as long as it is disclosed. (Study Session 1, LOS 1.b)

> Sample Scoring Key: 3 points for each correct response.

QUESTIONS 7–12

Source: Study Session 1

7. **C** Bracco has not violated any soft dollar standards. This is an example of *client-directed brokerage* where the client, in this case Stephen Carobilo, is allowed to direct the investment manager to use a specific broker to execute trades. Moreover, one could take the view that the client benefits in the sense that Stephen Carobilo knows he is helping his friend at First Trades Brokerage by utilizing them as the broker. A commingled fund is a fund that is comprised of different client's funds. (Study Session 1, LOS 1.b)

8. **C** Bracco is in violation of Standard II(A) Material Nonpublic Information, which states that members and candidates cannot trade or cause others to trade based on material nonpublic information that could affect the value of an investment. Even though Bracco has performed his own research and the information he acquired from McNulty and his colleague was an accident, it was nonetheless material nonpublic information and therefore cannot be traded upon. (Study Session 1, LOS 1.b)

9. **A** This is not a violation of an effective corporate governance system. Effective corporate governance requires that a majority of board members are independent. For effective corporate governance, boards should be composed of non-independent and independent members and others with relevant expertise. Clearly, James would not be considered an independent board member because she is paid as a consultant to the firm. The fact that James's husband also performs consulting work for Stiles Corporation is not a violation of effective corporate governance because he is not considered part of management. Board members are allowed to hire outside consultants without management's interference or approval, but James's husband was hired as a consultant to the firm and not the board. (Study Session 1, LOS 1.b)

10. **C** Short-term interest paid previously to the wrong accounts should not be taken away from those accounts which should have received the original shares, making Gun's statement incorrect. Accounts that do not meet the minimum transaction amount as described in the company's policies and procedures should not receive shares of the IPO, making Bracco's statement incorrect. (Study Session 1, LOS 1.b)

11. **A** McNulty has violated both the Code of Ethics and the Standards of Professional Conduct. The Code of Ethics states in part that members of CFA Institute must act with integrity, competence, diligence, respect, and in an ethical manner with employees and colleagues in the investment profession. The inappropriate behavior has violated the Code. The unethical behavior also violates Standard I(D) Misconduct. The Standard states in part that members and candidates must not commit any act that reflects adversely on their professional reputation, integrity, or competence. His inappropriate behavior, especially drinking heavily with Stiles' management, has violated this Standard. (Study Session 1, LOS 1.b)

12. **B** The information in the notebook is clearly material and non-public, as its public release will affect Stiles' stock price. As such, McNulty should have taken steps to protect it. His drinking and behavior at the party are the obvious blame for his accidentally losing the notebook, but the reasons for losing it are not the point here. Whether he intentionally or accidentally lost the notebook, McNulty has violated Standard III(E), Duties to Clients, by not taking steps to preserve the confidentiality of his client's planned offering. Sampson violated Standard II(A) by sharing material, non-public information with others and trading on it. (Study Session 1, LOS 1.b)

> Sample Scoring Key: 3 points for each correct response.

QUESTIONS 13–18

Source: Study Sessions 9, 10, and 15

13. **B**   When evaluating bond investment alternatives based on mean reversion analysis only, the bond that is most attractive is the one whose current spread is the largest positive number of standard deviations above the mean.

Bond issue YY has a current spread that is below its mean so it is not an attractive candidate. For the spread to revert to its mean, it must widen and the bond will depreciate in value.

The number of standard deviations above the mean is computed as follows:

Bond Issue VV: $(125 - 98) / 28 = 0.96$;   Bond Issue XX: $(100 - 75) / 15 = 1.67$

Morrison should purchase Bond Issue XX, since the current spread exceeds its mean spread by the greatest number of standard deviations. (Study Session 9, LOS 24.e)

14. **B**   Implication of cyclical and secular changes in the corporate bond market include:

Securities with embedded options will command a premium due to their scarcity, and the percentage of long-term issues will decline. Thus, Morrison is incorrect. Effective duration and aggregate interest rate risk sensitivity will decline.

Tabler's statement is correct. Credit-based derivatives will be used increasingly to achieve desired exposures to credit sectors, issuers, and structures. (Study Session 9, LOS 24.b)

15. **B**   To answer this question you have to bring to mind the price-yield graph for a callable bond. You will remember that the price-yield graph for a callable bond is concave below the coupon rate (i.e., the callable bond experiences negative convexity at very low interest rates). While a non-callable bond will continually increase in value as its required return falls, the value of the option in the callable bond increases as the required return falls and places a cap on the maximum value of the callable bond. Therefore, as rates fall below the coupon rate, the non-callable bond will outperform a comparable callable bond.

When rates are already below the coupon rate but are increasing, the callable bond will not fall in value as quickly, so it will outperform the non-callable bond. The difference between the values of the callable and comparable non-callable bond is the value of the embedded call option. Thus, as rates fall below the coupon rate, the value of the call option increases in value, consuming an increasing amount of the total value of the bond. When the required return is significantly higher than the coupon rate, the value of the call option goes to zero and both bonds behave as if they are non-callable. (Study Session 9, LOS 24.e)

16. **A**   Morrison is correct. Corporate spread curves, which measure the yield spreads between higher and lower rated bonds, tend to change with the economic cycle, so in order to properly conduct this analysis the analyst must carefully examine credit and yield curves. Tabler is also correct. Corporate spread curves narrow during upturns and widen during downturns. The reason for this is that default becomes more likely during a recession and yields on risky corporate bonds increase. Yield spreads decrease during an expansion because default is generally less likely. (Study Session 9, LOS 24.e)

17. **C** Both Morrison and Tabler are correct. There is a positive relationship between the federal funds rate and the repo rate. The use of collateral with limited availability decreases the repo rate. Furthermore, as credit quality and liquidity increase, the repo rate declines. As the term decreases, the repo rate decreases. Lastly, the repo rate will be lower if the collateral is delivered to the lender, rather than to the borrower's bank. (Study Session 10, LOS 25.b)

18. **B** The net interest paid is determined as follows:

Loan payment	−(LIBOR + 120 bp)
− Pay fixed in swap (5.20% + 100 bp)	−6.20%
+ Receive in swap	+LIBOR
Net =	−7.40%

LIBOR paid in the loan is cancelled by the LIBOR received in the swap. In net, the client will pay a fixed rate of 6.20% + 1.20% = 7.40%. (Study Session 15, LOS 38.a)

Sample Scoring Key: 3 points for each correct response.

QUESTIONS 19–24

Source: Study Sessions 10 and 14

19. **A** The provision responsible for Cramer's difficulty is the cross-default provision. A cross-default provision specifies that the borrower is in default of that agreement if it defaults on any of its borrowing/credit agreements. Jump-to-default risk is another name for current credit risk. (Study Session 14, LOS 34.i)

20. **B** Cramer is incorrect because current credit risk is not always a reliable indicator of potential credit risk. Firms currently having credit problems may be able to correct their situations, which will reduce potential credit risk. Alternatively, firms presently having no apparent current credit difficulties may lack the ability to honor obligations in the future.

    McNally is correct. Current credit risk relates to the possibility of default on current obligations, whereas future credit risk relates to potential default on future obligations. (Study Session 14, LOS 34.i)

21. **B** Current credit risk refers to the amount due now and there is none. However, the forward contract has positive value to the long of $50 minus the present value of $50, $\left[S - \dfrac{f}{(1+i)^t}\right]$, so there is potential credit risk (of future default) in that amount. Any position that has a positive value under the forward contract has potential credit risk because there is a risk that the counterparty will not pay. (Study Session 14, LOS 34.i)

22. **C** Cramer is incorrect. Although it is true that firms can control their credit risk by making use of netting arrangements, requiring collateral from counterparties, and requiring a periodic mark to market of asset positions, they should do business with an SPV, not create one. Doing business with SPVs can lower the probability of credit losses. Special purpose vehicles are created by dealer banks to offer higher credit-rated swaps that are protected from non-derivative claims against the parent company. SPVs are usually well capitalized and hedge their derivative risk. The parent is also liable for the SPV's debt up to the parent's equity investment.

    McNally is incorrect. In a total return swap, the purchaser receives cash flows over the life of the swap, usually determined by a floating rate, such as LIBOR, plus a spread. (Study Session 14, LOS 34.k)

23. **B** A credit spread call option will provide protection if the reference asset's spread (at option maturity) over the relevant risk-free benchmark increases beyond the strike spread (here 3%). The increase in the spread beyond the strike spread (i.e., the option being in the money) constitutes an identifiable credit event, in and of itself. These contracts may specify for the payoff to be delivery of a physical or a cash settlement.

    Credit spread puts are useful when one believes the credit spread will decline.

    In a credit default swap, the protection buyer (i.e., the asset holder) makes regular payments to the dealer and receives a payment when a specified credit event occurs. (Study Session 10, LOS 25.g)

24. **B**   Since the spread has widened, the credit spread forward results in a payoff to the **buyer** of $300,000:

FV = (actual spread − contract spread) × notional principal × risk factor

FV = (0.045 − 0.03) × $2 million × 10 = $300,000

(Study Session 10, LOS 25.g)

Sample Scoring Key: 3 points for each correct response.

QUESTIONS 25–30

Source: Study Sessions 9 and 10

25. **A**   In a cross hedge the manager enters into a forward contract to deliver the original foreign currency (the baht) for a second foreign currency (the won), which is predicted to appreciate against the domestic currency. The currency risk is changed from an exposure in the baht to one in the won.

In a proxy hedge the manager enters into a forward contract between the domestic currency and a second foreign currency highly correlated with the first foreign currency. Proxy hedges are typically employed when forward contracts are thinly traded or not available on the original foreign currency.

In the forward hedge, the baht would be delivered for the dollar.
(Study Session 10, LOS 25.j)

26. **C**   In the case of all three foreign countries, the cash rate is lower than the cash rate in the United States, which means that all three currencies will trade at a forward premium to the U.S. dollar.

The forward differential for each foreign currency relative to the dollar is approximated as the difference between the domestic and the foreign interest rates. Assume the U.S. dollar is currency d, the Thai baht is currency i, the Korean won is currency j, and the Japanese yen is currency k. Forward rates are denoted f, and the cash rates in each currency are denoted c.

$$f_{d,i} = c_d - c_i = 6.50 - 2.50 \quad = +4.00$$

$$f_{d,j} = c_d - c_j = 6.50 - 3.20 \quad = +3.30$$

$$f_{d,k} = c_d - c_k = 6.50 - 4.20 \quad = +2.30 \text{ (Study Session 10, LOS 25.j)}$$

27. **B**   In breakeven rate analysis, the analyst determines the yield change that makes the returns on bonds equivalent. Recall that we hold the short duration bond constant and examine the yield change in the longer duration bond that would make the returns equivalent.

To determine the yield change at which the investor would be indifferent between purchasing two bonds, we must first compare the bonds' yields over the holding period. Over the 1-year time horizon, the Nakhon Metals bond has a yield advantage of 0.70% (5.2% − 4.5%). For the returns to be equivalent over the 1-year time horizon (assuming the bonds are purchased at their current prices), the price for the Nakhon Metals bond must fall by 0.70%. For its price to fall, its yield must increase. The magnitude of the yield change is provided by rearranging the modified duration formula:

$$\%\Delta\text{price} = -\text{modified duration} \times \Delta\text{yield}$$

$$\frac{\%\Delta\text{price}}{-\text{modified duration}} = \Delta\text{yield}$$

$$\frac{-0.70\%}{-7.30} = 0.0959\% \text{ or } 9.59 \text{ basis points}$$

So if the yield for the Nakhon Metals bond increases by 9.59 basis points and the yield for the Powhatan Industries bond remains constant, the returns for the two bonds will be equivalent over the next year. Given that the Nakhon Metals bond has an initial yield advantage of 0.70%, its return will be higher as long as its yield does not increase by more than 9.59 basis points over the next year. In this case, the yield on the Nakhon Metals bond is expected to increase by 15 basis points, so the Powhatan Industries bond is more attractive. (Study Session 10, LOS 25.k)

28. **B**   Thomas is correct and Bentley's friend is incorrect. To determine whether a foreign currency-denominated investment should be hedged or not, the manager must compare the expected currency gain or loss implied by the respective cash rates to his expectations. Using the cash rates for the United States and Japan, the expected forward premium for the Yen is 6.5% − 4.20% = 2.3%. In other words, the market predicts the Yen will appreciate 2.3% against the dollar. According to Thomas's and Bentley's expectations, however, the yen should appreciate 3.5% against the dollar. Thomas's and Bentley's conclusion should be that the forward Yen is currently too cheap; it is not priced high enough relative to the dollar. Bentley's friend's statement is correct only if the forward differential implied by the cash rates is the same as Thomas's and Bentley's expectations. Since Thomas and Bentley expect the yen to appreciate more than predicted by the market, Thomas's U.S. managers would be better off not hedging. (Study Session 10, LOS 25.j)

29. **C**   Both Thomas and Bentley are correct. Both callable bonds and bonds with very long durations trade at a premium due to their scarcity. (Study Session 9, LOS 24.b)

30. **C**   When interest rates are near coupon rates and fall for callables and non-callables, non-callables will increase in value more than callables. This is because the price of a callable is depressed as the value of the embedded option increases with the drop in interest rates. Under scenario A, therefore, non-callables outperform callables.

When interest rates are historically very low and rise for both callables and non-callables, the value of the non-callable will fall faster than the value of the callable bond. Therefore, under scenario B the callable will outperform the non-callable. (Study Session 9, LOS 24.e)

Sample Scoring Key: 3 points for each correct response.

QUESTIONS 31–36

Source: Study Session 13

31. **A** The only possible answer from the given reasons is a high water mark provision. Since the firm had experienced losses for two years before increasing in value in the previous year, it is likely that the value of the fund had yet to achieve a previous "high water mark" that it must exceed in order for there to be an earned incentive fee. (Study Session 13, LOS 31.q)

32. **C** CTAs that specialize in systematic trading strategies typically apply sets of rules to trade according to or contrary to short, intermediate, and/or long-term trends. A discretionary CTA trading strategy generates returns on the managers' trading expertise, much like any active portfolio manager. CTAs can also be classified according to whether they trade in financial markets, currency markets, or diversified markets. (Study Session 13, LOS 31.t)

33. **C** Similar to a term structure of interest rates, the term structure of futures prices shows the relationship at a point in time between futures prices and time to maturity. When the term structure is negative (called backwardation), longer-term contracts have lower prices than shorter-term contracts, so the curve is downward sloping. With the passage of time, the maturity of a long-term contract shortens and its price rises to that of a shorter-term contract. Thus, an investor can go long a long-term contract and profit as time passes, and the steeper the curve (the greater the backwardation), the greater the potential returns. An upward-sloping term structure of futures prices is called contango. (Study Session 13, LOS 31.n)

34. **A** Cantori says he will research companies who do business in commodities. He feels that using the indirect method of buying the stock of those companies to gain commodity exposure is an efficient and effective method for gaining exposure to commodities. This is not necessarily true because those companies often hedge their exposure to commodities. The other statements are true. Agricultural commodities tend to be negatively correlated with inflation, but the broad commodity indices have been positively correlated with inflation. Also, commodities have not generally outperformed stocks and bonds. They are attractive in that they can provide a comparable return while diversifying the portfolio. (Study Session 13, LOS 31.o)

35. **A** Like interest rate swaps, the fixed value is a weighted average of the futures or forward values where the weights are slightly heavier for the contracts with a shorter maturity. Thus, the swap price is probably slightly more than $53. It is probably not much higher than $53 since the risk-free rate is so low. (Study Session 13, LOS 32)

36. **B** Commodity swaps can have both seasonal prices and notional principals. This should not be surprising since swaps are OTC contracts that the participants can design any way they choose. (Study Session 13, LOS 32)

> Sample Scoring Key: 3 points for each correct response.

QUESTIONS 37–42

Source: Study Sessions 10, 12, and 15

37. **B**   Edwards is incorrect. The value of the note goes down if interest rates increase. An interest rate call seller provides a payment to the buyer of the call when interest rates increase. If interest rates increase, a short position in interest rate calls would decrease in value, so this will not hedge the risk of the note.

   Palmer is correct. We know that the note must have a fixed rate because of the length of its duration. A floating rate note will have a duration significantly less than one year. The swap can effectively turn the fixed-rate note into a floating-rate note and reduce the duration of the position. If interest rates rise, Anderson receives the higher floating rate in the swap. (Study Session 15, LOS 38.a)

38. **A**   In order to calculate how much Anderson will receive in dollars as a result of the swap, first calculate the implied notional principal (NP) of a CHF-denominated swap that would produce quarterly cash flows of CHF12,000,000, given the Swiss interest rate of 6.6%:

$$NP\left(\frac{0.066}{4}\right) = CHF12,000,000$$

$$NP = \frac{CHF12,000,000}{\left(\dfrac{0.066}{4}\right)} = CHF727,272,727$$

   Next, calculate the dollar-equivalent principal at the current exchange rate and then calculate a dollar cash flow using the dollar interest rate of 2.8%:

$$CHF727,272,727 \times (\$/CHF1.24) = \$586,510,264$$
$$\$586,510,264 \times (2.80\%/4) = \$4,105,572 \qquad \text{(Study Session 15, LOS 38.f)}$$

39. **B**   The statement is accurate. Transaction exposure is from transactions already entered into and the amount to hedge is thus known (i.e., hedge the principal). Transaction exposures are the most commonly hedged exposures of a firm. Economic risk, the relationship between changing exchange rates and asset values, is not contractual and the amount to hedge is thus less certain, making it harder to hedge. Translation risk refers to the effect of exchange rate changes on the income statement and balance sheet and is often not hedged. (Study Session 15, LOS 36.f)

40. **A** Edwards is correct. If management predicts that interest rates will fall, they will not want to be stuck paying a high, fixed rate. To take advantage of falling rates, they can enter a pay-floating swap (or swaption). The fixed receipt from the swap will at least partially offset the fixed payment on the bonds, while the firm ends up paying a net floating rate. If desired, management could enter a second pay fixed swap after rates have fallen to lock in the lower fixed rate. The net duration on the first swap can be calculated as the duration of the fixed arm minus the duration of the floating arm, which is $3.75 - 0.25 = 3.5$. The notional principal for the swap can be calculated as follows:

$$\text{NP} = \$10,000,000 \left(\frac{4}{3.5} \right) = \$11,428,571$$

Note: Anderson will assume the receive-fixed arm of the swap, so its duration to Anderson is positive. Also, Anderson is not hedging price risk. That is, they are not trying to change the duration of the bond, so we enter the duration, as it is, in the equation.

Palmer is incorrect. Anderson is paying out a fixed rate, so to take advantage of falling rates, they should receive a fixed rate and pay out a floating rate in the swap. Because the fixed side of the swap has a greater duration than the floating side, Anderson's position in the swap will have a net positive duration. (Study Session 15, LOS 38.f)

41. **C** If $275,000 is invested in the U.S. bond and $155,000 is invested in the British bond, the total value of the portfolio is $430,000. The duration contribution of the U.S. bond is (275,000 / 430,000) × 4.0 = 2.56.

To obtain the duration contribution of the British bond to the U.S. portfolio, we must incorporate its yield beta. The yield beta tells us how much British bond yields will change, if U.S. bond yields change by 1%. Using the yield beta of 1.40, the duration contribution of the British bond is (155,000 / 430,000) × 8.5 × 1.40 = 4.29.

The duration of the entire bond portfolio from a U.S. perspective is then 2.56 + 4.29 = 6.85. (Study Session 10, LOS 25.i)

42. **A** Comment 1 is correct. Emerging market debt has been shown to have increased resiliency over time. When emerging debt markets are hit by some event, they tend to bounce back offering the potential for high returns. (Study Session 10, LOS 30.l)

Comment 2 is incorrect. It is true that emerging market debt is quite volatile due in part to political risk and that analysts should monitor the risk of these markets. However, the standard deviation would be a poor measure of risk because the returns for emerging market debt are often negatively skewed. This non-normal returns distribution makes the standard deviation a poor measure of risk because it assumes normality. (Study Session 12, LOS 30.c)

> Sample Scoring Key: 3 points for each correct response.

QUESTIONS 43–48

Source: Study Sessions 9, 14, and 15

43. **C** To hedge their Treasury bond position, Washington Capital should sell:

$$\#\,calls = \frac{1}{\delta} \times \left(\frac{V_p}{V_c}\right)$$

where:
V_p = total value of asset position
V_c = value covered by one call option

(1 / 0.4) × (5,000,000 / 100,000) = 125 calls. (Study Session 15, LOS 37.e)

44. **C** Thomas is correct. When the option is at-the-money or near expiration, it becomes more important for the portfolio manager to incorporate both gamma and delta into their option hedge analysis so as to increase the precision of the hedge.

    Bentley is correct. An increase in the price of the underlying would drive the call option into the money and increase delta, so the size of a delta hedge call position should be decreased. (Study Session 15, LOS 37.e,f)

45. **A** To return the portfolio to its original dollar duration, the manager could purchase additional amounts of each bond. Alternatively, the manager could select one of the bonds to use as a controlling position. Since the dollar duration has fallen and Bond 1 has the longest duration, the manager could use the least amount of additional cash by increasing only the holding in Bond 1 (i.e., using Bond 1 as the controlling position):

$$\text{desired increase in DD} = \text{target DD} - \text{current DD}$$
$$= \$157,200 - \$142,095 = \$15,105$$

$$\text{increase in Bond 1: new DD of Bond 1} = \$35,100 + \$15,105$$
$$= \$50,205$$

$$\text{required new value of Bond 1} = \frac{\$50,205}{\$35,100} \times \$780,000 = \$1,115,667$$

Thus, the manager could purchase another \$335,667 (= \$1,115,667 − \$780.000) of Bond 1. The new portfolio total value will be \$4,217,000 + \$335,667 = \$4,552,667, and the portfolio dollar duration will be back to its original level:

$$\begin{aligned}
DD_{new} &= [\$1,115,667(4.5)+\$2,500,000(3.4)+\$524,000(2.7)+\$413,000(1.9)](0.01)\\
&= [\$5,020,501.50+\$8,500,000+\$1,414,800+\$784,700](0.01)\\
&= \$15,720,002(0.01) = \$157,200 = DD_{Original}
\end{aligned}$$

(Study Session 9, LOS 23.g)

46. **A**   Given that LIBOR is above the FRA rate of 4.4%, if LIBOR remains at 4.6%, Canopy will receive a payment and bears the risk that the counterparty will default. If LIBOR is above the FRA rate at inception of the loan, Canopy will receive a payment based on the notional principal ($5,000,000), the term of the loan (nine months), a discount factor, and the difference between the LIBOR (4.60%) and the FRA rate (4.40%). The discount factor will be based on the LIBOR at the inception of the loan. The amount received is calculated as:

$$\text{payment from the FRA} = \$5,000,000 \times \frac{(0.046 - 0.044) \times (270/360)}{1 + \left[0.046 \times (270/360)\right]}$$

To find the current value of the credit risk, we calculate the present value of the expected proceeds from the FRA discounted at the risk-free rate:

$$PV = \frac{\$7,250}{(1.038)^{0.25}} = \$7,183$$
   (Study Session 14, LOS 34.i)

47. **B**   Thomas is incorrect. If they use bonds with high yields, it is true that the cost of immunization will be cheaper. Expected returns are higher so they will have to purchase fewer bonds. However, such bonds will also have higher credit risk and contingent immunization assumes no default. If one of the bonds defaults, the immunization strategy will not provide the terminal value required.

Bentley is correct. The risk from nonparallel shifts in the yield curve (immunization risk) can be minimized by concentrating the cash flows around the horizon date.
(Study Session 9, LOS 23.f)

48. **A**   If LIBOR does increase, the cost of Kershaw Ross's floating rate loan will increase. In this case the firm will want to pay a fixed rate and receive a floating rate in a swap. The payer swaption will allow them to pay a predetermined, lower fixed rate in a swap.

If interest rates increase and the fixed rate on swaps in one year (projected at 9.3%) exceeds the swaption fixed rate, the firm will exercise the swaption and pay 8.5%. They receive LIBOR from the swaption and pay in total 8.5% + 1.5% = 10% in the swap and the loan. The firm's first quarterly payment in net will be:

10% × £5,000,000 × 90 / 360 = £125,000.

Note that if swap fixed rates are less than 8.5% in one year, the firm would not exercise the swaption. The firm could either (a) enter a swap at that time and pay the lower fixed rate or (b) not enter a swap and just pay the floating rate in the loan.
(Study Session 15, LOS 38.h)

Sample Scoring Key: 3 points for each correct response.

QUESTIONS 49–54

Source: Study Session 16

49. **B** Gleeson is correct concerning the nature of uncertainty. Market orders have price uncertainty but no execution uncertainty, while limit orders eliminate price uncertainty but have execution uncertainty. However, he is incorrect concerning when these order types should be used. In most cases, information-motivated and liquidity-motivated trades should use market orders to ensure that execution takes place, while value-motivated and rebalancing trades should use limit orders because price is typically more important than the speed of execution. (Study Session 16, LOS 39.a)

50. **C** The quoted spread for the first trade = 22.36 − 22.18 = 0.18. The quoted spreads for the remaining three trades are 0.20, 0.19, and 0.26, so the **average quoted spread** = (0.18 + 0.20 + 0.19 + 0.26) / 4 = 0.2075.

    The mid-quote for the first trade = (22.36 + 22.18) / 2 = 22.27, and the effective spread = (22.33 − 22.27) × 2 = 0.12. The effective spreads for the remaining three trades are 0.20, 0.17, and 0.30, so the **average effective spread** = (0.12 + 0.20 + 0.17 + 0.30) / 4 = 0.1975.

    The **weighted average effective spread** = (900 / 3,000) × 0.12 + (600 / 3,000) × 0.20 + (700 / 3,000) × 0.17 + (800 / 3,000) × 0.30 = 0.1957. (Study Session 16, LOS 39.b)

51. **C** The VWAP for the day = (900 / 3,000) × 22.33 + (600 / 3,000) × 22.43 + (700 / 3,000) × 22.47 + (800 / 3,000) × 22.65 = 22.468, and the trader's goal would be to have an average cost that is less than the VWAP if they are buying. (Study Session 16, LOS 39.f)

52. **B** The benchmark price is 22.36, and the benchmark quantity is 5,000, so the benchmark investment = 22.36 × 5,000 = $111,800. The terminal benchmark value = 22.65 × 5,000 = $113,250, and the benchmark gain = 113,250 − 111,800 = $1,450.

    The actual portfolio cost = (900 × 22.33) + (600 × 22.43) + (700 × 22.47) + (800 × 22.65) = 67,404 + 210 = $67,614. The actual portfolio terminal value = 22.65 × 3,000 = $67,950, and the actual gain = 67,950 − 67,614 = $336.

    The implementation shortfall = (1,450 − 336) / 111,800 = 0.00996 or 0.996%. (Study Session 16, LOS 39.g)

53. **A** In general, implementation shortfall will be positive (i.e., profits will be foregone) if prices are rising when the trader is attempting to buy, or if prices are falling when the trader is attempting to sell, and all of the order is not completed. Cancellation of a buy order prior to a fall in price, or cancellation of a sell order prior to a rise in price will give rise to a negative implementation shortfall (i.e., the trader will be made better off by the cancellation). (Study Session 16, LOS 39.f)

54. **A** Because an algorithmic trading strategy involves mechanical rules to guide trading, one of the concerns is that the portfolio can become over-concentrated. For example, the portfolio could become over-concentrated in sectors that are more liquid and easier to trade when buying, and the opposite problem could occur when selling (i.e., the most liquid assets are sold first, leaving the portfolio over-concentrated in illiquid securities). (Study Session 16, LOS 39.m)

> Sample Scoring Key: 3 points for each correct response.

QUESTIONS 55–60

Source: Study Sessions 14 and 17

55. **C**   The time-weighted return is approximately 11.4% and money-weighted return is 6.8%. To calculate the time-weighted return, first calculate the returns for each period:

Sub-period 1 (Days 1–16):

$$r_{t,1} = \frac{(\$17,800,000 - \$4,000,000) - \$11,200,000}{\$11,200,000} = 0.2321 = 23.21\%$$

Sub-period 2 (Days 17–31):

$$r_{t,2} = \frac{\$16,100,000 - \$17,800,000}{\$17,800,000} = -0.0955 = -9.55\%$$

Compounding the returns together to calculate a monthly return:

$$r_{twr} = (1 + 0.2321)(1 - 0.0955) - 1 = 0.1144 = 11.44\%$$

To obtain the money weighted-return, we can use our financial calculator. We assume compounding every 15 days because the cash flow comes exactly in the middle of the month, such that it is 15 days from the beginning of the period and 15 days from the end of the period. Using the IRR function on the TI BAII Plus®:

$$MV_1 = MV_0(1 + R)^2 + CF_1(1 + R)$$
$$\$16,100,000 = \$11,200,000(1 + R)^2 + \$4,000,000(1 + R)$$
$$R = 3.36\%$$

Keystrokes on the TI BAII Plus®:

CF 2nd	CLR WORK
–11,200,000	ENTER ↓
–4,000,000	ENTER ↓↓
16,100,000	ENTER
IRR	CPT → 3.36

To convert this half-month return to a monthly return, we compound it over two periods:

$$MWR = (1.0336)^2 - 1 = 0.0683 = 6.8\% \quad \text{(Study Session 17, LOS 41.c)}$$

56. **C**   Mercer is incorrect, because although time-weighted return may be easy to calculate, it is not easy to administer. Accounts must be valued with every large, external cash inflow or outflow. For most accounts this would mean daily valuations. Marking to market daily can be expensive to administer and potentially introduces more errors.

Seagram is incorrect because the money-weighted return is influenced by the timing of external cash flows, over which the manager may have no control. In this example, the manager received a cash flow in the middle of the month. Thus, the return during the second half of the month was weighted more heavily than the return during the first half of the month. The manager's return during the first half of the month was quite impressive but the return during the second half of the month was negative. Consequently, the time-weighted return was 11.44% and money-weighted return was lower at 6.8%. The money-weighted return penalizes the manager, because the contribution was not received until later in the month and the manager had no control over this. (Study Session 17, LOS 41.c)

57. **C**   The M-squared measure for the Bison fund is 11.2%.

To calculate the M-squared ratio for Bison, use the following formula:

$$M_P^2 = \bar{R}_F + \left(\frac{\bar{R}_P - \bar{R}_F}{\hat{\sigma}_P} \right) \hat{\sigma}_M$$

$$M_P^2 = 0.035 + \left(\frac{0.141 - 0.035}{0.315} \right) 0.23 = 0.112 = 11.2\%$$

We compare the M^2 of 11.2% to the return on the market of 9% and conclude that, compared to the market, the Bison Fund had superior risk-adjusted performance over the period. (Study Session 17, LOS 41.f)

58. **A**   To evaluate the diversification of the two funds, we calculate the Jensen's alpha, Treynor, Sharpe, and M-squared measures for each fund. Using the Bison fund as an example, you would have obtained a Jensen's alpha of:

$$\hat{R}_{Bison} = R_F + \beta_{Bison} \left(\hat{R}_M - R_F \right) = 0.035 + 0.9 (0.09 - 0.035) = 8.45\%$$

$$\alpha_{Bison} = R_{Bison,t} - \hat{R}_{Bison}$$

$$\alpha_{Bison} = 0.141 - 0.0845 = 5.7\%$$

The Treynor ratio for Bison is calculated as:

$$T_{Bison} = \frac{\bar{R}_A - \bar{R}_F}{\beta_{Bison}}$$

$$T_{Bison} = \frac{14.1 - 3.5}{0.9} = 11.8$$

The Sharpe ratio for Bison would be calculated as:

$$S_{Bison} = \frac{\bar{R}_A - \bar{R}_F}{\hat{\sigma}_{Bison}}$$

$$S_{Bison} = \frac{14.1 - 3.5}{31.5} = 0.34$$

The M-squared measure is calculated in the answer for question 20.3. If we repeat these calculations for the Lunar fund, we arrive at the following:

	Bison	Lunar
Jensen's alpha	5.70%	5.20%
Treynor ratio	11.80	9.50
Sharpe	0.34	0.35
M-squared	11.20%	11.70%

The Bison fund ranks higher by Jensen's alpha and the Treynor ratio, but the Lunar fund ranks higher by the Sharpe and M-squared measures. Jensen's alpha and the Treynor ratio account only for systematic risk as measured by beta. The Sharpe and M-squared measures account for total risk. Thus, since the rankings using alpha and Treynor versus Sharpe and M^2 are reversed, it must be the case that Bison has more unsystematic risk than Lunar and that Lunar is better diversified.

Professor's Note: You did not have to calculate all four measures. Any two, as long as one utilizes beta and the other standard deviation, would have been sufficient to determine the funds' relative diversification.

To evaluate the relative performance considering downside risk only, we employ the Sortino ratio, which measures risk relative to the downside risk of returns. It is calculated as the portfolio return minus the minimum acceptable return (MAR) divided by a standard deviation that uses only returns below the MAR. The calculation for Bison is:

$$Sortino_{Bison} = \frac{14.1 - 4.5}{15.1} = 0.64$$

For Lunar, the Sortino ratio is 0.71. Thus, Lunar provides better performance according to the Sortino ratio. Sortino is similar to the Sharpe ratio in that an excess return is divided by a standard deviation. Note however that the Sharpe ratio (which uses the standard deviation in the denominator) examines all returns, whether they correspond to positive or negative alphas. The use of the Sharpe ratio could result in a measurement that is unfair to managers who have consistently outperformed their benchmark and whose variability of returns is primarily on the upside. (Study Session 14, LOS 39.l and Study Session 17, LOS 41.p)

59. **C** Mercer is correct because, although manager universes are measurable (after the fact), they are subject to survivor bias. Survivor bias refers to the tendency to include only those managers currently in existence in the benchmark, thereby ignoring those who have left the business or stopped reporting. The poorer performers' records are left out, creating an upward bias in the benchmark performance.

    Seagram is correct because manager universes possess only one quality of a valid benchmark, which is measurability. A valid benchmark should meet the following criteria: (1) specified in advance, (2) appropriate, (3) measurable, (4) unambiguous, (5) reflect current investment opinions, (6) accountable, and (7) investable. The median manager cannot be identified in advance and is therefore also ambiguous. The benchmark will differ from one period to another and is therefore not investable. It is impossible to determine its appropriateness and whether it is reflective of current opinion due to its ambiguity. It is also difficult to determine its accountability because fund sponsors must rely on the compiler's representations. (Study Session 17, LOS 41.e,f,h)

60. **C** Operations risk is not explicitly mentioned. The risk exposures an analyst should report as part of an enterprise risk management system include liquidity risk, settlement risk, credit risk, operations risk, model risk, sovereign risk, and regulatory risk. In this question, of the responses listed, operations risk is not explicitly mentioned. Operations risk is the potential for failures in the firm's operating systems due to personal or technological, mechanical, or other problems. Although Jaguar is sure to have exposure to operations risk, it is not explicitly described in these transactions. Credit risk is the potential for default, which is certainly a possibility in Jaguar's forward contract. Herstatt risk or settlement risk is the possibility that one party could default on a contract while the other is settling. This has been a problem in foreign exchange markets due to time differences and is certainly possible in Jaguar's currency swap.

    Note also that Jaguar's sale of the Mexican pesos is subject to liquidity risk. Liquidity risk refers to the potential for sustaining losses due to the inability to sell or buy a position quickly. (Study Session 14, LOS 34.d)

> Sample Scoring Key: 3 points for each correct response.

PRACTICE EXAM 3
MORNING SESSION ANSWERS

QUESTION 1
Source: Study Session 4, LOS 10.i,j

A. i. **For the Exam:**
   After-tax nominal return to support his annual living expenses and family support payments during retirement; maintain real value of portfolio.

   Discussion:
   This is an example of the wording for the answer coming directly from the vignette. CFAI has asked candidates to "formulate" the return objective many times, meaning they want you to put it into words, not calculations. Had you glanced at the questions quickly before reading the vignette, you would have known what was required and could have marked the appropriate parts of the vignette as you read them. Be careful, however. On occasion they have asked candidates to formulate the return objective and said to "show your calculations." They haven't done that in a while (I assume they figured out that it confused candidates), so you probably won't see that. If they should ask it that way on your exam, I recommend that you write out the objective as above and then perform the calculation that is required by the next part of this question. The key to answering is watching for the words, "Show your calculations."

   ii. To calculate the required return for the first year of retirement, you first need to determine the value of the portfolio at the beginning of that year. You then determine the after-tax cash flows that will be met by the portfolio over that year. The ratio of the two is the after-tax required return.

   The value of the portfolio at the beginning of the first year of retirement (the end of the current year in this case) is the portfolio value today plus all inflows for the year and minus all outflows for the year. If outflows are greater than inflows, the value of the portfolio at the beginning of next year will be smaller than the value today. Of course if inflows exceed outflows, the portfolio will increase in value. Total inflows and outflows for the year are equal in this case, so there is no change in the value of the portfolio over the year:

Year	Year before retirement (current year)	First year of retirement (next year)
Inflows		
Profits and Sale of Business	£3,000,000	
Interest income from cash savings (after-tax)	60,000	
Growth equity portfolio (after-tax return)[1]	2,040,000	
Total Inflows	**£5,100,000**	
Outflows		
Income tax @ 40%[2]	1,200,000	
Living Expenses	720,000	£748,800[3]
Family support payments	480,000	499,200[3]
Purchase of home	2,700,000	0
Total Outflows	**£5,100,000**	£1,248,000
Net Inflows/(Outflows)	0	(£1,248,000)

[1] Growth equity portfolio return = £24,000,000 × 8.5%
[2] Income tax = £3,000,000 × 40%
[3] Living/family support expenses increased 4% for inflation

©2011 Kaplan, Inc.

Current Investable Assets

Cash savings	£2,400,000
Growth equity portfolio	24,000,000
Total current investable assets	£26,400,000
Add: Net cash flows over the current year	0
Total investable assets at retirement	£26,400,000

Outflows during first year of retirement (from previous table)	£1,248,000
Req'd after-tax real rate of return = 1,248,000 / 26,400,000	4.73%
Add: Inflation rate	4.00%
Required after-tax nominal rate of return (arithmetic) = 4.73% + 4.00% =	8.73%

Required after-tax nominal rate of return (geometric) = (1.0473)(1.04) −1 = 8.92%

Note: The ocean-front home is not included in investable assets.

Sample Scoring Key: (maximum 14 points)
2 points for part i and 12 points for the correct return calculation for part ii.

Source: Study Session 4, LOS 10.i,j

Answer for Question 1-B

Two factors that increase Williams's ability to take risk.
• Long time horizon • Large asset base relative to expenses • Could start another company (flexibility) • Could reduce his living expenses (flexibility)
Two factors that decrease his ability to take risk.
• Investment portfolio is only source of income • Wants to maintain real value of portfolio
Determine Williams's ability to take risk
Above Average
Discussion: Even though Williams will depend on the portfolio to meet all living expenses, his significant time horizon and wealth, in combination with his flexibility, give him an above-average ability to take risk.

Sample Scoring Key: (maximum 6 points)
1 point for each correct factor listed (4 total).
2 points for circling the correct ability level of risk tolerance.

QUESTION 2

Source: Study Session 4 LOS 10.n, Study Session 8 LOS 21.l

A.   **For the exam:**

1. Monte Carlo provides distribution of outcomes; mean-variance provides single point estimates.
2. Monte Carlo incorporates effects of inflows and outflows over a multi-year planning horizon.

Discussion:

The data in Exhibit 2 provide an endorsement for Monte Carlo (MC) simulation. The Monte Carlo program uses distributions of all inputs along with liquidity requirements (outflows; spending needs) to project the value of the portfolio at a time in the future; in this case at the expected time of death. It also demonstrates how the final value of the portfolio depends on the value path (interim cash flows and returns) the portfolio takes.

MC simulation considers the cash inflows and outflows of the portfolio over time, while the standard mean-variance analysis does not. Investment returns can vary significantly from year to year, so they play a significant part in the value path the portfolio takes over the planning horizon.

MC allows the investor to decide on the allocation that meets an acceptable tradeoff between potential excess portfolio value and the probability of falling short and running out of assets or having to reduce retirement spending. Based on Behavioral Finance theory, individuals prefer a planning method that quantifies the probability that they will not meet their desired retirement lifestyle rather than portfolio standard deviation and expected return, the traditional mean variance risk and return measures.

 Professor's Note: This is an example of a scenario in which the client is unconcerned with maintaining the portfolio principal. It is clearly stated that he is most concerned with maintaining his lifestyle.

> Sample Scoring Key: (maximum 4 points)
> 2 points for each correct explanation.

Source: Study Session 8 LOS 21.d,l

B.   **For the exam:**

1. Asset-liability management specifically considers liquidity needs.
2. Asset-liability management controls risk better than asset-only.

Discussion:

By using Monte Carlo simulation as part of an asset-liability management (ALM) planning strategy, the individual is provided with a distribution of possible outcomes, based on portfolio returns and any inflows to the portfolio as well as planned outflows over the planning horizon. It is best utilized to demonstrate to the client the possibility of running out of funds or not being able to maintain a given retirement lifestyle (shortfall risk). An asset-only (AO) approach, on the other hand, considers only the portfolio value by maximizing expected return within risk constraints.

An AO approach is better employed by an individual as part of pre-retirement planning. The financial adviser determines the appropriate size of the portfolio at retirement based on the client's desired retirement lifestyle and capital market expectations. With that portfolio value as the required terminal portfolio value, a MC output can show the expected value and resulting portfolio returns, additional savings, changing tax rates etc., over the planning horizon. Note that even though we might consider this an AO approach, it is effectively an ALM approach because the investor uses the required terminal value as a target, making it a pseudo liability.

> Sample Scoring Key: (maximum 4 points)
> 2 points for each correct statement.

Source: Study Session 4 LOS 10.n, Study Session 8 LOS 21.l

C.   **For the exam:**
       Allocation 2; 95% probability will not run out of assets.

Discussion:
Given that Bush is already retired and maintaining the level of retirement spending is crucial to him, Allocation 2 (the moderate allocation) is the most appropriate for Bush. The main objective of his portfolio is to be able to fund his spending needs for his life expectancy of 20 years. Bush has indicated an interest in earning a greater return than is necessary, but his situation warrants less risk than present in the aggressive allocation. Of the three, Allocation 2 is the only one that provides a positive value under all scenarios. For Allocation 2, we know there is less than a 5% chance of running out of funds and at least a 95% chance of funds remaining before the 20 years are up.

> Sample Scoring Key: (maximum 2 points)
> 1 point for choosing the correct allocation.
> 1 point for the justification.

QUESTION 3

Source: Study Session 4, LOS 10.e,f

Answer for Question 3

	Client Statement	Investor Type	Explanation
1.	"In general, I don't like to see much turnover in my account since I don't believe in market timing strategies. Those strategies seem likely to have a low probability of actually making money. What I find more important is preserving the value of my portfolio against inflation."	Cautious	**For the exam:** Focus on maintaining principal only. **Discussion:** This individual desires low turnover, which is characteristic of a cautious investor, and focuses on losses and inflation rather than earning high returns.
2.	"Most of the time I don't want to be bothered with stock tips from my broker. I read the same research they read, and I often think the analysts writing the reports don't have a clue what they are talking about. The majority of my investments have been selected using my own careful research, but there are a few stocks in my portfolio that I just had a feeling about so I bought them."	Individualistic	**For the exam:** Confidence in own research. **Discussion:** This individual exhibits confidence by preferring own research to analyst tips. Not afraid to invest based on own research. Uses data from multiple sources.
3.	"I like to have broad access to quality reports from analysts and economic researchers so I can stay abreast of key market developments. I do not appreciate, however, receiving calls from my stockbroker regarding the latest investment strategy that is also being sold to everyone else in the market. Most of the time the recommended strategy is too risky and doesn't fit with my portfolio."	Methodical	**For the exam:** Wants as much information as possible. **Discussion:** This individual strives to keep up to date on the latest information. The statement about brokers' recommendation being too risky indicates a conservative nature.
4.	"I need to have access to market information quickly so I can keep up-to-date on where the hot money is. I read research occasionally but the analysts are usually talking over my head about some boring blue-chip company. Everyone in my investment club generally agrees that the analysts are overrated. I like my portfolio to be reasonably liquid so I can move funds quickly."	Spontaneous	**For the exam:** Wants the latest investment. **Discussion:** This individual seems more interested in liquidity and being able to act quickly to capitalize on the latest stock tip.

Sample Scoring Key: (maximum 8 points)
1 point each for identification.
1 point for a brief justification.

QUESTION 4

Source: Study Session 13, LOS 31.m

Answer for Question 4-A

Alternative	Type	Comment
Futures contracts	Direct	**For the exam:** Good exposure; value of futures directly impacted by value of commodity. **Discussion:** Direct exposure to energy commodity prices, either through purchasing the underlying asset itself or through derivatives such as futures contracts, provides the best exposure to changes in energy prices.
Energy stocks	Indirect	**For the exam:** Poor exposure; energy firms usually hedge energy inputs. **Discussion:** Overweighting energy stocks could provide some exposure to changes in energy prices, but many commodity producing firms hedge their exposure to price changes through the internal use of derivatives. This alternative would be the least likely to achieve Cady's objective for the MU endowment.
ETFs	Indirect	**For the exam:** Partial exposure; index contains non-energy commodities. **Discussion:** While an ETF investment is considered indirect, the suggested ETF based on the GSCI would give the MU endowment significant exposure to energy-related commodities. However, the GSCI includes non-energy related commodities as 30–40 percent of its weighting. This non-energy component would reduce the potential benefit sought by Cady.

Sample Scoring Key: (maximum 6 points)
For each alternative, 1 point for direct/indirect; 1 point for comment.

Source: Study Session 13, LOS 31.n

B. The roll return is the change in the futures price that is not attributable to changes in the spot price of the underlying asset. The calculation based on Figure 1 would be:

June 15 futures price – May 15 futures price – change in spot price

Award 1 point for each correct calculation:

Contract	Roll return calculation
July	$83.25 – $82.55 – $0.50 = $0.20
October	$82.35 – $81.70 – $0.50 = $0.15
January	$81.75 – $81.20 – $0.50 = $0.05

Sample Scoring Key: maximum 3 points.

Source: Study Session 13, LOS 31.n

Answer for Question 4-C

Future pricing	Justification
Backwardation	**For the exam:** Futures curve downward sloping. **Discussion:** When the contracts with longer maturities have lower futures prices, the market is said to be in backwardation. Because the January contracts are priced below the October contracts, and the October contracts are priced below the July contracts, the oil futures market is in backwardation.

Sample Scoring Key: (maximum 2 points)
1 point for backwardation.
1 point for justification

Source: Study Session 13, LOS 31.e,n

D.   Total return = roll return + spot return + collateral return

$$= 6.4 + 10.2 + 7.1 = 23.70\%$$

Discussion:
The largest weighted sector in the GSCI is energy. The GSCI has exposure to non-energy related commodities, such as metals and agricultural products. The weights in the GSCI are based on a five-year moving average of world production for each commodity.

Sample Scoring Key: maximum 3 points.

Source: Study Session 13, LOS 31.f,m,o

E.   **For the exam:**
   i.   Inflation: Prices of storable commodities tend to be positively correlated with inflation.

   ii.   Diversification: Historically low correlation with stocks and bonds.

Discussion:
   i.   Inflation hedging: Commodities, and particularly energy-related commodities, have been shown to be effective as inflation hedges. Commodities offer the most benefit as inflation hedges when there are unexpected changes in the rate of inflation.

   ii.   Diversification: For the past 15 years, the correlation between commodity returns and stock/bond returns has been at or near zero, suggesting significant diversification benefits from adding commodities to a traditional portfolio such as MU's endowment. Adding energy-related commodities to the MU portfolio would certainly hedge some of the risk of higher energy costs, and alleviate some of the related budgetary issues.

Sample Scoring Key: maximum 4 points.

QUESTION 5

Source: Study Session 13, LOS 31.g

Answer for Question 5-A

Memorandum	Agree or Disagree	Justification
"Based solely on real estate benchmarks, it would appear that direct investment in real estate tends to be more volatile than indirect investment."	Disagree	**For the exam:** 1. NCREIF less volatile because smoothed by appraisal data. 2. NCREIF de-leveraged. 3. NAREIT uses actual trade prices. **Discussion:** The NCREIF (benchmark of the National Council of Real Estate Investment Fiduciaries) is published quarterly and reflects **direct** real estate investment values. Since values are based predominantly on appraisals, the benchmark tends to be smoothed (i.e., reflect less volatility than if actual market value data were readily and consistently available on direct real estate transactions). Further, the estimated market values are asset values only and as such do not reflect the use of leverage. Since the values and resulting returns reflect "cash" prices, they also do not reflect the additional returns volatility caused by leverage. The NAREIT (National Association of Real estate Investment Trusts) is a benchmark for **indirect** investment (i.e., real estate investment through a fund similar to a mutual fund). Since REITs are publicly traded, values of the NAREIT reflect "live" data. Hence the volatility of the NAREIT reflects changes in market values, which should include the effects of leverage.

Sample Scoring Key: (maximum 3 points)
1 point for disagree.
2 points for justification.

Source: Study Session 13, LOS 31.e

Answer for Question 5-B

Strength	**For the exam:** Based on holdings of large institutions. **Discussion:** The NCREIF index is an index of properties held by large institutions. CREFs manage real estate assets for large institutions (primarily pensions). In that sense, the NCREIF is an appropriate index for CREFs.
Weakness	**For the exam:** NCREIF unleveraged. CREFs use leverage. **Discussion:** Closed-end CREFs take leveraged positions in properties, and the NCREIF is an unleveraged index, which is a weakness of the NCREIF as a benchmark for closed-end CREF performance.

Sample Scoring Key: (maximum 4 points) 2 points for a brief explanation of each.

Source: Study Session 13, LOS 31.e,f

Answer for Question 5-C

Decision	Justification
Disagree	**For the exam:** NAREIT based on many types of REITs while Von Wilstrom Fund is specialized. **Discussion:** While it is true that the Von Wilstrom Fund underperformed the NAREIT index, Ketter should point out that the Von Wilstrom Fund is an apartment REIT fund. It is not designed to be a well-diversified REIT fund (as represented by the NAREIT index). Therefore, the more appropriate benchmark for the Von Wilstrom Fund is the Apartment REIT component of the NAREIT index. Von Wilstrom's return was higher than the Apartment REIT index and its standard deviation was less than the Apartment REIT index. Therefore, the Von Wilstrom Fund performed well within its stated REIT objective.

Sample Scoring Key: (maximum 3 points) 1 point for disagree. 2 points for justification.

QUESTION 6

Source: Study Session 7, LOS 19.a,b

Answer for Question 6-A

Factor	Factor Change (circle direction)
Production efficiency	Increase / (Decrease)
Environmental controls	(Increase) / Decrease
Children per household	Increase / (Decrease)

The change (growth) in real economic output is determined by the country's total factor productivity, TFP, the change in capital inputs, K, and the change in the labor force, L. The equation shows how the three variables can be considered separately:

$$\%\Delta Y \cong \%\Delta TFP + \alpha(\%\Delta K) + (1-\alpha)\%\Delta L$$

In determining the effect of a change in a single factor, you must consider it alone. Do not attempt to analyze how its change could impact the other variables:

- Think of production efficiency as total factor productivity, TFP, the economy's overall efficiency in utilizing inputs. All else equal, as TFP falls, real economic output falls.
- New environmental controls can have a dampening effect on production through a negative impact on the output elasticity of capital, α, and/or a decline in the value of capital employed, K. The result is a temporary or permanent decrease in economic output. Think of α as the efficiency with which the economy converts growth in capital into economic growth.
- A decrease in the number of children per household decreases the population (the labor input) and economic output.

Sample Scoring Key:
1 point each for correctly identifying the direction of the factor change.

Answer for Question 6-B

$$\%\Delta Y \cong \%\Delta TFP + \alpha(\%\Delta K) + (1-\alpha)\%\Delta L$$

where:
$\%\Delta Y$ = percent change in real economic output
$\%\Delta TFP$ = percent change in total factor productivity
$\%\Delta K$ = percent change in capital stock
$\%\Delta L$ = percent change in labor input
α = output elasticity of capital stock
$(1-\alpha)$ = output elasticity of labor, β

expected sustainable real growth rate $= 1.0\% + (0.3 \times 4.0\%) + (0.7 \times 0.7\%) = 2.69\%$

Sample Scoring Key:
2 points for correctly calculating the expected sustainable real growth rate.

Answer for Question 6-C

$$V_0 = \frac{D_0}{r - g_L}\left[(1 + g_L) + \frac{N}{2}(g_S - g_L)\right]$$

where:
V_0 = intrinsic value of the index
D_0 = current dividend
r = real required rate of return
g_L = long-term sustainable growth rate
g_S = supernormal growth rate
N = length of growth rate decline period

estimated intrinsic value $= \dfrac{31}{0.09 - 0.0269}\left[(1 + 0.0269) + \dfrac{10}{2}(0.0925 - 0.0269)\right] = 665.6403$

Mantrovia's stock market is slightly undervalued because the current value of 645 is less than the estimated intrinsic value of 665.64.

Sample Scoring Key:
1 point for correctly selecting the H-Model.
2 points for correctly calculating the intrinsic value.
1 point for correctly indentifying the market as undervalued.

QUESTION 7 (Note: For the Exam answers are not appropriate here.)

Source: Study Session 17, LOS 41.k

Answer for Question 7-A

Portfolio	Calculation	Return
Sterling	$(0.6 \times 12.5) + (0.25 \times 16.0) + (0.15 \times 10.0) =$ 1 point 1 point 1 point	13.00% 1 point
Benchmark	$(0.5 \times 10.0) + (0.3 \times 18.5) + (0.2 \times 9.0) =$ 1 point 1 point 1 point	12.35% 1 point
Circle one		
Outperform 2 points		

Sample Scoring Key: maximum 10 points.

Source: Study Session 17, LOS 41.e,l

Answer for Question 7-B

Effect	Calculation	Final Answer
Pure sector allocation effect	1 point $(0.6 - 0.5) \times (10.0 - 12.35)$ + 1 point $(0.25 - 0.30) \times (18.5 - 12.35)$ + 1 point $(0.15 - 0.20) \times (9.0 - 12.35) =$	−0.375% 1 point
Within-sector selection effect	1 point $[0.50 \times (12.5 - 10.0)]$ + 1 point $[0.3 \times (16.0 - 18.5)]$ + 1 point $[0.2 \times (10.0 - 9.0)] =$	0.70% 1 point

Discussion:

The pure sector allocation effect measures the manager's ability to over-weight outperforming sectors and under-weight underperforming sectors. It is calculated by multiplying the difference in the weights of sector i in the portfolio and benchmark by the difference between the return for sector i in the benchmark and the overall return on the benchmark and then summing across all sectors:

$$\text{pure sector allocation effect} = \sum_{j=1}^{s} \left(w_{P,j} - w_{B,j} \right) \left(R_{B,j} - R_B \right)$$

The within-sector-selection effect, or security selection effect, measures the manager's ability to select outperforming securities to represent the sectors in the portfolio. It is calculated by multiplying the weight of sector i in the benchmark by the difference between the returns for sector i in the portfolio and benchmark:

$$\text{within-sector selection effect} = \sum_{j=1}^{s}\left(w_{B,j}\right)\left(R_{P,j} - R_{B,j}\right)$$

Sample Scoring Key: maximum 8 points.

Source: Study Session 17, LOS 41.e,l

C.   3 points—The outperformance is due to the within-sector selection effect; value added by the segment managers.

         3 points—The Rawls Group hurt performance with their pure sector asset allocation decisions.

Sample Scoring Key: maximum 6 points.

QUESTION 8

Source: Study Session 5, LOS 16.b,c

A.   **For the exam:**

1. High ratio of active to inactive lives suggests a greater allocation to equities for increases in future real wages.
2. High ratio of active to inactive lives suggests a greater allocation to TIPS to cover inflation component of future wages.
3. Small proportion of inactive lives suggests lower allocation to nominal bonds.

Discussion
Smith Hospital Corporation has a relatively young workforce with an average age of 31, indicating a fairly long time horizon. In addition, the ratio of active to inactive participants is very high. To meet future pension liabilities, a greater percentage of assets must be invested in equities than in Weekly's proposal. In other words, to meet the increased future liability generated by the real growth component in wages, Smith Hospital Corporation should invest a significant percentage of the plan's assets in equities.   Even though pension benefits are fixed at retirement and do not offer an inflation adjustment, the growth in future wages earned by the large number of active participants will have an inflation component. The significant liability created by this inflation component will require a greater percentage of pension assets invested in Treasury inflation-protected securities (TIPS) or some other type of inflation-protected securities.   The high percentage allocated to nominal bonds would reduce the company's overall risk profile, but the portfolio would likely not generate the returns needed to cover the growing pension liability caused by the inflation component in future wage increases. The percentage allocated to nominal bonds should be reduced. As the percentage of inactive participants rises, a larger proportion of the pension plan's assets can be invested in nominal bonds since employee benefits are fixed after retirement.

Sample Scoring Key: (maximum 6 points)   2 points for each benchmark discussion.

Source: Study Session 5, LOS 17.b

B.   **For the exam:**
Only the calculations would be required on the exam (no discussion). I always recommend writing out any related formulas, however, for potential partial credit.

	Market Value	Beta		Market Value	Beta
Operating assets (core)	500	0.48**	Debt	200	0
Pension assets	100	0.60*	Pension liabilities	100	0
			Equity	300	1.0
Total assets	600	0.5	Total L&E	600	0.5

1 point for calculating pension asset beta:
* (equity allocation) (pension plan equity beta) = 0.80 × 0.75 = 0.60
**The total (overall) asset beta is calculated as the weighted average of the operating (core) asset beta and the pension asset beta. To solve for the operating asset beta, the total asset beta equation is used with the known variables as follows:

$\beta_A = W_{A,P}\beta_{A,P} + W_{A,O}\beta_{A,O}$
$0.5 = [(100/600)\ 0.6] + [(500/600) \times \beta_{A,O}]$
$\beta_{A,O} = [0.5 - (100/600) \times 0.6] / (500/600) = 0.48$

2 points for calculating overall WACC:
$WACC = R_F + \beta_A(\text{market risk premium}) = 0.04 + 0.48(0.07) = 0.0736$

Sample Scoring Key: maximum 5 points.

Source: Study Session 5, LOS 17.b

C.   **For the exam:**
1.   Using only core WACC ignores the risk of the pension assets.
2.   Using only core WACC usually overstates WACC.
3.   Using only core WACC can lead to rejection of profitable projects.
4.   Using only core WACC can suppress stock price.

Discussion:
WACC is used as the discount rate when appraising potential projects, which means that we want it to reflect the risk of all the company's assets. The problem with the so-called "core WACC" is that it has been inferred from the company's asset beta ignoring the effect of the pension fund assets.

This can be seen if we calculate the WACC as in part B, but ignore the pension fund and use an asset beta based on the firm's operating assets only:

Using the 0.6 beta in the CAPM gives us 0.04 + 0.6(0.07) = 0.082 [8.2%]

A comparison of the above calculation with that in part B shows that the 8.2% "core WACC" is based on an overstated operating asset beta—we are ignoring the impact of the pension plan assets on the company's beta. The WACC adjusted for the pension plan of 7.4% is a fairer rate to use for capital budgeting purposes, since it considers the risk of all the firm's assets. In overestimating the discount rate by 0.8%, management will potentially exclude value-added projects.

Sample Scoring Key: maximum 4 points.

QUESTION 9

Source: Study Session 5, LOS 17.c
A. For the Exam

Pension plan asset allocation	Impact on SHC's equity beta and WACC; change in D/E to maintain current equity beta	
100% equity	Impact on equity beta:	Increased due to increase in total asset risk.
	Impact on WACC:	Increased due to increased operating asset beta.
	Required change in D/E:	Issue equity to buy back outstanding debt and decrease leverage ($\downarrow$D/E)
100% fixed income	Impact on equity beta:	Decreased due to decreased total asset risk.
	Impact on WACC:	Decreased due to decreased operating asset beta
	Required change in D/E:	Issue debt to buy back outstanding equity and increase leverage ($\uparrow$D/E)

Answer: Discussion

The firm's equity beta is observable in the market and, thus, reflects the firm's overall risk, including the balance sheet assets, the pension plan assets and liabilities, and the firm's use of leverage in its capital structure (D/E ratio). Increasing the pension asset allocation from 50% equities to 100% equities would increase the risk of the pension assets and the risk of the firm's total assets (left hand side of the combined balance sheet). When the total asset beta increases and the capital structure is left unchanged, the equity beta will increase to reflect the increased asset risk.

Thus, the equity beta observed when the pension plan is invested 100% in equities will be greater than if the plan is invested 50% in equities. To return the equity beta to its previous level, management would have to reduce the firm's overall risk by issuing equity to repurchase outstanding debt.

If the plan is moved to 100% fixed income, the total asset and equity betas will fall and management would have to increase the firm's overall risk by increasing the D/E ratio.

Sample Scoring Key: (maximum 6 points) 1 point for each correct WACC answer. 2 points for each correct optimal capital structure answer.

©2011 Kaplan, Inc.

Source: Study Session 5, LOS 15.a

B.   **For the exam:**
1.   Plan sponsor: Make required annual contributions; provide investment alternatives.
2.   Participant: Faces investment risk; determine fund allocations.

Discussion:

1. Plan sponsor (SHC)	SHC must contribute only the amount owed to the employee. SHC must provide the employee with a diversified selection of investment alternatives and investment education to help them make appropriate allocation decisions. Sponsor does not face investment risk.
2. Participant (employee)	The employee is responsible for all investment decisions and performance; faces all investment risk. The employee owns the assets and can move them if he or she leaves the company.

Sample Scoring Key: maximum 4 points.

QUESTION 10

Source: Study Session 12, LOS 30.b,c

A.   **Discussion:**
Many emerging market liberalizations have occurred that give foreign investors a greater opportunity to invest in emerging market equity securities. These market liberalizations also give investors located in the emerging countries the ability to transact in foreign equity securities. However, this liberalization process does not guarantee that market integration will occur, either because investors do not accept the changes as permanent or foreign investors have access to the emerging market through other means. The general and specific market integrations that account for the higher correlation between the emerging market and developed market investment returns include:

1.   Government reforms in emerging markets.
2.   Corporate governance reforms in emerging markets.
3.   Stronger trade relationships have resulted in a more integrated world economy (globalization).
4.   The greater number of companies with international operations.
5.   The emerging markets have a more developed trading process that leads to fairer and more accurate pricing.
6.   Efficient trading processes have led to lower transaction costs and higher quantities of shares being traded without affecting prices.
7.   Solid investment returns have attracted foreign capital flows which are helping to expand the emerging market economies.
8.   Lower systematic risk has reduced the cost of capital of emerging market firms. The lower cost of capital leads to greater investment opportunities for firms.
9.   Emerging markets have implemented disciplined monetary policies that have reduced inflation rates.
10.   Emerging markets have a more diversified economic base.
11.   Emerging market countries have enjoyed higher and more sustainable GDP growth rates.
12.   Fiscal and monetary management have reduced external borrowing requirements by emerging market governments.

Sample Scoring Key: (maximum 4 points)
1 point each for any four of the 12 reasons given for a total of 4 points.

Source: Study Session 12, LOS 31.c and Study Session 7, LOS 20.e

Answer for Question 10-B

Circle one	Justify with two reasons
Disagree	**For the exam:** Correlations not 1.0 **Discussion:** Gamez is correct that the higher correlation between emerging markets and developed markets will reduce diversification benefits, but as long as the correlation is less than perfect, there are diversification benefits to investing in these markets. **For the exam:** Falling risk. **Discussion:** The standard deviation of emerging market investment returns has fallen from 27.2% to 21.0%. **For the exam:** Reduced portfolio standard deviation. **Discussion:** The benefits of the lower standard deviation will partially offset the increased correlation. In other words, emerging market investments still provide attractive diversification benefits. **For the exam:** Did not consider returns. **Discussion:** Gamez did not consider the return portion of the risk/return trade-off. The outstanding growth opportunities presented by emerging market equities must be considered to fully evaluate their investment merits. The higher growth rates generated by emerging markets are being realized through a combination of improved domestic economies and strong international trade. In addition, emerging market fiscal and monetary policies are typically supportive of their growth opportunities.

Sample Scoring Key: (maximum 5 points) 1 point for disagreeing; points as indicated for defense. 2 points each for any two correct reasons.

QUESTION 11

Source: Study Session 5, LOS 15.j

Answer for Question 11-A

Objectives	
1. Return	**For the exam:** $(1.05)(1.02)(1.0275) - 1 = 10.0\%$ **Discussion:** The foundation needs to earn sufficient return to award 5% in annual grants, cover inflation of 2.75% and expenses of 2%. Note that foundations do not pay taxes in Grik, so the return is not grossed up for taxes.
2. Risk	**For the exam:** Above average ability to take risk. **Discussion:** Since they have no contractually obligated payout, foundations have above average ability to take risk. To meet the return objective, the foundation must be willing to accept a relatively high risk level. Fortunately, the foundation most likely has sufficient ability to take the necessary risk.
Constraints	
1. Liquidity	**For the exam:** 7% of assets annually: 5% payout plus 2% expenses. **Discussion:** The liquidity requirements for the foundation are the anticipated 5.0% payout, plus expenses, plus any unanticipated needs for cash in excess of contributions made by the foundation.
2. Time horizon	**For the exam:** Long-term. **Discussion:** Unless they are created with a finite time horizon, foundations are considered perpetual.
3. Taxes	**For the exam:** Tax exempt. **Discussion:** Since the foundation is to be located in Grik, it will be tax exempt. In the United States, a foundation is tax exempt on investment income as long as it meets its stated objectives and awards the required grants, although income earned by contributed businesses may be subject to taxes. Since they are (mostly) tax-exempt, foundations should not invest in tax-exempt investments, such as municipal bonds. This foundation will be subject to any peculiarities associated with being located in Grik.
4. Unique circumstances	**For the exam:** SRI and 60% in foreign countries. **Discussion:** Foundations and endowments are frequently subject to various forms of investment constraints, such as socially responsible investing. We are told in the vignette that the foundation requires that all investments to pass a socially acceptable screen. Also, the foundation requires 60% of its assets be invested in foreign countries in which the company does business.

Sample Scoring Key: maximum 12 points.

Source: Study Session 8, LOS 21.n,o

B.   **For the exam:** (2 points for selecting C and 2 points each for any three justifications.)

Portfolio C
1.   10.3% required return.
2.   Highest Sharpe ratio of eligible portfolios.
3.   Meets 60% requirement.
4.   Meets 5% minimum investment in each asset class.

Discussion:

Total return: Portfolio C generates 10.3% in total return, which exceeds the total return requirement of 10%.

Sharpe ratio: Portfolio C has a better risk-adjusted return, as measured by its Sharpe ratio, than Portfolio A, which is the only other portfolio that meets the objectives and constraints of Great Northern.

Foreign investment: Portfolio C meets the 60% foreign investment constraint.

Diversification: Portfolio C meets the 5% minimum investment in all asset classes requirement.

An answer that took the approach of rejecting the other portfolios without addressing the issues above favoring Portfolio C could earn a maximum of four points, 1 point each for any of the following:

Portfolio A offers an inferior risk-adjusted return based on its Sharpe ratio.

Portfolio B does not meet the total return requirement.

Portfolio D violates the 60% foreign investment requirement.

Portfolio E violates the 5% minimum asset class investment requirement.

Sample Scoring Key: maximum 8 points.

Source: Study Session 8, LOS 22.a,g

C.   **For the exam:**
    1. SRI can lead to growth bias.
    2. 60% foreign investment means on-going foreign currency management.
    3. Required minimum for asset classes but no stated maximum.
    4. Foundation performance highly correlated with Great Northern.
    5. Large foreign bond investment means significant transaction exposure.

Discussion:

The social screening process could impact the total return expectations by screening out certain investments that, while socially unacceptable to the foundation, may have large total return potential. Also, it has been shown that SRI can lead to a growth bias in the portfolio, if it leads to investing in new, eco-friendly companies.

The 60% international investment requirement stipulates that the investments must be in countries where Great Northern does business. This may impact the return expectations generated by the consultant. The countries in which Great Northern does business may have significantly lower available returns than what is available elsewhere.

Because Portfolio C has a 45% investment in the international fixed income asset class, it will have significant translation risk as well as cash flow risk. If interest rates unexpectedly rise in the foreign countries where Great Northern operates, the subsequent fall in foreign currency values (relative to the domestic currency) along with the fall in bond prices would result in significant reduction in balance sheet values as well as the values of the coupon payments.

Sample Scoring Key: maximum 6 points.

QUESTION 12

Source: Study Session 16, LOS 39.h

A.   **For the exam:** (2 points each for any two)
1. VWAP can be gamed.
2. Does not evaluate missed or delayed trades.
3. Not good for trades that dominate trading.
4. Does not account for market movements or trading volume.

Discussion:
Measuring execution costs by implementing a VWAP benchmark can lead to higher trading costs as traders attempt to time orders based on the benchmark. For example, if a trader buying shares recognizes the security is moving higher as the market closing approaches, he may wait for the next trading day rather than purchase the full position by day's end. The next day the trader is able to finish buying the security in the VWAP range rather than incur a higher price relative to the VWAP the previous day. This is good for the trader's performance measurement, but the portfolio's performance suffers as shares are purchased at higher prices than could have been obtained the previous day.

The VWAP becomes an ineffective measure of trading if the trade orders are delivered to the trading desk just after the opening bell. The trade is compared with a VWAP calculated over the full day, while the actual trade is not. This may help or hurt the trader's measured performance.

> Sample Scoring Key: maximum 4 points.

Source: Study Session 16, LOS 39.j,k

B.   **For the exam:** (1 point for each)
Value trades: Capture over- or under-pricing; limit order.
Information trade: Speed required to capture the value of information not already incorporated into price; market order.

Discussion:
In a value trade the manager has identified a miss-priced security. Assuming the manager does not have to trade the security, the manager would most likely submit a limit order that can expire unfilled if the limit price is not met.

In an information trade, information has hit the market or the manager has uncovered information that could be incorporated into the security price at any moment. Thus, time is of the essence and the manager will want the trade executed immediately. Market orders are orders to trade as quickly as possible at the best available price.

> Sample Scoring Key: maximum 4 points.

Source: Study Session 16, LOS 39.n,o

C.   **For the exam:**

1 point each for any 4 of the following:

- Attempt to improve performance while meeting fiduciary responsibilities.
- On-going process/multiple trades over time.
- Cannot be measured for single trade.
- Cannot be determined ex ante.
- Must be judged within the context of the investment decision.
- Relationships and practices are integral.
- Written policies for attaining best execution.
- Provide disclosure to clients on how practice best execution.

Discussion:

This question basically asks for the definition of best execution, which is discussed thoroughly in the SchweserNotes™ Book 5, page 29.

Sample Scoring Key: maximum 4 points.

QUESTION 13

Source: Study Session 3, LOS 8.b,c,d and LOS 9.a and Study Session 4, LOS 10.h

Answer for Question 13

Comment	Is the statement correct or incorrect? (circle one)	Explanation, if incorrect
"Many of our investors use a mental accounting or pyramiding approach to investment planning. Even though this approach might help them achieve a degree of self-control, it is a form of emotional bias that must be overcome for clients to effectively meet their long-term goals."	Incorrect	For the exam: Mental accounting is a cognitive error.
"An investment policy statement should be reviewed and considered for possible revision when an investor experiences a change in personal circumstances or when external conditions change significantly. For example, a change in tax laws may trigger an investment policy statement review."	Correct	
"We have a lot of clients I would classify as independent individualists. Due to their tendency toward emotional decisions, they can be very difficult to advise."	Incorrect	For the exam: Independent individualists are primarily subject to cognitive errors.

Discussion:

Because they put goals and related assets into mental accounts, investors' portfolios tend to resemble layered pyramids of assets. As a result, investors subconsciously ignore the correlations of assets and, thus, may not achieve an optimal asset allocation. They also may consider income and capital gains separately rather than as parts of the same total return. Rather than reinvest, they spend current income, which could lead to a decrease in real portfolio value over time. They could also take too much risk in search of high potential current income, as with low-rated, high-risk bonds.

To help the client mitigate mental accounting, have the client look at all investments as if they are part of the same portfolio and then analyze their correlations. This also leads to a clearer perception of the true portfolio allocation, which might be less evident when assets are not considered together.

The second statement is correct. An investment policy statement should be reviewed and considered for possible revision when an investor experiences a change in personal circumstances or when external conditions change significantly. Examples of the former include a change in marital status, health, and income. Examples of the latter include a change in tax laws, capital market expectations, and asset availability. A large loss in the portfolio could also trigger an investment policy statement review.

The independent individualist is an active investor who is willing to risk his own capital and give up security to gain wealth. He has moderate to high risk tolerance and suffers from cognitive biases. He is strong-willed, likes to invest, does his own research, and tends to be a contrarian. The independent individualist tends to be difficult to advise but will listen to sound advice. Therefore, the best approach to advising him is regular education on investing concepts relevant to the investor.

Sample Scoring Key: (maximum 9 points)
1 point each for correctly identifying whether the statement is correct or incorrect.
2 points for each explanation.
0 points possible if the correct/incorrect decision is wrong.

EXAM 3
AFTERNOON SESSION ANSWERS

To get detailed answer explanations with references to specific LOS and SchweserNotes content, and to get valuable feedback on how your score compares to those of other Level III candidates, use your Username and Password to gain Online Access at *www.schweser.com* and choose the left-hand menu item "Practice Exams Vol. 2."

1.	A	25.	B	49.	C
2.	A	26.	A	50.	A
3.	A	27.	C	51.	B
4.	C	28.	B	52.	C
5.	C	29.	A	53.	C
6.	B	30.	C	54.	C
7.	A	31.	C	55.	C
8.	A	32.	B	56.	A
9.	B	33.	C	57.	A
10.	A	34.	B	58.	B
11.	C	35.	A	59.	C
12.	B	36.	C	60.	B
13.	C	37.	B		
14.	B	38.	C		
15.	A	39.	B		
16.	B	40.	A		
17.	B	41.	A		
18.	C	42.	C		
19.	B	43.	C		
20.	A	44.	C		
21.	B	45.	C		
22.	B	46.	A		
23.	C	47.	A		
24.	A	48.	B		

Exam 3
Afternoon Session Answers

QUESTIONS 1–6

Source: Study Session 17

1. **A**   Harrison is correct. Since the Treynor ratio uses beta, which measures only systematic risk, it is only appropriate for assessing the performance of well-diversified portfolios or individual stocks held in well-diversified portfolios. Recall that unsystematic risk is diversified away in a well-diversified portfolio.

     Powell is incorrect. The Sharpe ratio uses the standard deviation as the measure of risk, which is useful when the portfolio is not well-diversified and reflects unsystematic or firm specific risk. Since the Treynor ratio uses systematic risk as the relevant measure of risk, it may rank portfolios differently than the Sharpe ratio. Consider a portfolio with low systematic risk but high unsystematic and total risk. This portfolio may rank highly using the Treynor ratio but quite low using the Sharpe ratio. (Study Session 17, LOS 41.p)

2. **A**   The pure sector allocation effect is calculated by taking the differences between the portfolio and benchmark weights for each sector and multiplying it by the difference between the benchmark return for that sector and the total benchmark return. The products are then summed across the sectors:

$$\text{pure sector allocation} = \sum_{j=1}^{s} \left(W_{P,j} - W_{B,j} \right) \left(R_{B,j} - R_B \right)$$

benchmark return = (0.6)(0.286) + (0.25)(0.124) + (0.15)(0.0885) = 0.216

The pure sector allocation effect = (0.5 − 0.6)(0.286 − 0.216) + (0.3 − 0.25)(0.124 − 0.216) + (0.2 − 0.15)(0.0885 − 0.216) = −1.80%.

So TopTech does not demonstrate superior ability to choose sectors, because the allocation effect is negative at −1.80%. (Study Session 17, LOS 41.l)

3. **A**   The within-sector selection effect measures the manager's ability to select superior securities to represent each sector in the portfolio. It is the sum of the weight for each sector in the benchmark times the difference in that sector's return in the portfolio and in the benchmark:

$$\text{within-sector selection} = \sum_{j=1}^{s} W_{B,j} \left(R_{P,j} - R_{B,j} \right)$$

Within-sector selection effect = (0.60)(0.187 − 0.286) + 0.25(0.158 − 0.124) + (0.15)(0.125 − 0.0885) = −0.0594 + 0.0085 + 0.0055 = −0.0454 = −4.54%.

In sum, in the financial and large cap sectors, the manager chose superior stocks, so they show superior ability there. The overall within-sector selection effect is negative (−4.54%), however, so they do not show a consistent overall ability to select stocks.

The remaining component of attribution analysis (the allocation/selection interaction effect) can be calculated as the difference between the portfolio and benchmark weights for each sector multiplied by the difference between the return for the sector in the portfolio and the return for the sector in the benchmark. The total allocation/selection interaction effect is the sum of these products:

$$\text{allocation/selection interaction} = \sum_{j=1}^{s}\left(W_{P,j} - W_{B,j}\right)\left(R_{P,j} - R_{B,j}\right)$$

Allocation/selection interaction effect = (0.50 − 0.60)(0.187 − 0.286) + (0.30 − 0.25)(0.158 − 0.124) + (0.20 − 0.15)(0.125 − 0.0885) = 0.0099 + 0.0017 + 0.0018 = 0.0134 = 1.34%.

The total excess return for the manager is then −1.80% + 1.34% − 4.54% = −5.00%.

This should be equal to the excess return calculated using the total returns for the benchmark and the portfolio. The total return for the benchmark is calculated above as 21.6%. For the portfolio it is: = (0.5)(0.187) + (0.3)(0.158) + (0.2)(0.125) = 16.6%. Thus, the excess return calculated using the total returns for the portfolio and the benchmark is 16.6% − 21.6% = −5.0%. (Study Session 17, LOS 41.l)

4. C   Benchmarks are used to measure investment skill—a manager's ability to select superior securities or apply superior trading strategies. We compare the actively managed portfolio to the performance of a benchmark representing the same risk factor exposures, style, asset classes, and so on, to see if the manager added value or if we would have been better off investing directly in the benchmark itself.

TopTech compares its managers to the top ten managers in their particular areas of specialty, so they appear to be utilizing a variation of the median manager approach. In the mean-manager approach, the active manager is expected to beat the average manager when managers from the same manager universe are ranked from best to worst. TopTech seems to take this a step further by requiring their managers to place in the upper 10%.

From a valid benchmark perspective, there are several problems with the median manager and, for that matter, TopTech's approach. For a benchmark to be considered valid, it must be: (1) unambiguous; (2) investable; (3) measurable; (4) appropriate; (5) reflective of current investment opinions; (6) specified in advance; and (7) owned.

1. *Unambiguous* means the benchmark's contents or factor exposures can be clearly identified.
    * The TopTech benchmarks are identifiable only at the end of the measurement period, and must therefore be ambiguous at the beginning of the period.

2. To be *investable*, an investor must be able to actually hold the benchmark.
    * Again, since the benchmarks are not known until the end of the period, the managers (or the client) could not elect at the beginning of the period to invest in the benchmarks instead of the active portfolios.

3. A benchmark is *measurable* if its return can be calculated with reasonable frequency.
    * At the end of the period, the returns for the top 10% of managers are available, while even the identities of the managers are not necessarily known. Purely from the perspective of being able to compare the TopTech managers to the top performing managers, the benchmarks could be considered measurable.

4. A benchmark is *appropriate* if it reflects the manager's style or area of expertise.
   - Since the benchmarks are unknown at the beginning of the period, they cannot be deemed appropriate. Manager universes are subject to survivor bias and the contents of the benchmark managers' portfolios (even the identities of the managers for that matter) cannot be determined, so we cannot say that the benchmarks are appropriate even if TopTech is careful in applying their benchmark selection criteria.

5. *Reflective of current investment opinions* means that the manager has knowledge of and opinions about the benchmark contents or factor exposures.
   - TopTech appears to be careful in selecting benchmarks that are reflective of their managers' positions. For this reason, it is possible that the benchmarks are reflective of the managers' current investment opinions.

6. *Specified in advance* is straightforward. The manager knows the benchmark prior to entering the measurement period.
   - Ranking of the manager universe takes place at the end of the period, so the top ten performers can only be determined at that time. Thus, TopTech cannot specify the benchmarks in advance.

7. *Owned* means that the manager agrees to be held accountable for any difference in performance between his portfolio and the benchmark.
   - Whether the TopTech managers own the benchmarks isn't made clear by the statements, but to own their benchmarks, managers must agree that differences between their portfolios' performance and that of the benchmarks are the result of active management decisions, not differences in the construction of the portfolios and benchmarks.
   (Study Session 17, LOS 41.f)

5. **C** Harrison is incorrect. The benchmark level examines the difference between the return to custom benchmarks reflecting the managers' styles and the return to a broad asset category. Essentially the benchmark return measures the return to style bets resulting from the policy weighting in various styles. Harrison actually describes the investment managers level.

   Powell is incorrect. Although the investment manager's level does reflect the return from active management, it uses the policy weights established for each manager. Returns due to differences between policy weights and the amounts actually allocated to each manager do not show up until the last level of macro attribution analysis (i.e., allocation effects). (Study Session 17, LOS 41.k)

6. **B** Benchmark B is the best benchmark for the small-cap value manager. A good benchmark will have a beta relative to the portfolio that is close to one, so the tracking error (i.e., the standard deviation of the excess return of the portfolio relative to the benchmark) will be low. The benchmark turnover should be low so that it is investable by a passive manager. The correlation between the return to the manager's active management (A) and the return to the manager's style (S) should be low. Otherwise, the benchmark has not adequately captured the manager's style.

   Benchmark B is the best benchmark using all four measures.
   (Study Session 17, LOS 41.i)

Sample Scoring Key: 3 points for each correct response.

QUESTIONS 7–12

Source: Study Session 1

7. **A**   According to Standard V(B) Communication with Clients and Prospective Clients, he is required to distinguish between fact and opinion in his research reports. He has fully conformed to this requirement. The statement is in accordance with CFA Institute Standards. The mosaic theory allows combining public information with nonmaterial nonpublic information on which to base a decision.
(Study Session 1, LOS 1.b)

8. **A**   His action is not supported by reasonable and adequate basis in fact, and thus constitutes a violation of Standard V(A) Diligence and Reasonable Basis. In fact, he totally missed the Reuters report, which would indicate a lack of due diligence.
(Study Session 1, LOS 1.b)

9. **B**   Standard II(B) Market Manipulation states that members and candidates must not engage in practices that distort prices or artificially inflate trading volume with the intent to mislead market participants. Legitimate orders in thinly traded securities could overwhelm the liquidity of the security, causing significant changes in the price of the security. This is different from efforts to artificially affect the price of the security; thus, Lepage did not engage in market manipulation.
(Study Session 1, LOS 1.b)

10. **A**   CFA Institute Standard III(B) Fair Dealing requires that members and candidates deal fairly with clients when taking investment actions (including trade allocations). Recommended procedures to comply with this Standard include allocating trades on a pro rata basis when the entire order is being filled over time such that the prices are the same in all accounts. Lepage has conformed with the Standards in his execution and allocation of the shares of Spectra Vision. (Study Session 1, LOS 1.b)

11. **C**   Shareholders are most often concerned with the long-term prospects for the company. Giving management a large number of options that expire in the current year creates strong incentive for management to engage in behavior that puts the long-term value of the company at risk in favor of short-term gains in the stock price (thus maximizing the value of management's stock options). The base salary should be a small proportion of the overall compensation package and can be supplemented by performance-based bonuses (not a guaranteed bonus structure). Use of company assets for personal use should be restricted, whether or not the manager does a good job for the shareholders. (Study Session 1, LOS 1.b)

12. **B**   Lepage's first statement is incorrect. While it is a noble goal for a board to structure management compensation packages to align the managers' interests with those of the shareholders, best practices in corporate governance dictate that the board must continue to evaluate the effectiveness of management in managing the firm in accordance with shareholders' interests. Lepage's second statement is correct. Good corporate governance practices provide the audit committee independence from firm management and the authority to hire an auditor and scrutinize the auditor's work, including any financial statements produced internally. (Study Session 1, LOS 1.b)

Sample Scoring Key: 3 points for each correct response.

QUESTIONS 13–18

Source: Study Sessions 6 and 12

13. **C**   Ms. So is referring to psychological traps and model and input uncertainty. Psychological traps are behavioral characteristics such as anchoring, status quo, overconfidence, etc. The main point is that these traps can result in biased capital market expectations. Problems relating to the choice of models and accuracy of data are known as model and input uncertainty. The analyst wants to choose the model that most correctly describes the market valuation process, but any time there is a choice, there is a chance that the incorrect model will be chosen.
    (Study Session 6, LOS 18.b)

14. **B**   The required return on the Singapore index can be estimated with the dividend discount model.

$$3,750 = \frac{90(1.06)}{(R_M - 0.06)} \Rightarrow R_M = 8.544\%$$

The market risk premium for Singapore = 8.544 − 2.4 = 6.144%. The market risk premium for Taiwan = 6.144 × 1.10 = 6.76, so the required return on the market in Taiwan is 6.76 + 2.7 = 9.46%. Thus, we can estimate the intrinsic value of the Taiwan index.

$$\frac{450(1.045)}{(0.0946 - 0.045)} = 9,481$$

(Study Session 6, LOS 18.c)

15. **A**   The presenter is incorrect on both counts. For any pair of freely traded currencies, interest rate parity is governed by arbitrage and must hold in the short run. On the other hand, the relative form of purchasing power parity is not governed by arbitrage, and currency values can deviate widely from their PPP value in the short run. However, the evidence suggests that PPP is a useful forecasting tool for the long run.
    (Study Session 6, LOS 18.l)

16. **B**   Although it is true that, in general, emerging market sovereign debt has increased in quality and emerging market governments have the ability to access global capital (e.g., World Bank), these generalities in and of themselves do not necessarily present any specific return-enhancing capabilities. Also, it is true that emerging market debt can be highly volatile with negatively-skewed returns distributions. This characteristic, however, presents an increased probability of low or negative returns (increased risk). Expected returns (prices) will compensate for the increased risk, but this again does not in and of itself present any specific return-enhancing capability. It is also true that the EMBI+ index is dominated by the debt securities of Latin American countries. Ordinarily an investor would not want to invest in a concentrated index, due to its lack of diversification. However, with such a concentrated index, the investor is faced with both unsystematic and systematic risk and, hence, an increased return potential. Thus, combining the index with a well-diversified portfolio of fixed income securities presents the global fixed income manager the potential to generate enhanced returns.
    (Study Session 12, LOS 30.a)

17. **B** When an economic crisis, such as that which began in Thailand in 1997, spreads to other countries, this is known as contagion. The fact that emerging market asset returns may exhibit greater non-normality makes it more difficult to apply parametric models (e.g., those based upon the statistical concepts of mean and standard deviation). In such instances, the analyst should consider non-parametric approaches, such as bootstrapping techniques and Monte Carlo simulation to estimate risk. (Study Session 6, LOS 18.m)

18. **C** All else being equal, the economic statistics presented favor Russia over Brazil for hard currency bond investment. Russia has a relatively greater level of foreign exchange relative to short-term debt, implying that short-term ability to pay is greater, and the overall indebtedness relative to GDP is lower.

   While India and China each have the advantage in two of the four economic growth statistic categories, in aggregate, the statistics presented favor China for equity investment.

   estimated long-term growth = population growth + labor force

   participation growth + growth in capital spending + growth in total factor productivity

   estimated long-term growth for China: 0.8 + 1.8 + 1.3 + 0.9 = 4.8%

   estimated long-term growth for India: 1.3 + 0.5 + 1.4 + 0.4 = 3.6%

   In addition, China enjoys a relatively more favorable savings to investment balance, implying that the growth may be more sustainable. (Study Session 6, LOS 18.r)

QUESTIONS 19–24

Source: Study Session 9

19. **B** The cushion spread is the difference between the safety net return (minimum acceptable return) and prevailing immunized rate. In this case, the cushion spread is 8% – 6% = 200 basis points. (Study Session 9, LOS 23.i)

20. **A** Assuming the present value of the liability at the safety net return is $100 million:

$$\$100 \text{ million} = \frac{L}{(1.03)^{10}}$$

L = $100 million$(1.03)^{10}$ = $134.39 million

The amount required to achieve the required terminal value at the current immunization rate of 8% over the five remaining years is $134.39 million / $(1.04)^{10}$ = $90.79 million.

So, the dollar safety margin is $100 million – $90.79 million = $9.21 million. (Study Session 9, LOS 23.i)

21. **B** After one year, the value of the portfolio is the price of the bond plus accumulated interest. The price of the bond is computed as follows:

FV = 100; N = 18; I/Y = 4.5; PMT = 4; CPT → PV = 93.92

The accumulated value of the coupon payments is the compounded value of the first coupon at 4% (= 8% / 2) for one 6-month period plus the value of the second coupon payment received at the end of the first year, or:

4(1.04) + 4 = 4.16 + 4 = $8.16

Thus, the value of the portfolio after one year is 93.92 + 8.16 = 102.08, or $102.08 million.

The required terminal value is $134.39 million. The portfolio value necessary to achieve the required terminal value at the prevailing immunization rate of 9%, compounded semiannually, over the four remaining years, is:

$134.39 million / $(1.045)^{8}$ = $94.50 million

So, the dollar safety margin is: $102.08 million – $94.50 million = $7.58 million. (Study Session 9, LOS 23.i)

22. **B** The dollar safety margin hits zero when the portfolio value nears the minimum value necessary to achieve an immunization strategy, and that value is the present value of the liability at the current immunized rate. The present value of $134.39 million at the immunized rate of 11% (for 5 years) is ($134.39 million)/$(1.055)$10 = $78.676 million. To answer the question, therefore, we determine the required return that will push the portfolio value ($100 million, 10-year, 8%, semi-annual bonds) to that amount:

FV = 100,000,000; PMT = $8 / 2 = 4,000,000; N = 10 × 2 = 20; PV = –$78,676,000; CPT → I/Y = 5.83 × 2 = 11.67%

If the required return on the portfolio of bonds increases to 11.67%, the present value of the bonds will be exactly the minimum amount necessary to implement an immunization strategy at the current immunized rate. (Study Session 9, LOS 23.i)

23. **C** Price has correctly described cash flow matching but has incorrectly described horizon matching. Cash flow matching involves finding a bond with a maturity date equal to the liability payment date, buying enough in par value of that bond so that the principal and final coupon fully fund the last liability, and continuing this process, using a recursive procedure, until all liabilities are matched. Features of multi-cash flow immunization include ensuring that assets and liabilities have the same present values and durations. Horizon matching (a.k.a. combination matching) is a combination of cash flow matching in the early years and multiple liability immunization. (Study Session 9, LOS 23.m)

24. **A** Immunization risk can only be eliminated by investing in zero-coupon bonds (e.g., Treasury strips) with a maturity and face value equal to that of the liability, so that statement is correct. That strategy is rarely followed, however, due to the high asset cost (low return potential). His statement about the dispersion of cash flows around the horizon date is correct, because the greater the dispersion the higher the reinvestment risk; the less the dispersion the lower the reinvestment risk. Note that using zeros is the extreme example of concentrating the asset maturities and cash inflows at the horizon date. (Study Session 9, LOS 23.f)

> Sample Scoring Key: 3 points for each correct response.

QUESTIONS 25–30

Source: Study Sessions 8, 10, 14, and 15

25. **B** RS is using a balanced mandate approach, in which the manager is allowed discretion for hedging currency risk within the guidelines of the investor's investment policy statement. This approach manages currency risk as an integral part of the portfolio. It allows the manager to view the interaction between the risk of the assets and the currencies. The currency overlay approach would assign the currency hedging process to another manager when the portfolio manager does not have the necessary hedging expertise. The overall process is still managed within the guidelines established by the investment policy statement. The currency as a separate asset allocation approach manages currency risk separate from the rest of the portfolio, such that the cash manager decides which currencies to hedge. (Study Session 14, LOS 35.i)

26. **A** The hedging of currency risk with options should focus on buying an option, not writing (selling) them. In this case, the purchase of a put on Japanese yen provides RS with a minimum amount of Canadian dollars they will receive for the sale of Japanese yen. The sale of a call on Japanese yen would provide income enhancement but would not provide a complete hedge against adverse currency movements. The sale of a put on Canadian dollars is the same position as the sale of a call on Japanese yen (RS is giving the counterparty the right to sell them dollars in exchange for the counterparty buying Japanese yen). (Study Session 14, LOS 35.f)

27. **C**

$$\text{\# contracts} = \left(\frac{\beta_{target} - \beta_{current}}{\beta_{futures}} \right)\left(\frac{V_P}{V_F} \right)$$

$$= \left(\frac{1.80 - 0.60}{1.02} \right)\left(\frac{2,000,000}{110,000} \right) = 21.39 \ (\text{buy 21 contracts})$$

(Study Session 15, LOS 36.a)

28. **B** RS would be least likely to hedge the currency risk of the British manufacturers. The currency hedging decision should consider the correlation between the asset and the currency. In developed markets, there is often a negative correlation between the currency and the equity. The reasoning is that when the currency depreciates, the country's exports are more competitive on international markets. Such a scenario is most likely for the developed market manufacturing firm here that exports. The stocks of service industries in general, and even more so in emerging markets, tend to be positively correlated with changes in the country's currency. To avoid the simultaneous drop in asset and currency values, RS is likely to hedge these exposures.
(Study Session 8, LOS 22.c)

29. **A** The CWC International mortgage has a higher coupon rate than newly issued mortgages. As such, it is likely to be called (i.e., homeowners will refinance) when interest rates decline and it has negative convexity (just as with any callable bond). If rates decline, the mortgage price rise will be capped at the call price. The price rise in the MBS will be less than the loss in the short futures position. Thus, the mortgage and hedge combination would have a weak return if interest rates fall.
(Study Session 10, LOS 26.a)

30. **C** Both Rolle and Sims are correct. Since mortgage securities exhibit negative convexity, two Treasury bond futures contracts are typically used as a hedge. If the volatility of interest rates increases, an investment in an MBS declines in value. The mortgage holder has sold the borrower an interest rate call that allows him to refinance the mortgage. As with any option, an increase in the underlying's volatility increases the value of the option. (Study Session 10, LOS 26.b)

Sample Scoring Key: 3 points for each correct response.

QUESTIONS 31–36

Source: Study Sessions 9 and 10

31. **C** To calculate the number of futures contracts necessary for the hedge, we must first obtain the dollar durations for the CTD and Bond Q:

The dollar duration for a given change in interest rates at time t is expressed as:

DD_t = duration$_t$ × assumed change in interest rates × value of asset at time t

DD_{CTD} is given as $13,245.46.

$DD_Q = 10.32 \times 0.01 \times 1.0498 \times \$10,000,000 = \$1,083,394$

The number of futures contracts necessary for the hedge can be computed as:

$$\text{\# contracts} = \left(\frac{DD_T - DD_P}{DD_{CTD}/\text{conversion factor}}\right)(\text{yield beta})$$

$$\text{\# contracts} = \left(\frac{0 - \$1,083,394}{\$13,245.46/1.3698}\right)(1.00) = -112.04$$

Therefore, sell 112 contracts.

(Study Session 10, LOS 25.e)

32. **B** The portfolio's dollar duration is the sum of the individual bond's dollar durations:

$$DD_P = DD_Q + DD_R + DD_S$$

$$= [(1.0498 \times 10,000,000) \times 0.01 \times 10.32]$$

$$+ [(0.9836 \times 25,000,000) \times 0.01 \times 8.67]$$

$$+ [(1.0121 \times 15,000,000) \times 0.01 \times 7.38]$$

$$= 1,083,394 + 2,131,953 + 1,120,395 = \$4,335,742$$

(Study Session 9, LOS 23.g)

33. **C** DD_P (in one year) $= 0.01\big[(10m \times 1.0498 \times 9.46) + (25m \times 0.9836 \times 7.83) + (15m \times 1.0121 \times 6.51)\big]$
$= \$3,906,822$

rebalancing ratio $= 4,901,106 / 3,906,822 = 1.2545$

We must increase the value of the portfolio by the rebalancing ratio, which assumes a proportionate increase in each bond. To do this, multiply the necessary percentage increase by the total value of the portfolio.

required cash $= 0.2545$ (Total value of Bond Q, Bond R, and Bond S)

required cash $= 0.2545\big[(10m \times 1.0498) + (25m \times 0.9836) + (15m \times 1.0121)\big] = \$12,793,588$

(Study Session 9, LOS 23.g)

34. **B**   Rawlins is incorrect. If the slope coefficient from Tejada's regression was greater than one, the number of futures contracts needed to hedge a position would *increase* because the yield on the underlying bond would be more volatile than the yield on the hedge instrument.

Tejada is correct. The yield beta is obtained from using a regression equation in the following form:

yield on bond to be hedged = a + b(yield on CTD issue) + error

The yield beta, *b*, measures the relationship between changes in yields. If the yield spread between the bond being hedged and the CTD issue is assumed to be constant, the yields must move together and the yield beta must equal one.
(Study Session 10, LOS 25.e)

35. **A**   Rawlins's basis for trading would most likely be characterized as that of yield pickup. He favors the bond with the higher yield and ignores the potential change in price of either bond. Rawlins should be examining both yield differentials and potential changes in both bonds' prices (a total return approach).

Tejada's basis for trading would most likely be characterized as a total return approach. He correctly evaluates both yield differentials and potential price changes in the bonds under evaluation. (Study Session 9, LOS 24.d)

36. **C**   To determine which bond would be more attractive using breakeven analysis, we use modified duration. Recall the formula:

$$\%\Delta price = -modified\ duration \times \Delta yield \Rightarrow \Delta yield = \frac{\%\Delta price}{-modified\ duration}$$

For the returns to the two bonds to be equal over the next three months, the price for the Dynacom bond must fall by 0.5% (its yield advantage calculated by Rawlins in the vignette), holding the yield for the Bergamo bond constant. The change in yield that would result in this price change is:

$$\Delta yield = \frac{-0.5\%}{-5.13} = 0.0975\%$$

If the yield on the Dynacom bond rises 0.0975%, the return on the two bonds will be equal. So Tejada is correct because if the yield on the Dynacom bond rises by 0.75%, its price will fall such that its return will be lower than the return on the Bergamo bond over the next three months.

Rawlins is correct as well. Note that breakeven analysis uses the duration relationship, which provides only an approximate price change. Recall that the use of duration ignores any nonlinearity (i.e., convexity) in the bond price/yield relationship.
(Study Session 10, LOS 25.k)

Sample Scoring Key: 3 points for each correct response.

QUESTIONS 37–42

Source: Study Sessions 7, 10, 14. and 15

37. **B**   All the BRIC countries except Russia are expected to remain below the G6 countries in terms of per capita income. Because developing countries currently utilize relatively low amounts of capital, an increase in investment capital will result in a relatively high level of output. Furthermore, as developing countries adopt technology available in developed countries, their productivity will increase. (Study Session 7, LOS 20.a,b,c)

38. **C**   Amsler's portfolio is invested in European stocks that are denominated in the euro. She is therefore long European stocks and long the euro. In order to hedge, short positions should be taken in both the European stocks and the euro. If the European equity index or euro decline in value, the short positions in the derivative contracts will rise, therefore offsetting the losses in the underlying equity and currency positions. (Study Session 15, LOS 36.a,f)

39. **B**   Tavinsky is incorrect. He has ignored the relative betas of the portfolio and futures contract and simply divided the value of the portfolio by the value of a futures contract:

$$\frac{-15,000,000}{120,000} = -125$$

The correct number of futures contracts can be calculated as:

$$N_f = \left(\frac{0-1.15}{0.975}\right)\left(\frac{15,000,000}{120,000}\right) = -147.44 \Rightarrow \text{short 147 contracts}$$

Treblehorn is correct. In a "hedging the principal" strategy, the investor simply sets the principal of the forward contract equal to the beginning principal value of the investment. The reason that the investor uses the beginning value and not an estimated future value is that, especially in equity investments, the future value of the investment is very difficult to predict with accuracy.
(Study Sessions 14 and 15, LOS 35.a and 36.a)

40. **A**   If the local market declined by 12%, the equity position will decline an estimated (−12%)(1.15) = −13.8%. This would translate into a portfolio worth €15,000,000 × (1 − 0.138) = €12,930,000 at the end of the year. The ending position in dollars is worth (€12,930,000)($1.12 / €) = $14,481,600. Since the beginning portfolio value was worth (€15,000,000)($1.05 / €) = $15,750,000, this translates into a U.S. dollar loss of 8.05%. (Study Session 14, LOS 35.a)

41. **A**   If the futures position was a perfect hedge, the euro rate of return on the equity portfolio will be the local risk-free rate of 2%. This would translate into an ending portfolio value of €15,300,000. The dollar equivalent of that portfolio would be (€15,300,000)($1.12 / €) = $17,136,000, which is an 8.8% return ($17,136,000 / $15,750,000 − 1).

 Professor's Note: Looking at it another way, the investor earns 2% in the local market and 6.67% [(1.12 / 1.05) − 1] on the euro appreciation. [(1.02) × (1.0667)] −1 = 8.8% total return.

(Study Session 14, LOS 35.a)

42. **C**   Tavinsky is incorrect. By covered interest rate parity, the forward rate between two currencies must reflect the current spot rate times the ratio of one plus the interest rates:

$$F_{\$/\mathbb{\euro}} = S_{\$/\mathbb{\euro}} \times \left(\frac{1+i_\$}{1+i_\mathbb{\euro}} \right)$$

$$= \$1.05 \times \left(\frac{1.04}{1.02} \right) = \$1.070588$$

If a perfect hedge took place using equity futures, then the rate of return on the equity portfolio would be the local risk-free rate of 2%. This would translate into an ending portfolio value of €15,300,000.

If the €15,300,000 is sold in one year at the forward rate of ($1.070588 / €), the value of the portfolio in dollars will be $16,379,996. The starting portfolio value in dollars was (€15,000,000)($1.05 / €) = $15,750,000. So the investor's return in dollars, hedging both equity and currency risk, would be 4% ($16,379,996 / $15,750,000 − 1).

 Professor's Note: We could have arrived at this answer more quickly by recognizing that by interest rate parity, the return on a currency-hedged, risk-free foreign investment must equal the return on a domestic risk-free investment. So if interest rate parity holds the return must be 4%.

Treblehorn is incorrect. As noted previously, the forward rate must reflect interest rate differentials between the two countries. In this case, the forecasted spot rate of $1.12 / € does not equal the forward rate dictated by covered interest rate parity (i.e., $1.070588 / €). (Study Session 10, LOS 25.j)

> Sample Scoring Key: 3 points for correct response.

QUESTIONS 43–48

Source: Study Sessions 14 and 17

43. **C**   The information ratio is calculated as average excess return (alpha) divided by the standard deviation of alpha (a.k.a. tracking error, active risk, or tracking risk). The information ratio shows not only the manager's ability to generate alpha, but his ability to *consistently* generate alpha. The greater the volatility of alpha compared to the average alpha, the less consistent the manager's performance. That is, as the information ratio decreases, the distribution of the manager's alpha increases (i.e., widens) relative to his average alpha. As the distribution of alpha increases, the probability of a zero or negative alpha in any single measurement period increases. A higher information ratio, therefore, generally indicates a superior ability to consistently generate alpha over time. (Study Session 17, LOS 41.p)

44. **C**   The risk governance and risk budgeting statement (the second statement) is correct. Risk governance is part of the firm's overall corporate governance system and is the process of developing a risk management system and putting it into operation. A decentralized risk governance system puts risk management into the hands of those closest to the risk (e.g., individual managers). The primary drawback to a decentralized system is the inability for individual managers to gain a sense of how their risk affects the firm's overall risk. A centralized system is called an Enterprise Risk Management (ERM) system. ERM systems are overseen by top management who are better positioned to view and analyze the firm's overall risk.

        Risk budgeting is the process of determining which risks are acceptable and how total risk is allocated across business units or portfolio managers. Through the ERM system upper management allocates capital across portfolio managers, each with an associated VAR.

        The ERM statement (the third statement) is incorrect. Individual managers cannot determine the correlation of their portfolio risk to that of other managers, so only upper management is in a position to measure and monitor firm risk. In an ERM system upper management allocates capital to each manager based on the manager's risk and the desired overall firm risk. (Study Session 14, LOS 34.a)

45. **C**   Liquidity risk is the possibility of sustaining losses due to the inability to take or liquidate a position quickly at a fair price. It is considered a financial risk. (Study Session 14, LOS 34.d)

46. **A**   The Monte Carlo statement is correct. The main advantage of the Monte Carlo Method is the ability to incorporate any returns distribution or asset correlation. The historical VAR statement is incorrect. The variance/covariance VAR, not the historical method, is based on MPT. (Study Session 14, LOS 34.f)

47. **A**   To calculate the daily VAR, we must first calculate a daily expected return and daily standard deviation. Note that to obtain a daily standard deviation from an annual standard deviation, we must divide the annual standard deviation by the square root of 250. We then calculate a daily percent VAR by subtracting 1.65 times the daily standard deviation from the daily expected return. The daily dollar VAR is calculated last using the fund's asset base:

daily expected return = 12.1% / 250 = 0.0484%

daily standard deviation = 18.2% / $(250)^{0.5}$ = 1.1511%

daily percent VAR = 0.0484% − (1.65 × 1.1511%) = −1.8509%

daily dollar VAR = $140 × 1.8509% = $2.59 million

(Study Session 14, LOS 34.e)

48. **B**   Incremental VAR (IVAR) is used to measure the impact of a single asset on the portfolio VAR. By measuring the VAR of the portfolio with and without the asset, IVAR captures the effects of the correlations of the individual assets on the overall portfolio VAR. (Study Session 14, LOS 34.g)

Sample Scoring Key: 3 points for each correct response.

QUESTIONS 49–54

Source: Study Sessions 10 and 15

49. **C**   The sale has resulted in transaction exposure; a change in revenues or costs that result from changes in foreign exchange rates. If the size of Smiler's sales to Frexa were to change as a result of a change in the $/€ rate this would be economic exposure. The third type of exposure is translation exposure, and it occurs when financial statements are converted from foreign currency to home currency.

Assuming Smiler hedges the long position in €10,000,000 by selling euros for dollars at the 90-day forward rate, the proceeds from the forward contract = €10m × 1.45$/€ = $14.5 million. (Study Session 15, LOS 36.f)

50. **A**   The cost of the call is 0.000943443 × 25 million = $23,586.

The future value of this premium at the beginning of the loan period based on current 90-day LIBOR plus the 150 bp spread is:

23,586 × [1 + (0.048 + 0.015) 90 / 360] = $23,957, making the net loan:

25,000,000 − 23,957 = $24,976,043

The payoff on the call = ($25,000,000)(0.0573 − 0.048)(180 / 360) = $116,250.

The effective dollar interest cost = ($25,000,000)(0.0573 + 0.0150)(180 / 360) − $116,250 = $787,500.

Alternatively, the interest on the loan can also be calculated as the exercise rate plus the spread because the call is in the money at expiration: (0.048 + 0.015) × 180 / 360 × 25,000,000 = $787,500.

The annualized rate on the loan is ($25,787,500 / $24,976,043)$^{365/180}$ − 1 = 6.6982%. The call premium increased the cost of the loan from (4.8 + 1.5 =) 6.3% to 6.698%. (Study Session 15, LOS 37.c)

51. **B**   The equation to determine the number of contracts and the direction of the trade (long or short) is:

$$\text{number of contracts} = \left(\frac{\beta_{\text{Target}} - \beta_{\text{Current}}}{\beta_{\text{Futures}}}\right)\left(\frac{\text{portfolio value}}{\text{future contract value}}\right)$$

which in numeric terms is:

$$\text{number of contracts} = \left(\frac{0.9 - 1.25}{0.98}\right)\left(\frac{\$52,750,000}{1,050 \times \$250}\right) = -71.77; \text{ short 72 contracts.}$$

(Study Session 15, LOS 36.a)

52. **C**   The dollar duration of the $25,000,000 corporate bond at issue is expected to be:

$25,000,000 \times 0.01 \times 9.90 = \$2,475,000$

$$\text{number of contracts} = \frac{DD_T - DD_P}{DD_{CTD}/\text{conversion factor}}(\text{yield beta}) \qquad [DD_T = 0]$$

$$= \frac{-\$2,475,000}{\$6,932.53/1.259}(1.05) = -472$$

(Study Session 10, LOS 25.e)

53. **C**   The futures contract has an expiration date that coincides with the expected date of the bond issuance, so the basis will be zero and does not have to be estimated. (Study Session 10, LOS 25.e)

54. **C**   Ng has an investment in British stocks, which he will be converting to U.S. dollars in one year. The problem with hedging the foreign exchange rate risk of an equity investment is that the investor does not know how much to hedge because the investment's value fluctuates. (Study Session 15, LOS 36.f)

Sample Scoring Key: 3 points for each correct response.

QUESTIONS 55–60

Source: Study Session 2

55. **C**   The IPS review policy is inadequate. It is good that IPS are reviewed at any time upon client request, but it is also likely that clients may be unaware of when such a review might be appropriate. It is incumbent upon the manager to initiate a review of the client's IPS. The Asset Manager Code recommends such reviews on an annual basis, or more frequently if changes in client circumstances justify them. The process for making changes in style/strategy is adequate. (Study Session 2, LOS 6.b)

56. **A**   The IPO program creates a substantial conflict of interest between managers and clients. Managers wanting to boost their participation in an IPO would be motivated to place orders in accounts where such an investment might not be appropriate. The employee participation in and of itself might be acceptable, so long as clients' interests were placed ahead of employees'. In this case, there is no evidence of such a priority of transactions, and further, the fact that CA has no exact numbers on the program indicates that the firm is not tracking employee trading activity, which is poor policy. (Study Session 2, LOS 6.b)

57. **A**   It is perfectly reasonable for CA to offer certain services or products only to clients meeting specified criteria, such as assets under management. (Study Session 2, LOS 6.b)

58. **B**   Riley was incorrect. The pricing methodology should be disclosed to clients, whether one or multiple sources are used. Simpson was correct. Multiple sources are acceptable, so long as full disclosure is made. (Study Session 2, LOS 6.b)

59. **C**   This type of trading is clearly market manipulation. Even though the 100 shares may be insignificant, the trade sets the price for the entire position. Such trades, especially entered as buy orders, are an unethical attempt to manipulate prices higher and justify a higher return for the period. However, even a sell transaction made under similar circumstances would be market manipulation. (Study Session 2, LOS 6.b)

60. **B**   BTN obviously assists in the investment decision-making process at CA. Using soft dollars to purchase BTN is acceptable. BTR might assist in the investment decision-making process, but managers have not performed any due diligence to verify the quality of the service. With no proven track record or other apparent means of verifying BTR's value, buying the service violates the managers' duty to have a reasonable basis for making investment decisions. Also, the very small capitalization firms may not be suitable for all clients. Unless CA has specific policies and monitoring in place to ensure only soft dollars from appropriate accounts are used to purchase research from BTR, they could also be in violation of Standard III: C, Suitability, as well as AMC Standard B:5.a. (Study Session 2, LOS 6.b)

> Sample Scoring Key: 3 points for each correct response.

Notes

Notes

Notes

Notes

Notes

Notes

Notes

Notes

Notes

Notes

Notes

Notes

Notes